Contents

Mathematics

Cursive Writing

Grammar and Reading

Social Studies

Science

Art

Counting by 3s

Count by 3s.

1.	Start at 12, **15**, 18, 21, 24, 27, 30
2.	Start at 45, 48, 51, 54, 57, 60, 63
3.	Start at 57, 60, 63, 66, 69, 72, 75
4.	Start at 87, 90, 93, 96, 99, 102, 105
5.	Start at 33, 36, 39, 42, 45, 48, 51

Count back by 3s.

6.	Start at 39, **36**, 33, 30, 17, 14, 11
7.	Start at 96, 93, 90, 87, 84, 81, 87
8.	Start at 51, 48, 45, 42, 39, 36, 33
9.	Start at 27, 24, 21, 18, 15, 12, 76
10.	Start at 72, 69, 66, 63, 60, 57, 54

Counting by 4s

Count by 4s.

1.	Start at 16, **20**, 24, 28, 32, 36, 40
2.	Start at 24, 28, 32, 36, 40, 44, 48
3.	Start at 44, 48, 52, 58, 62, 68, 78
4.	Start at 80, 84, 88, 82, 86, 90, 94
5.	Start at 52, 56, 60, 64, 68, 70, 72

Count back by 4s.

6.	Start at 72, **68**, 64, 60, 56, 52, 48
7.	Start at 68, 64, 60, 56, 52, 48, 44
8.	Start at 60, 56, 52, 48, 44, 40, 38
9.	Start at 36, 32, 28, 24, 20, 16, 12
10.	Start at 92, 88, 84, 80, 76, 72, 68

Counting by 5s and 25s

Count by 5s.

1.	Start at 310, **315** , _____, _____, _____, _____, _____
2.	Start at 545, _____, _____, _____, _____, _____, _____
3.	Start at 780, _____, _____, _____, _____, _____, _____

Count back by 5s.

4.	Start at 495, **490** , _____, _____, _____, _____, _____
5.	Start at 675, _____, _____, _____, _____, _____, _____
6.	Start at 160, _____, _____, _____, _____, _____, _____

Count by 25s.

7.	Start at 675, **700** , _____, _____, _____, _____, _____
8.	Start at 225, _____, _____, _____, _____, _____, _____

Count back by 25s.

9.	Start at 700, **675** , _____, _____, _____, _____, _____
10.	Start at 425, _____, _____, _____, _____, _____, _____

Counting by 10s

Count by 10s.

1.	Start at 170, **180**, _____, _____, _____, _____, _____
2.	Start at 233, _____, _____, _____, _____, _____, _____
3.	Start at 800, _____, _____, _____, _____, _____, _____
4.	Start at 655, _____, _____, _____, _____, _____, _____
5.	Start at 400, _____, _____, _____, _____, _____, _____

Count back by 10s.

6.	Start at 200, **190**, _____, _____, _____, _____, _____
7.	Start at 90, _____, _____, _____, _____, _____, _____
8.	Start at 383, _____, _____, _____, _____, _____, _____

BRAIN STRETCH

A box has 10 snack bars. Write how many snack bars are in

a) 2 boxes _____   b) 3 boxes _____   c) 5 boxes _____   d) 7 boxes _____

Counting by 100s

Count by 100s.

1.	Start at 100, **200**, _____, _____, _____, _____, _____
2.	Start at 209, _____, _____, _____, _____, _____, _____
3.	Start at 198, _____, _____, _____, _____, _____, _____
4.	Start at 345, _____, _____, _____, _____, _____, _____
5.	Start at 174, _____, _____, _____, _____, _____, _____

Count back by 100s.

6.	Start at 986, **886**, _____, _____, _____, _____, _____
7.	Start at 621, _____, _____, _____, _____, _____, _____
8.	Start at 863, _____, _____, _____, _____, _____, _____

BRAIN STRETCH

There are 100 jelly beans in one bag. Write how many jelly beans are in

a) 6 bags _____   b) 4 bags _____   c) 9 bags _____

Growing Number Patterns

In a growing pattern, the number increases.

$\overset{(+3)}{}\qquad\overset{(+3)}{}\qquad\overset{(+3)}{}\qquad\overset{(+3)}{}\qquad\overset{(+3)}{}\qquad\overset{(+3)}{}$

3   6   9   12   15   18   21

The pattern rule is add 3 each time.

Make a growing pattern by adding.

1. The pattern rule is add 7 each time.

   Start at 7, __14__, _21_, _28_, _35_, _42_, _49_, _56_

2. The pattern rule is add 10 each time.

   Start at 20, _____, _____, _____, _____, _____, _____, _____

3. The pattern rule is add 5 each time.

   Start at 5, _____, _____, _____, _____, _____, _____, _____

4. Make your own. The pattern rule is add _____ each time.

   Start at 7, _____, _____, _____, _____, _____, _____, _____

Shrinking Number Patterns

In a shrinking pattern, the number decreases.

$\bigodot{-4}$ $\bigodot{-4}$ $\bigodot{-4}$ $\bigodot{-4}$ $\bigodot{-4}$ $\bigodot{-4}$

32   28   24   20   16   12   8

The pattern rule is subtract 4 each time.

Make a shrinking pattern by subtracting.

1. The pattern rule is subtract 3 each time.

Start at 40, __37__, _____, _____, _____, _____, _____, _____

2. The pattern rule is subtract 5 each time.

Start at 70, _____, _____, _____, _____, _____, _____, _____

3. The pattern rule is subtract 10 each time.

Start at 100, _____, _____, _____, _____, _____, _____, _____

4. Make your own. The pattern rule is subtract _____ each time.

Start at 30, _____, _____, _____, _____, _____, _____, _____

Odd and Even Numbers

Look at the ones digits to see if a number is odd or even.
Odd numbers end in 1, 3, 5 , 7, or 9.
Even numbers end in 0, 2, 4, 6, or 8.

Colour the even numbers orange. Colour the odd numbers green. Write your own odd and even numbers and colour the balloons.

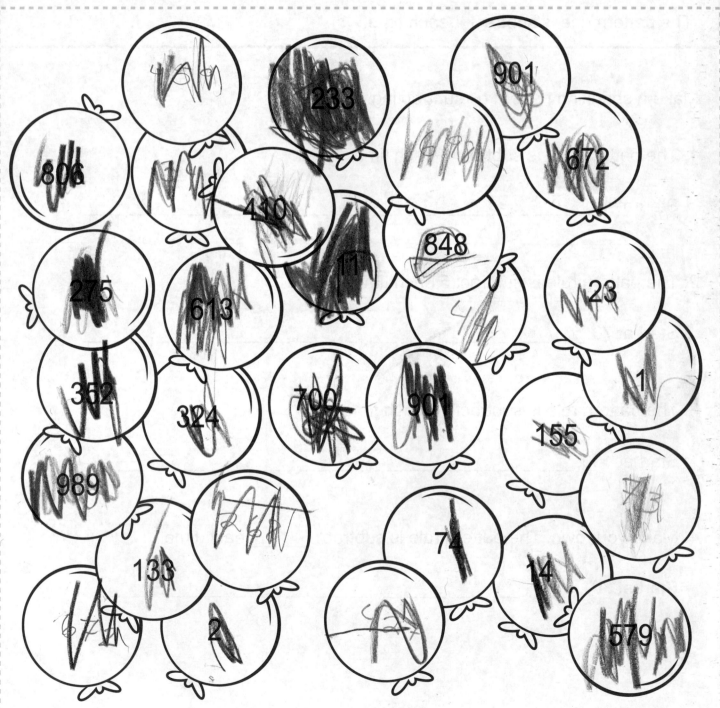

Comparing and Ordering Numbers

1. Count by 10s. Fill in the missing numbers.

Just before: **33** , 43, 53	Just before: _____, 61, 71
Just after: 9, 19, _____	Just before and after: _____, 74, _____
Between: 58, _____, 78	Just after: 46, 56, _____

2. Circle the larger number in each pair.

a) 342 or 324   b) 987 or 798   c) 301 or 103   d) 672 or 627

e) 120 or 102   f) 440 or 484   g) 715 or 751   h) 800 or 790

3. Order each group of numbers from smallest to largest.

164, 439, 181, 219, 170, 322   _____, _____, _____, _____, _____, _____

440, 463, 459, 330, 500, 143   _____, _____, _____, _____, _____, _____

4. Order each group of numbers from largest to smallest.

95, 84, 123 _____, _____, _____   245, 212, 289 _____, _____, _____

Hundreds, Tens, and Ones

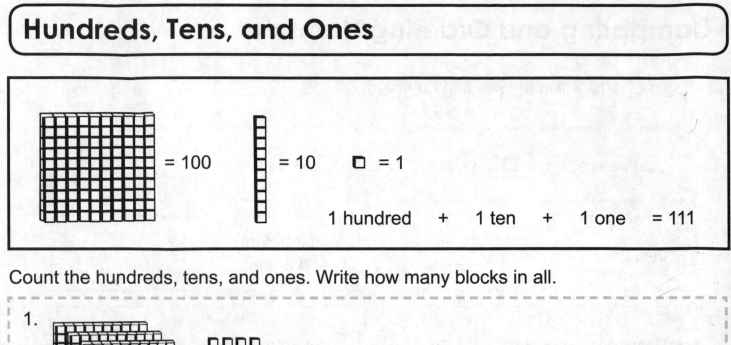

= 100   = 10   □ = 1

1 hundred + 1 ten + 1 one = 111

Count the hundreds, tens, and ones. Write how many blocks in all.

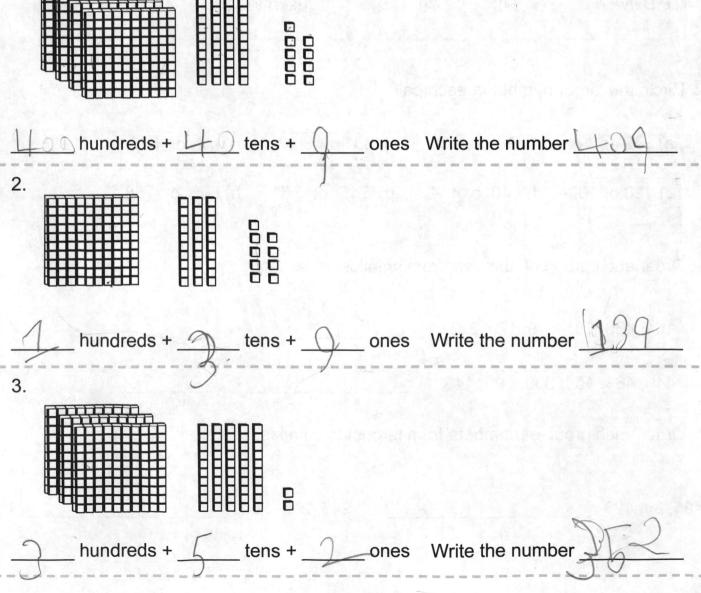

1. _400_ hundreds + _40_ tens + _9_ ones   Write the number _409_

2. _1_ hundreds + _3_ tens + _9_ ones   Write the number _139_

3. _3_ hundreds + _5_ tens + _2_ ones   Write the number _352_

Hundreds, Tens, and Ones (continued)

Count the hundreds, tens, and ones. Write how many blocks in all.

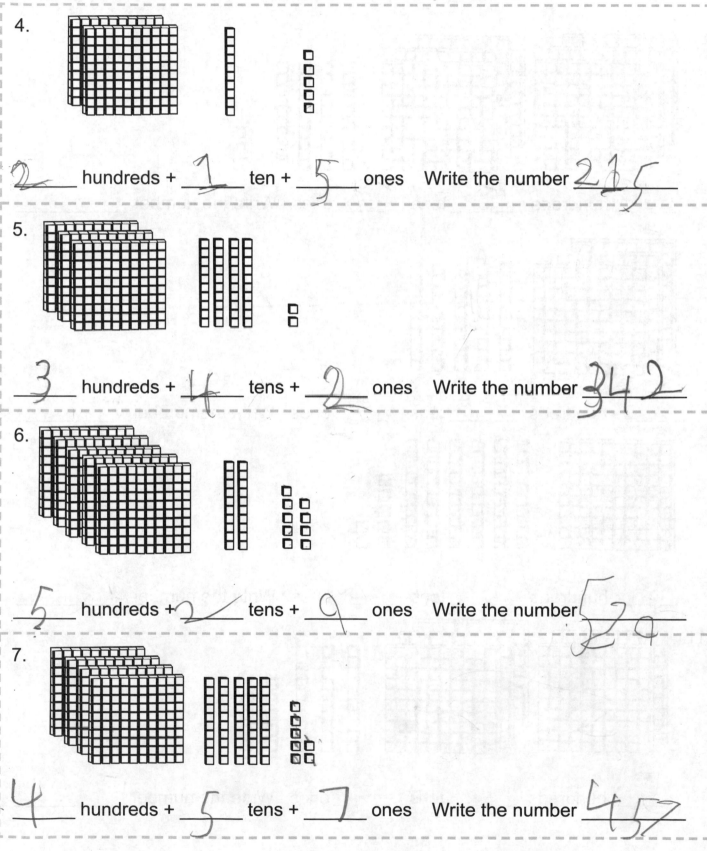

4.

__2__ hundreds + __1__ ten + __5__ ones   Write the number __215__

5.

__3__ hundreds + __4__ tens + __2__ ones   Write the number __342__

6.

__5__ hundreds + __2__ tens + __9__ ones   Write the number __529__

7.

__4__ hundreds + __5__ tens + __7__ ones   Write the number __457__

Hundreds, Tens, and Ones (continued)

Count the hundreds, tens, and ones. Write how many blocks in all.

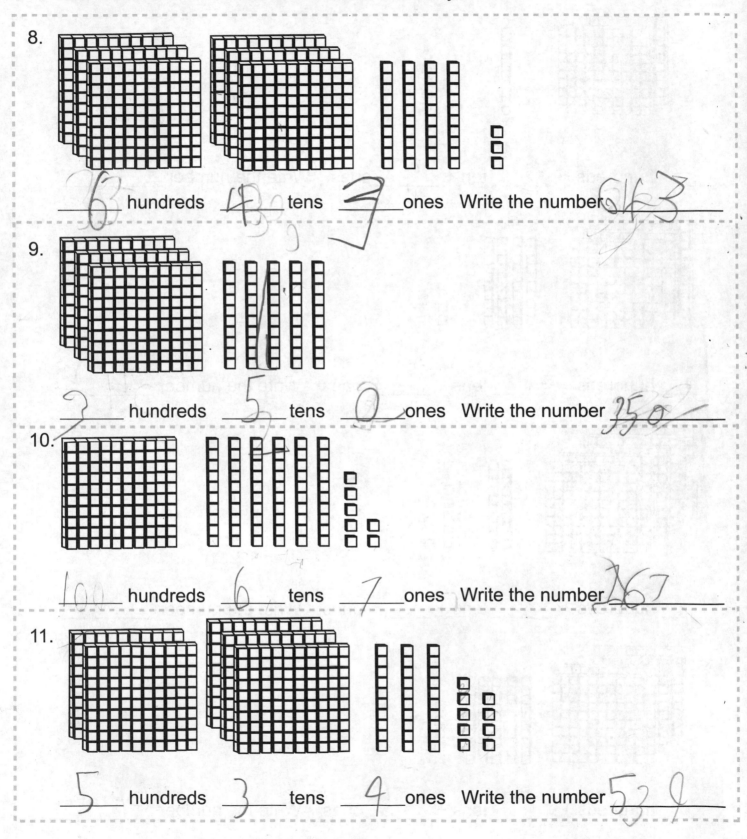

8. _3_ hundreds _4_ tens _3_ ones   Write the number _643_

9. _3_ hundreds _5_ tens _0_ ones   Write the number _350_

10. _100_ hundreds _6_ tens _7_ ones   Write the number _167_

11. _5_ hundreds _3_ tens _4_ ones   Write the number _534_

Place Value

Place value is the value of where the digit is in the number, such as ones, tens, hundreds, etc. For example, in the number 725,

7 stands for 700
2 stands for 20
5 stands for 5

725 in expanded form is **700 + 20 + 5**

Write the place value of the underlined digit.

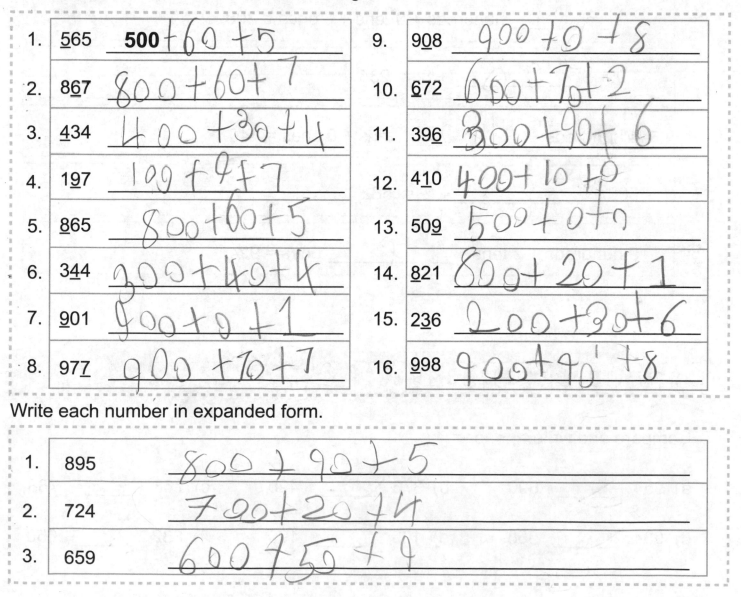

1.	5̲65	**500** + 60 + 5
2.	86̲7	800 + 60 + 7
3.	4̲34	400 + 30 + 4
4.	1̲97	100 + 9 + 7
5.	8̲65	800 + 60 + 5
6.	34̲4	300 + 40 + 4
7.	9̲01	900 + 0 + 1
8.	97̲7	900 + 70 + 7

9.	9̲08	900 + 0 + 8
10.	6̲72	600 + 70 + 2
11.	39̲6	300 + 90 + 6
12.	41̲0	400 + 10 + 0
13.	50̲9	500 + 0 + 9
14.	8̲21	800 + 20 + 1
15.	23̲6	200 + 30 + 6
16.	9̲98	900 + 90 + 8

Write each number in expanded form.

1.	895	800 + 90 + 5
2.	724	700 + 20 + 4
3.	659	600 + 50 + 9

What Is the Value?

Write the missing value.

1. 600 + 30 + _____5_____ = 635

2. _____900_____ hundreds + 4 tens + 7 ones = 947

3. 800 + 90 + _____1_____ = 891

4. _____3_____ hundreds + 0 tens + 8 ones = 308

5. 200 + _____30_____ + 8 = 238

6. 4 hundreds + _____40_____ tens + 0 ones = 440

7. 500 + _____80_____ + 2 = 582

8. 9 hundreds + 2 tens + _____4_____ ones = 924

BRAIN STRETCH

Compare and write >, <, or =.

a) 954 __>__ 890   b) 376 __<__ 420   c) 768 __=__ 768

d) 534 __<__ 558   e) 165 __<__ 190   f) 832 __>__ 650

Writing Numbers in Different Ways

Circle two correct ways to express each number.

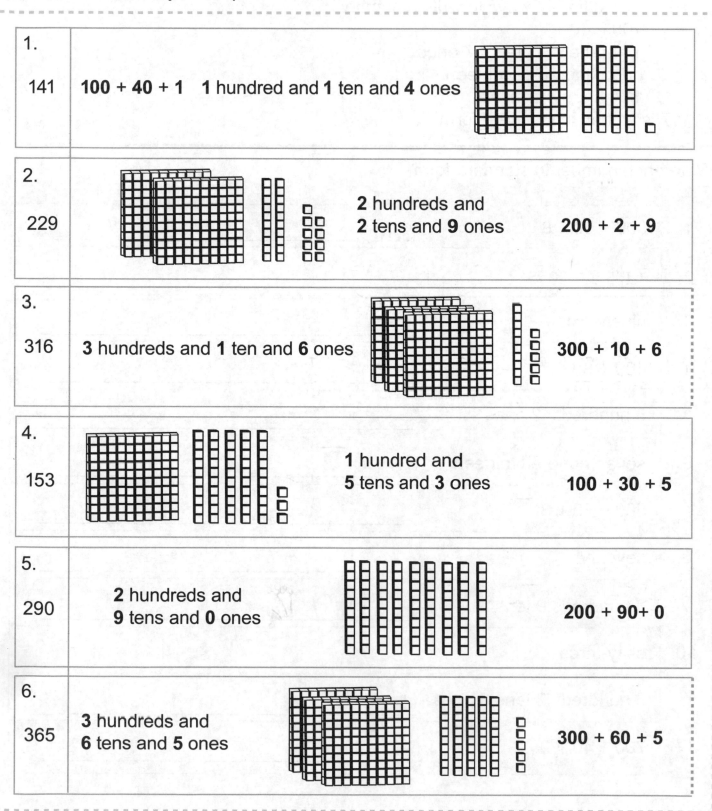

1. 141	**100 + 40 + 1** **1** hundred and **1** ten and **4** ones
2. 229	**2** hundreds and **2** tens and **9** ones **200 + 2 + 9**
3. 316	**3** hundreds and **1** ten and **6** ones **300 + 10 + 6**
4. 153	**1** hundred and **5** tens and **3** ones **100 + 30 + 5**
5. 290	**2** hundreds and **9** tens and **0** ones **200 + 90 + 0**
6. 365	**3** hundreds and **6** tens and **5** ones **300 + 60 + 5**

Writing Numbers in Standard Form

There are different ways to write a number.

100 + 10 + 7

1 hundred + 1 ten + 7 ones

one hundred seventeen

117

117 is written in standard form.

Write each number in standard form.

1.	600 + 50 + 8	658
2.	7 tens 5 ones	75
3.	ninety-nine	99
4.	400 + 30 + 7	437
5.	8 hundreds 2 ones	802
6.	seven hundred thirteen	713
7.	500 + 40 + 3	543
8.	seventy	70
9.	3 hundreds 9 tens	309
10.	sixty-three	603
11.	6 hundreds 2 tens 8 ones	628
12.	700 + 40 + 9	749

Writing Number Words

Number words for the teens:
eleven twelve thirteen fourteen fifteen sixteen seventeen eighteen nineteen

Number words for the tens:
twenty thirty forty fifty sixty seventy eighty ninety

The number word for 285 is **two hundred eighty-five**.

1. Write the number word.

   a) 121 **one hundred twenty-one**

   b) 572 _five hundred - seventy - two_

   c) 415 _four hundred - one - five_

   d) 268 _two - hundred - sixty - eight_

   e) 923 _nine hundred - twenty - three_

2. Write the number word.

   a) There are _twelve_ months in one year.
   12

   b) There are _fifty - two_ weeks in a year.
   52

   c) There are _six hundreds - five_ days in a year.
   365

   d) Some months of the year have _threety_ days.
   30

   Other months have _threety - one_ days.
   31

   e) There are _twenty - four_ hours in a day.
   24

   f) There are _sixty_ minutes in one hour.
   60

Number Roundup

To round to the nearest tens place, look at the ones digit.
If the ones digit has a 0, 1, 2, 3, or 4, round **down**.
If the ones digit has a 5, 6, 7, 8, or 9, round **up**.

To round to the nearest hundreds place, look at the tens digit.
If the tens digit has a 0, 1, 2, 3, or 4, round **down**.
If the tens digit has a 5, 6, 7, 8, or 9, round **up**.

Round each number.

	Number	Round to nearest 10	Round to nearest 100
1.	553		
2.	201		
3.	845		
4.	397		
5.	172		
6.	664		
7.	489		
8.	736		
9.	953		
10.	888		

Ordinal Numbers

An **ordinal number** describes the numerical position of an object in a rank or sequential order.

1. Write the ordinals. Hint: Use the **bold** part to help you.

   fir**st** __1st__   seco**nd** _2nd_   thi**rd** _3rd_

   fou**rth** _4th_   fif**th** _5th_   six**th** _6th_   seven**th** _7th_

   eigh**th** _8th_   nin**th** _9th_   ten**th** _10th_

2. What is   a) the first letter in the alphabet? ____

   b) the 6th letter in the word "snowboard"? ____

   c) the second letter in the word "ballet"? ____

   d) the 10th letter in the alphabet? ____

   e) the fourth letter in the word "Canada"? ____

3. Some students had a contest to find out whose paper airplane flew the farthest.

   a) Helen came in seventh. Who came in first? _____

   b) Who came in fifth? _____

   c) In which position was Lisa? _____

   d) In which position was Paul? _____

   e) Jess came in _____

   f) Who came in 4th? _____

   Chris   Jess   Lisa   Mandy   Jason   Paul   Helen

Adding or Subtracting

You can find the sum of two numbers by counting on.

14 + 5 = 19   Count: 14, 15, 16, 17, 18, 19

You can find the difference between two numbers by counting back.

29 − 4 = 25   Count: 29, 28, 27, 26, 25

Use the number line to help find the sum or difference.

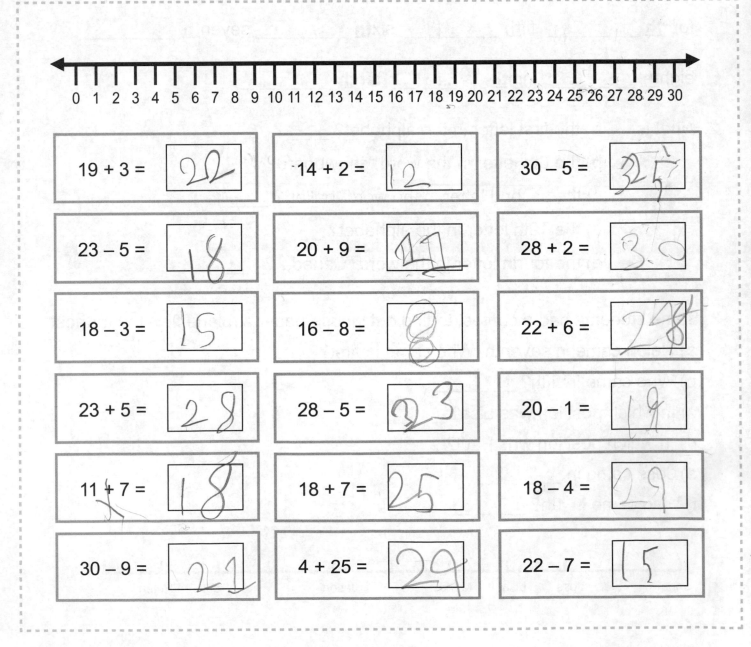

19 + 3 = 22	14 + 2 = 12	30 − 5 = 25
23 − 5 = 18	20 + 9 = 11	28 + 2 = 30
18 − 3 = 15	16 − 8 = 8	22 + 6 = 28
23 + 5 = 28	28 − 5 = 23	20 − 1 = 19
11 + 7 = 18	18 + 7 = 25	18 − 4 = 29
30 − 9 = 21	4 + 25 = 29	22 − 7 = 15

Adding Tens

Think of an addition fact to add tens.

Find 40 + 20.

Think 4 + 2 = 6.
4 tens + 2 tens = 6 tens
40 + 20 = 60

1. Use an addition fact to help you add tens.

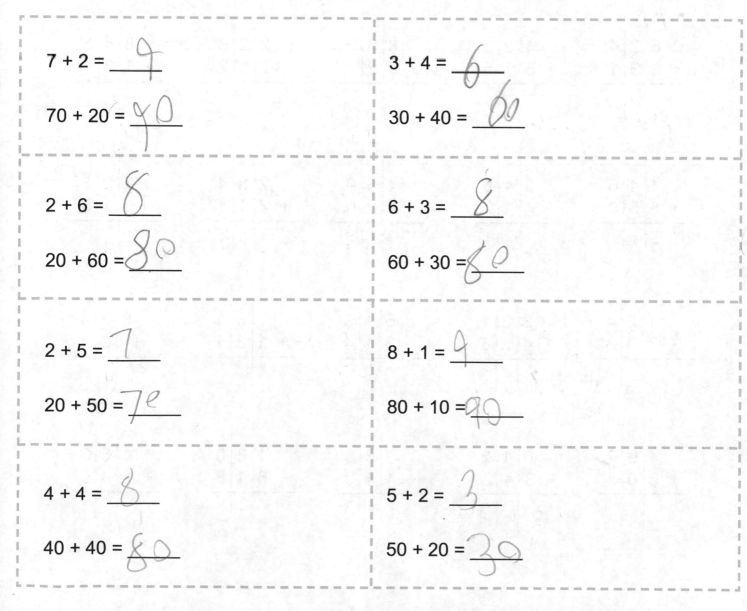

7 + 2 = _9_

70 + 20 = _90_

3 + 4 = _6_

30 + 40 = _60_

2 + 6 = _8_

20 + 60 = _80_

6 + 3 = _8_

60 + 30 = _80_

2 + 5 = _7_

20 + 50 = _70_

8 + 1 = _9_

80 + 10 = _90_

4 + 4 = _8_

40 + 40 = _80_

5 + 2 = _3_

50 + 20 = _30_

Three-Digit Addition Without Regrouping

Line up the ones, tens, and hundreds.	First add the ones.	Next add the tens.	Then add the hundreds.
	hundreds / tens / **ones**	hundreds / **tens** / ones	**hundreds** / tens / ones
	2 2 3 + 3 4 5 —— 8	2 2 3 + 3 4 5 —— 6 8	2 2 3 + 3 4 5 —— 5 6 8

1. Use a hundreds, tens, and ones chart to help you add. Shade the ones column yellow. Shade the tens column orange. Shade the hundreds column green.

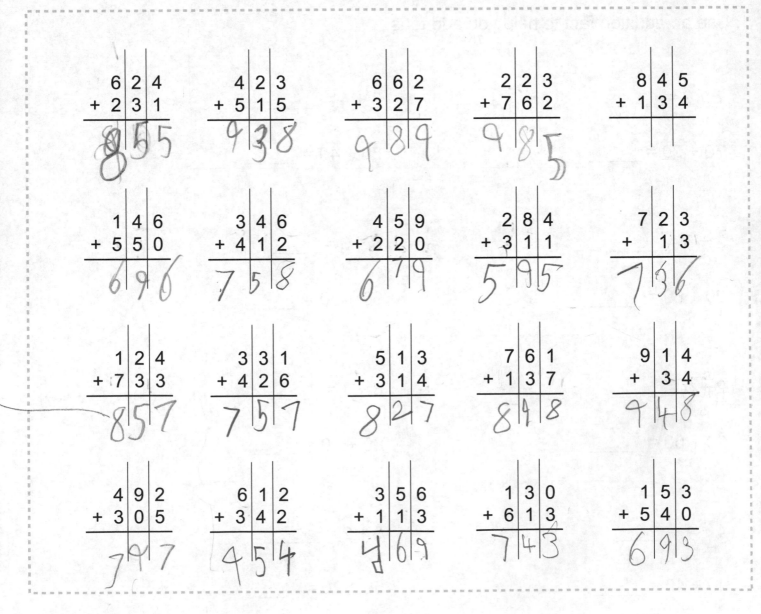

6 2 4 + 2 3 1 8 5 5	4 2 3 + 5 1 5 9 3 8	6 6 2 + 3 2 7 9 8 9	2 2 3 + 7 6 2 9 8 5	8 4 5 + 1 3 4 9 8 5
1 4 6 + 5 5 0 6 9 6	3 4 6 + 4 1 2 7 5 8	4 5 9 + 2 2 0 6 7 9	2 8 4 + 3 1 1 5 9 5	7 2 3 + 1 3 7 3 6
1 2 4 + 7 3 3 8 5 7	3 3 1 + 4 2 6 7 5 7	5 1 3 + 3 1 4 8 2 7	7 6 1 + 1 3 7 8 9 8	9 1 4 + 3 4 9 4 8
4 9 2 + 3 0 5 7 9 7	6 1 2 + 3 4 2 9 5 4	3 5 6 + 1 1 3 4 6 9	1 3 0 + 6 1 3 7 4 3	1 5 3 + 5 4 0 6 9 3

Three-Digit Addition Without Regrouping (continued)

2. Use the hundreds, tens, and ones chart to add. Shade the ones column yellow.
   Shade the tens column orange. Shade the hundreds column green.

455 + 14 **469**	735 + 132 **867**	166 + 502 **668**	246 + 323 **569**	570 + 325 **895**
314 + 341 **655**	543 + 222 **765**	377 + 202 **579**	432 + 243 **675**	317 + 532 **849**
235 + 113 **348**	713 + 222 **935**	132 + 713 **845**	254 + 444 **698**	264 + 313 **577**
342 + 332 **674**	111 + 163 **274**	581 + 412 **993**	623 + 136 **759**	350 + 225 **575**
712 + 246 **958**	213 + 534 **747**	400 + 215 **615**	824 + 133 **957**	421 + 116 **537**

Three-Digit Addition with Regrouping

Line up the ones, tens, and hundreds.
Add the ones.
Then add the tens.

If there are more than 9 tens,
trade 10 tens for 1 hundred.
Regroup in the hundreds column.
Write the tens.
Add the hundreds.

hundreds	tens	ones
¹3	3	6
+ 2	9	3
6	2	9

Trade 10 tens from 120 for 1 hundred.
Regroup by writing 1 in the hundreds column.

1. Use a hundreds, tens, and ones chart to help you add. Shade the ones column yellow. Shade the tens column orange. Shade the hundreds column green.

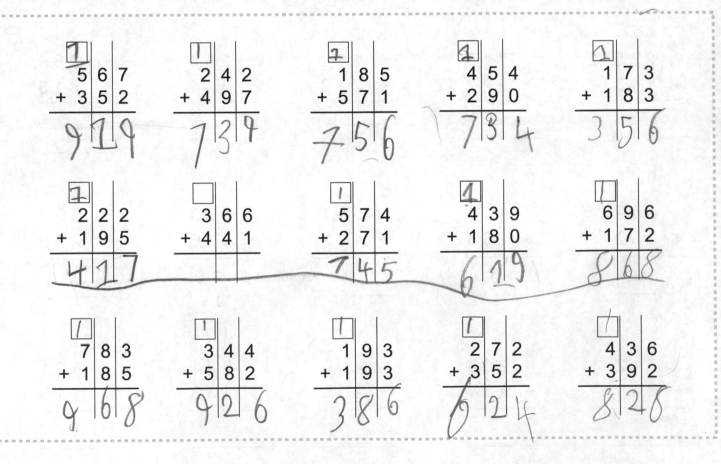

Three-Digit Addition with Regrouping (continued)

2. Use the hundreds, tens, and ones chart to add. Hint: If there are more than
   9 ones, trade 10 ones for 1 ten. Regroup in the tens column.

☐ 1	☐ ☐	☐ ☐	☐ ☐	☐ ☐
239	378	464	547	735
+ 412	+ 219	+ 418	+ 117	+ 225
651				

☐ ☐	☐ ☐	☐ ☐	☐ ☐	☐ ☐
524	236	342	519	513
+ 338	+ 26	+ 229	+ 264	+ 338

☐ ☐	☐ ☐	☐ ☐	☐ ☐	☐ ☐
445	335	829	359	627
+ 419	+ 148	+ 19	+ 431	+ 226

3. Add. Regroup in the tens column and the hundreds column.

1 1	☐ ☐	☐ ☐	☐ ☐	☐ ☐
488	695	269	355	282
+ 23	+ 128	+ 166	+ 257	+ 138
511				

Subtracting Tens

Think of a subtraction fact to subtract tens.

Find 40 – 20.
Think 4 – 2 = 2.
4 tens – 2 tens = 2 tens

40 – 20 = 20

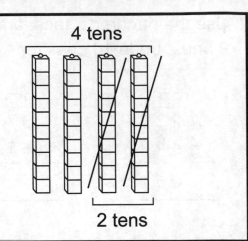

1. Use a subtraction fact to help you subtract tens.

7 – 4 = 3
70 – 40 = 30

9 – 8 = 1
90 – 80 = 10

8 – 4 = 4
80 – 40 = 40

8 – 5 = 3
80 – 50 = 30

8 – 7 = 1
80 – 70 = 10

6 – 2 = 4
60 – 20 = 40

9 – 3 = 6
90 – 30 = 60

3 – 2 = 1
30 – 20 = 10

Using Tens to Make an Easier Problem

1. Make an easier problem using tens. Then subtract.

23 – 18 =

23 – 18 = **25** – 20 = __5__
I know 18 + 2 = 20.
So I add 2 to each number.
Then I subtract.

---

29 – 17 =

29 – 17 = ___ – ___ = ___

Add 1 to each number.

---

42 – 18 =

42 – 18 = ___ – ___ = ___

Add ___ to each number.

---

34 – 19 =

34 – 19 = ___ – 20 = ___

Add __ to each number.

---

28 – 19 =

28 – 19 = ___ – 20 = ___

Add ___ to each number.

---

22 – 16 =

22 – 16 = ___ – 20 = ___

Add ___ to each number.

---

31 – 16 =

31 – 16 = ___ – 20 = ___

Add ___ to each number.

---

34 – 19 =

34 – 19 = ___ – ___ = ___

Add ___ to each number.

Three-Digit Subtraction Without Regrouping

Line up the ones, tens, and hundreds.	Subtract the ones.		Then subtract the tens.		Then subtract the hundreds.	
	hundreds	tens	**ones**			

Subtract the ones.

hundreds	tens	**ones**
4	8	7
− 1	4	4
		3

Then subtract the tens.

hundreds	**tens**	ones
4	8	7
− 1	4	4
	4	3

Then subtract the hundreds.

hundreds	tens	ones
4	8	7
− 1	4	4
3	4	3

1. Use a hundreds, tens, and ones chart to help you subtract. Shade the ones column yellow. Shade the tens column orange. Shade the hundreds column green.

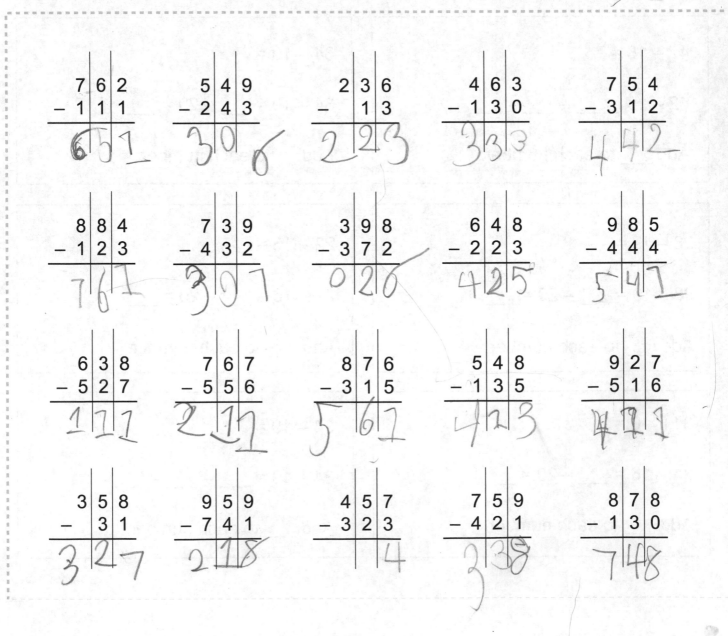

7	6	2
− 1	1	1
6	5	1

5	4	9
− 2	4	3
3	0	6

2	3	6
−	1	3
2	2	3

4	6	3
− 1	3	0
3	3	3

7	5	4
− 3	1	2
4	4	2

8	8	4
− 1	2	3
7	6	1

7	3	9
− 4	3	2
3	0	7

3	9	8
− 3	7	2
0	2	6

6	4	8
− 2	2	3
4	2	5

9	8	5
− 4	4	4
5	4	1

6	3	8
− 5	2	7
1	1	1

7	6	7
− 5	5	6
2	1	1

8	7	6
− 3	1	5
5	6	1

5	4	8
− 1	3	5
4	2	3

9	2	7
− 5	1	6
4	1	1

3	5	8
−	3	1
3	2	7

9	5	9
− 7	4	1
2	1	8

4	5	7
− 3	2	3
		4

7	5	9
− 4	2	1
3	3	8

8	7	8
− 1	3	0
7	4	8

Three-Digit Subtraction Without Regrouping (continued)

Line up the ones, tens, and hundreds.	Subtract the ones.	Then subtract the tens.	Then subtract the hundreds.
	hundreds tens **ones**	hundreds **tens** ones	**hundreds** tens ones
	4 8 7	4 8 7	4 8 7
	− 1 4 4	− 1 4 4	− 1 4 4
	3	4 3	3 4 3

2. Use the hundreds, tens, and ones chart to subtract.

579 − 236 343	662 − 120 542	747 − 134 613	244 − 114 130	864 − 431 433
276 − 40 236	474 − 232 242	337 − 320 017	195 − 60 135	993 − 73 920
555 − 110 445	783 − 341 442	618 − 312 306	648 − 623 025	574 − 450 124
888 − 234 654	266 − 125 141	457 − 343 114	948 − 225 723	238 − 122 116

Taking Apart to Make Tens for Subtraction

31 – ⑥ = 31 + **4** – 6 + **4** = 35 – 10 = 25

6 + 4 = 10   So, add 4 to each number.

1. Make an easier problem using 10. Then subtract.

a) 15 – 9 = 15 + **1** – 9 + **1** = ___ – ___ = ___ Add **1** to each number.

b) 19 – 7 = 2 + 1 – 3 + 4 = 6 – 6 = ___ Add 1 to each number.

c) 16 – 8 = X + 1 – 2 + 3 = 4 – ___ = ___ Add ___ to each number.

d) 27 – 9 = ___ + ___ – ___ + ___ = ___ – ___ = ___ Add ___ to each number.

e) 54 – 6 = ___ + ___ – ___ + ___ = ___ – ___ = ___ Add ___ to each number.

f) 61 – 5 = ___ + ___ – ___ + ___ = ___ – ___ = ___ Add ___ to each number.

g) 42 – 7 = ___ + ___ – ___ + ___ = ___ – ___ = ___ Add ___ to each number.

Three-Digit Subtraction with Regrouping

Line up the ones, tens, and hundreds.
Subtract the ones.

Trade 1 hundred from the hundreds for
10 tens in the tens column.
Subtract the tens.
Then subtract the hundreds.

hundreds	**tens**	ones
	5	16
8	6̶	6̶
− 5	4	9
3	1	7

You cannot take 8 from 4. So, trade 1 hundred from the hundreds for 10 tens. Now there are 14 tens.

1. Use a hundreds, tens, and ones chart to help you subtract. Shade the ones column yellow. Shade the tens column orange. Shade the hundreds column green.

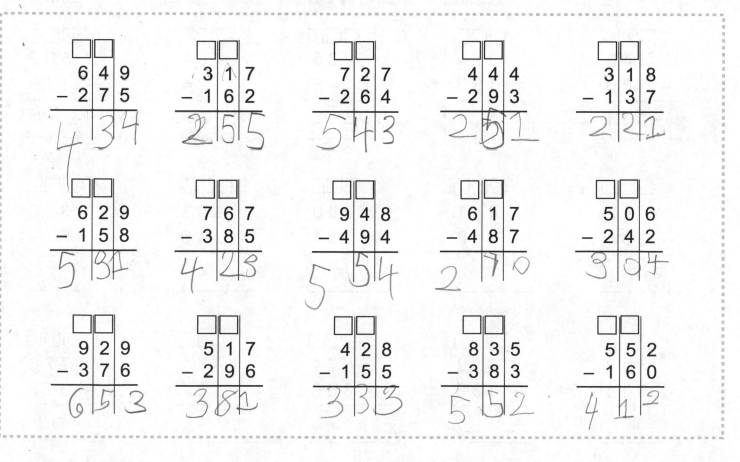

```
  6 4 9       3 1 7       7 2 7       4 4 4       3 1 8
- 2 7 5     - 1 6 2     - 2 6 4     - 2 9 3     - 1 3 7
  4 3 4       2 5 5       5 4 3       2 5 1       2 2 1


  6 2 9       7 6 7       9 4 8       6 1 7       5 0 6
- 1 5 8     - 3 8 5     - 4 9 4     - 4 8 7     - 2 4 2
  5 3 1       4 2 3       5 5 4       2 7 0       3 0 4


  9 2 9       5 1 7       4 2 8       8 3 5       5 5 2
- 3 7 6     - 2 9 6     - 1 5 5     - 3 8 3     - 1 6 0
  6 5 3       3 8 1       3 3 3       5 5 2       4 1 2
```

Three-Digit Subtraction with Regrouping (continued)

Line up the ones, tens, and hundreds.

Trade 1 ten from the tens column for 10 ones.

Subtract the ones.

Subtract the tens.

Then subtract the hundreds.

hundreds	tens	ones
	5	16
8	6̶	6̶
− 5	4	9
3	1	7

You cannot take 9 from 6. So, trade 1 ten from the tens for 10 ones. Now there are 16 ones.

2. Use the hundreds, tens, and ones chart to subtract. You will need to regroup the tens.

```
  ☐ 3 10        ☐☐☐          ☐☐☐          ☐☐☐          ☐☐☐
  4 4̶ 0̶        3 7 4        9 8 6        4 5 1        5 9 2
− 1 2 9      − 1 6 5      − 1 4 8      − 1 2 4      − 1 7 6
─────────    ─────────    ─────────    ─────────    ─────────
  3 1 1        2 1 1        8 4 8        3 3 3        4 2 4
```

```
  ☐☐☐          ☐☐☐          ☐☐☐          ☐☐☐          ☐☐☐
  7 9 2        4 4 1        6 8 0        8 9 3        3 3 8
− 3 6 6      − 1 1 8      − 2 3 4      − 2 4 5      − 2 1 9
─────────    ─────────    ─────────    ─────────    ─────────
  4 3 4        3 3 7        4 5 4        6 5 2        1 2 1
```

```
  ☐☐☐          ☐☐☐          ☐☐☐          ☐☐☐          ☐☐☐
  6 4 2        6 8 3        6 7 4        4 6 1        7 7 6
− 3 1 4      − 1 3 9      − 3 5 6      − 1 3 7      − 3 1 8
─────────    ─────────    ─────────    ─────────    ─────────
  3 3 2        5 5 6        3 2 2        3 3 6        4 6 2
```

Word Problems

Decide if you need to add or subtract. Underline any words that help you decide. Circle Add or Subtract. Then solve the problem. Show your work.

1. Donisha had 234 stamps. She gave 29 to Dave. How many stamps does she have left?

   Add

   Subtract

   There are _Add_ stamps left.

2. Ms. Stevens's class had 136 tulip bulbs to plant. The class planted 79 tulip bulbs. How many tulip bulbs still need to be planted?

   Add

   Subtract

   There are _Subtract_ tulip bulbs to be planted.

3. Ethan scored 560 points on a computer game. Ben scored 298 points. How many points did they score altogether?

   Add

   Subtract

   They scored _Add_ points altogether.

4. Jose collected 400 stamps. Jill collected 187 stamps. How many stamps did they collect altogether?

   Add

   Subtract

   There are _Add_ stamps in all.

Counting with Coins

Find the value of the coins. Remember to use the $ sign.

1. $\qquad$ 1003

2. $\qquad$ 35

3. $\qquad$ 28

4. $\qquad$ 30

5. $\qquad$ 32

Estimating Coins

1.

Estimate $_____._____   Count $_____._____

2.

Estimate $_____._____   Count $_____._____

3.

Estimate $_____._____   Count $_____._____

4.

Estimate $_____._____   Count $_____._____

Trading Coins

1. Trade each set of coins for fewer coins. Draw the coins. Check your work.

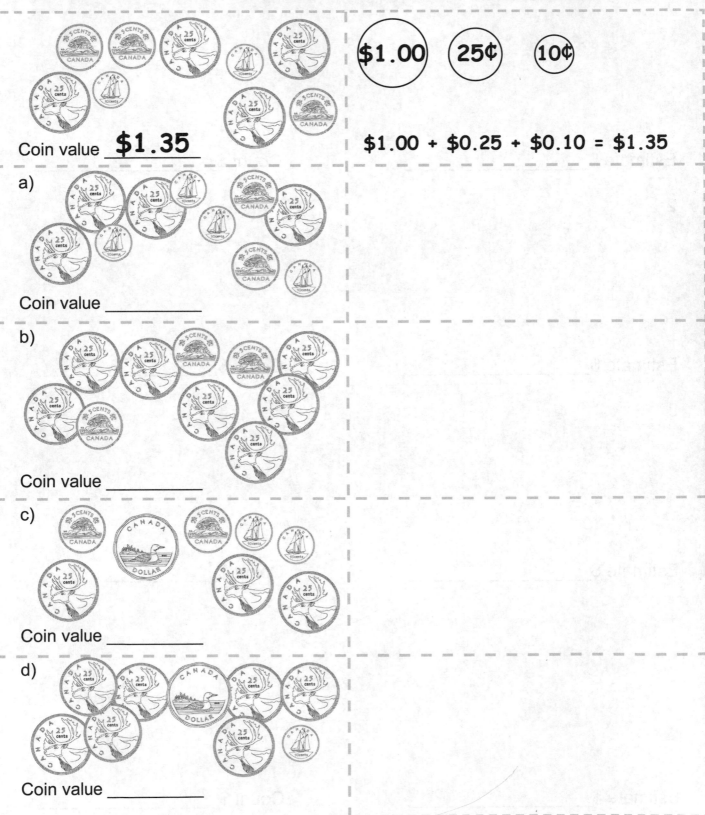

Coin value __$1.35__

$1.00 + $0.25 + $0.10 = $1.35

a)

Coin value _____

b)

Coin value _____

c)

Coin value _____

d)

Coin value _____

Comparing Money Values

1. Compare and write >, <, or = in the ◯ .

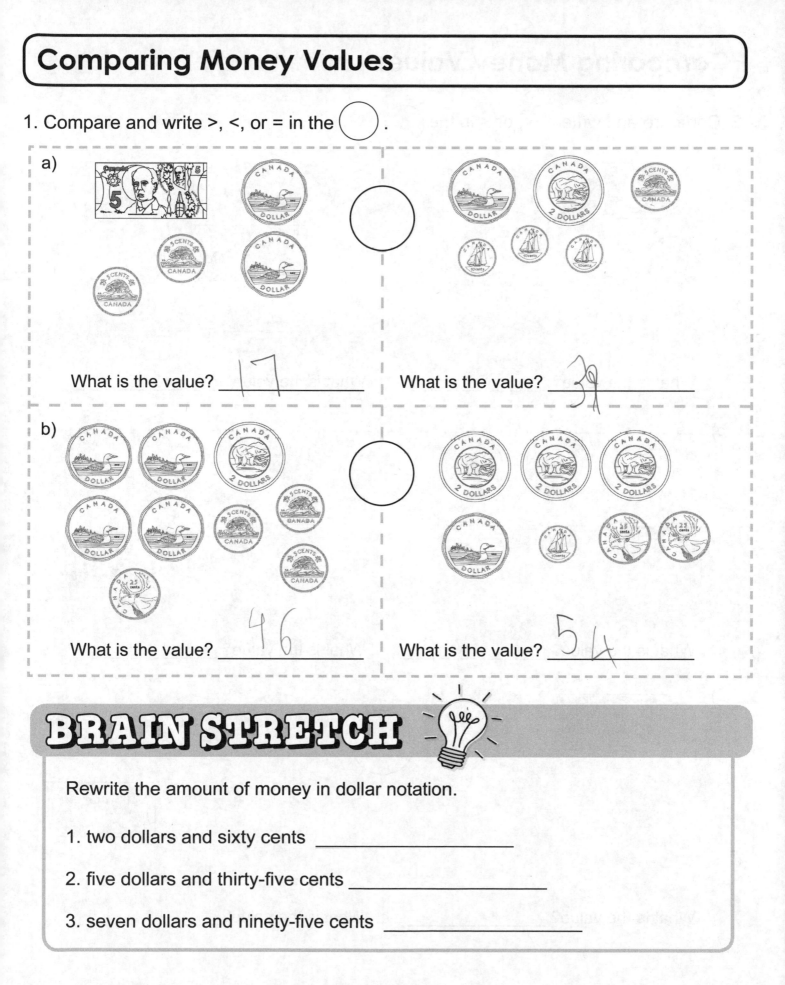

a)

What is the value? ___17___

What is the value? ___39___

b)

What is the value? ___46___

What is the value? ___54___

BRAIN STRETCH

Rewrite the amount of money in dollar notation.

1. two dollars and sixty cents _____

2. five dollars and thirty-five cents _____

3. seven dollars and ninety-five cents _____

Comparing Money Values (continued)

2. Compare and write >, <, or = in the ◯ .

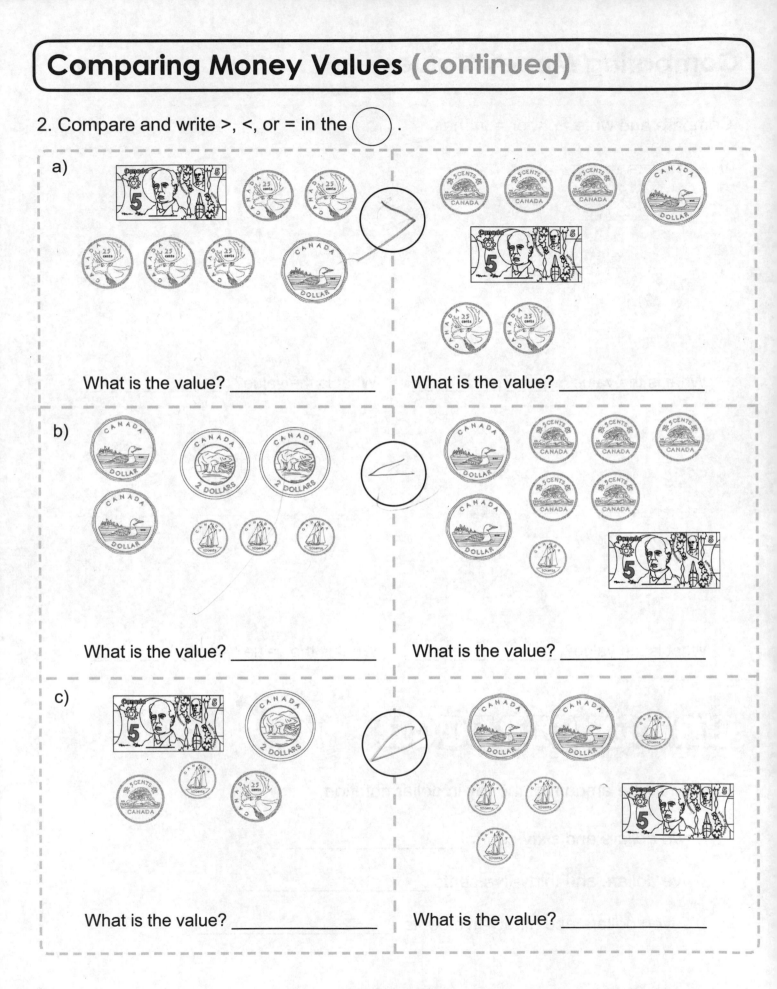

a)

What is the value? _____

What is the value? _____

b)

What is the value? _____

What is the value? _____

c)

What is the value? _____

What is the value? _____

Fractions: Equal Parts

There are three equal parts.
Each part is one third.

$\frac{1}{3}$ means that 1 out of 3 equal parts is shaded.

Shade one part of each shape. Write the fraction.

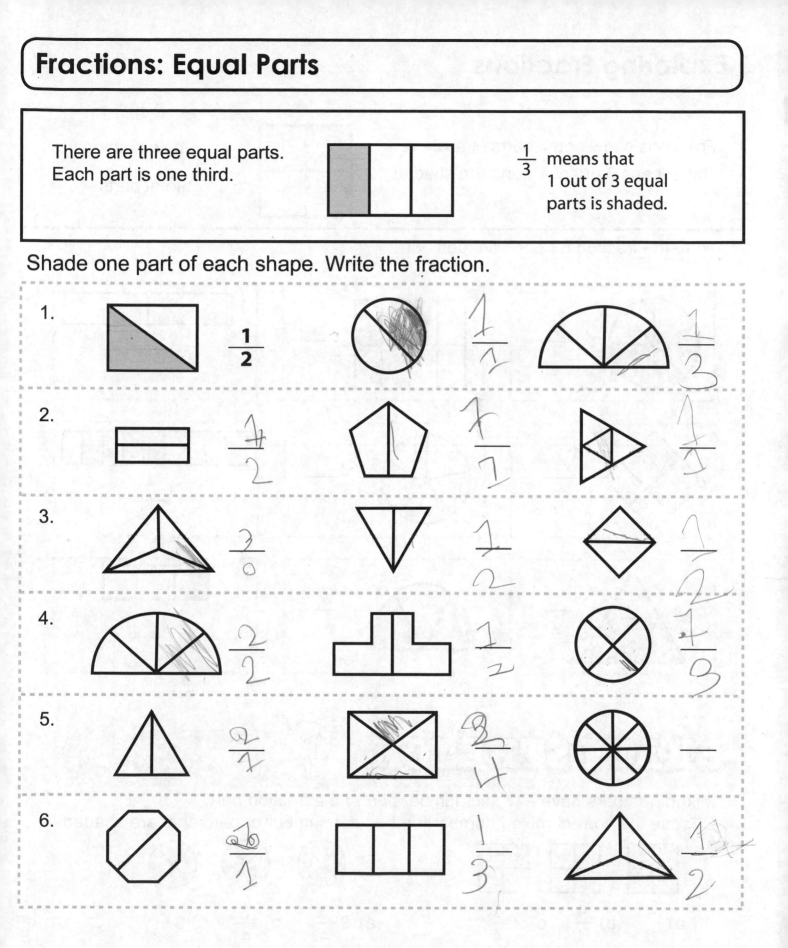

1. $\frac{1}{2}$ $\frac{1}{1}$ $\frac{1}{3}$

2. $\frac{7}{2}$ $\frac{7}{7}$ $\frac{1}{1}$

3. $\frac{2}{0}$ $\frac{1}{2}$ $\frac{1}{2}$

4. $\frac{2}{2}$ $\frac{1}{2}$ $\frac{1}{3}$

5. $\frac{2}{7}$ $\frac{2}{4}$ —

6. $\frac{2}{1}$ $\frac{1}{3}$ $\frac{11}{2}$

Exploring Fractions

Fractions show equal parts of a whole.
This means 3 out of 4 parts are shaded.

$\dfrac{3}{4}$ — how many parts
— total parts

1. Write the fraction for each shaded part.

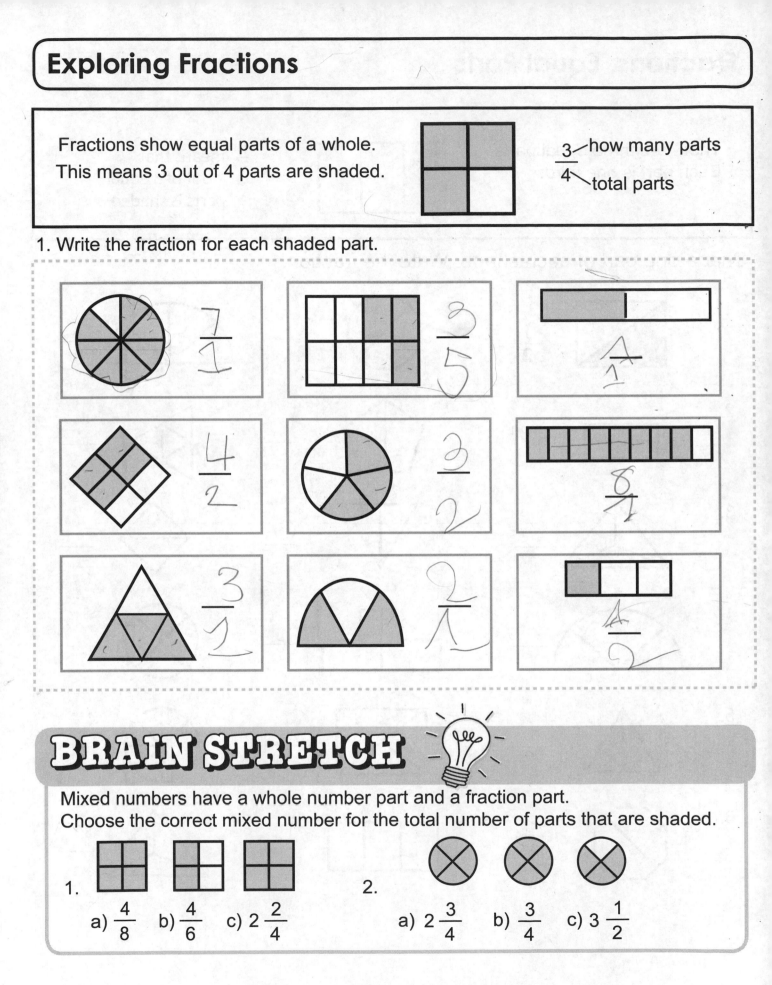

$\dfrac{7}{1}$

$\dfrac{3}{5}$

$\dfrac{4}{1}$

$\dfrac{4}{2}$

$\dfrac{3}{2}$

$\dfrac{8}{1}$

$\dfrac{3}{1}$

$\dfrac{2}{1}$

$\dfrac{4}{3}$

BRAIN STRETCH

Mixed numbers have a whole number part and a fraction part.
Choose the correct mixed number for the total number of parts that are shaded.

1.
a) $\dfrac{4}{8}$ b) $\dfrac{4}{6}$ c) $2\dfrac{2}{4}$

2.
a) $2\dfrac{3}{4}$ b) $\dfrac{3}{4}$ c) $3\dfrac{1}{2}$

Exploring Fractions (continued)

2. Write a fraction to show how much of the shape is not shaded.

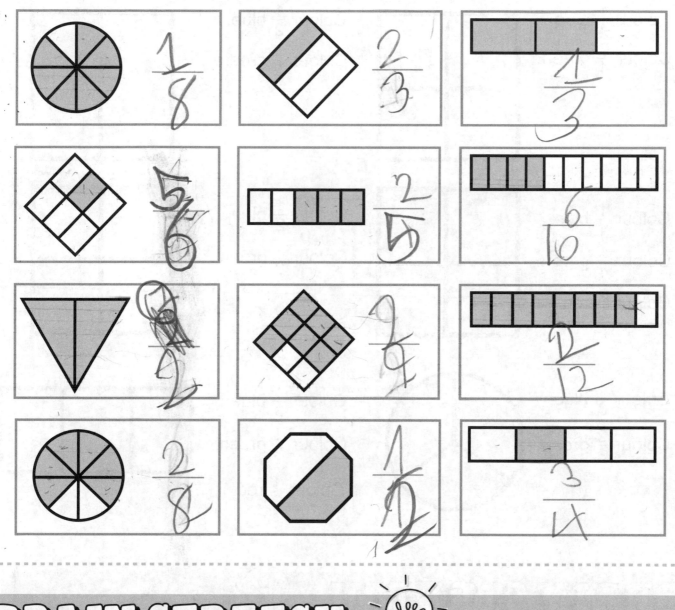

$\dfrac{1}{8}$

$\dfrac{2}{3}$

$\dfrac{1}{3}$

$\dfrac{5}{6}$

$\dfrac{2}{5}$

$\dfrac{6}{10}$

$\dfrac{1}{2}$

$\dfrac{4}{4}$

$\dfrac{2}{12}$

$\dfrac{2}{8}$

$\dfrac{1}{2}$

$\dfrac{3}{4}$

BRAIN STRETCH

a) Paige has 9 red beads and 4 blue beads. What fraction of Paige's beads are blue?

b) Tony has 4 oranges and 6 apples. What is the fraction of apples?

Colouring Fractions

Colour the fractions.

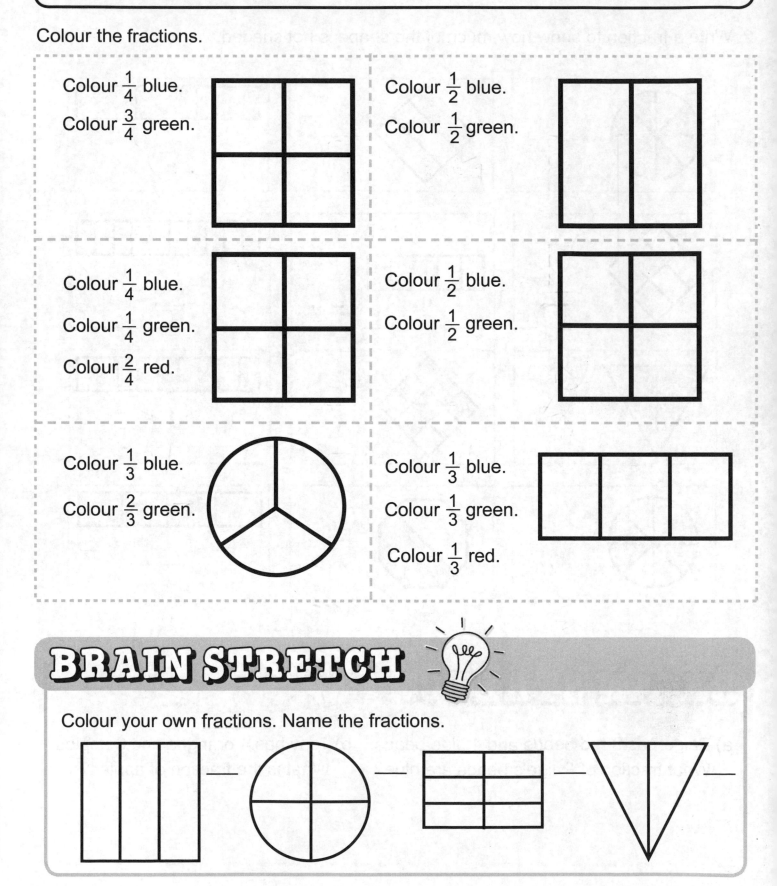

Colour $\frac{1}{4}$ blue.

Colour $\frac{3}{4}$ green.

Colour $\frac{1}{2}$ blue.

Colour $\frac{1}{2}$ green.

Colour $\frac{1}{4}$ blue.

Colour $\frac{1}{4}$ green.

Colour $\frac{2}{4}$ red.

Colour $\frac{1}{2}$ blue.

Colour $\frac{1}{2}$ green.

Colour $\frac{1}{3}$ blue.

Colour $\frac{2}{3}$ green.

Colour $\frac{1}{3}$ blue.

Colour $\frac{1}{3}$ green.

Colour $\frac{1}{3}$ red.

BRAIN STRETCH

Colour your own fractions. Name the fractions.

Fractions as Part of a Group

Colour the fraction.

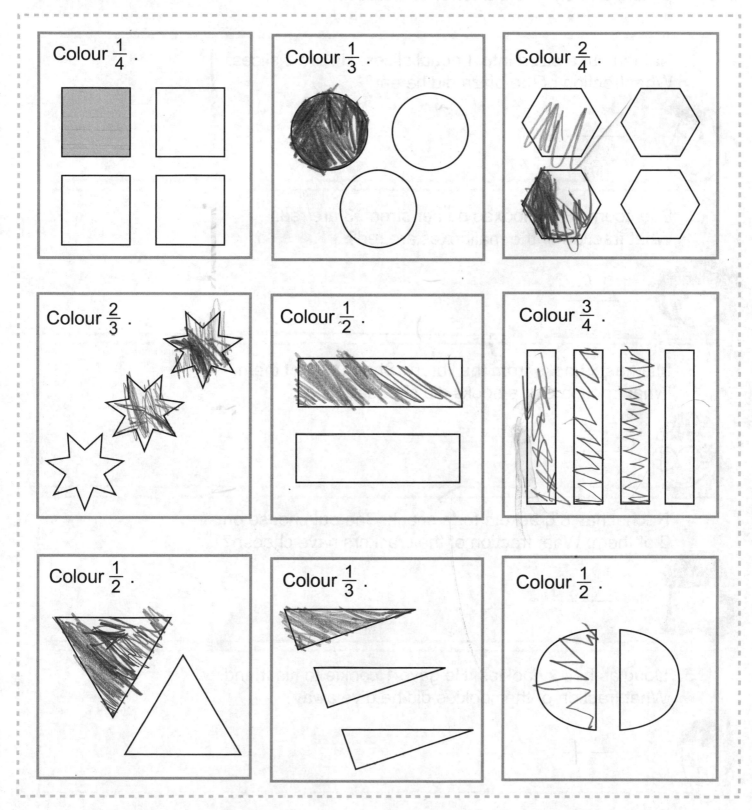

Colour $\frac{1}{4}$.

Colour $\frac{1}{3}$.

Colour $\frac{2}{4}$.

Colour $\frac{2}{3}$.

Colour $\frac{1}{2}$.

Colour $\frac{3}{4}$.

Colour $\frac{1}{2}$.

Colour $\frac{1}{3}$.

Colour $\frac{1}{2}$.

Fraction Problems

Draw a picture and show the answer as a fraction.

1. Nathan cut a pizza into 4 equal slices. He ate 2 slices. What fraction of the pizza did he eat?

   $\dfrac{2}{\quad}$

2. Sue counts 8 mailboxes on her street. 3 are red. What fraction of the mailboxes are red?

   $\dfrac{5}{\quad}$

3. Mia has 3 books from the library. She read 1 of them. What fraction of the books did she read?

   $\dfrac{2}{\quad}$

4. Rachel has 8 crackers for a snack. She put cheese on 2 of them. What fraction of the crackers have cheese?

   $\dfrac{6}{\quad}$

5. Douglas has 2 cookies. He gave 1 cookie to his friend. What fraction of the cookies did he give away?

   $\dfrac{\quad}{\quad}$

48

Exploring Polygons

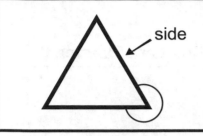side

A polygon is a 2D shape with at least 3 **sides**.
A regular polygon has all sides equal and all angles equal.

A corner of a polygon is a **vertex**.
The plural is **vertices**.

1. Fill in the chart.

Shape	Trace the Shape	Number of Sides	Number of Vertices
triangle		3	3
square		4	4
pentagon		5	5
hexagon		6	6
octagon		8	8

Exploring Polygons (continued)

2. Fill in the chart.

Shape	Trace the Shape	Number of Sides	Number of Vertices
rectangle		4	4
rhombus		4	4
parallelogram		4	4
trapezoid		4	4

BRAIN STRETCH

An irregular polygon does **not** have all sides equal and all angles equal.
Draw two irregular polygons.

Example:

Exploring Polygons (continued)

3. Put an X if it is **not** a polygon. Colour the regular polygons blue.
   Colour the irregular polygons red.

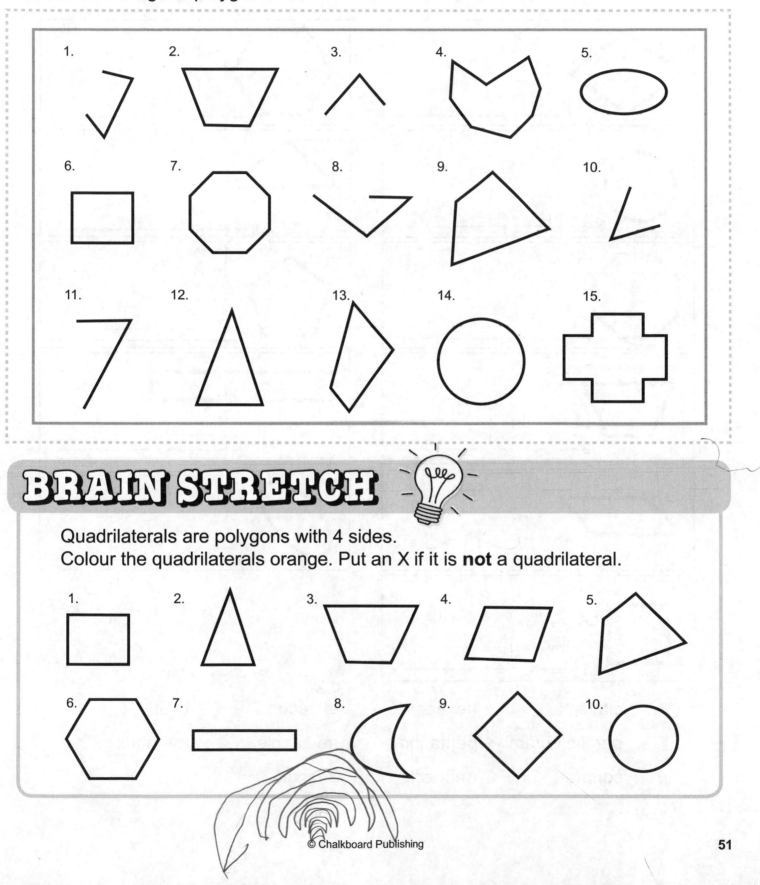

BRAIN STRETCH

Quadrilaterals are polygons with 4 sides.
Colour the quadrilaterals orange. Put an X if it is **not** a quadrilateral.

2D Shapes

Use the words below to write the correct name for each 2D shape.

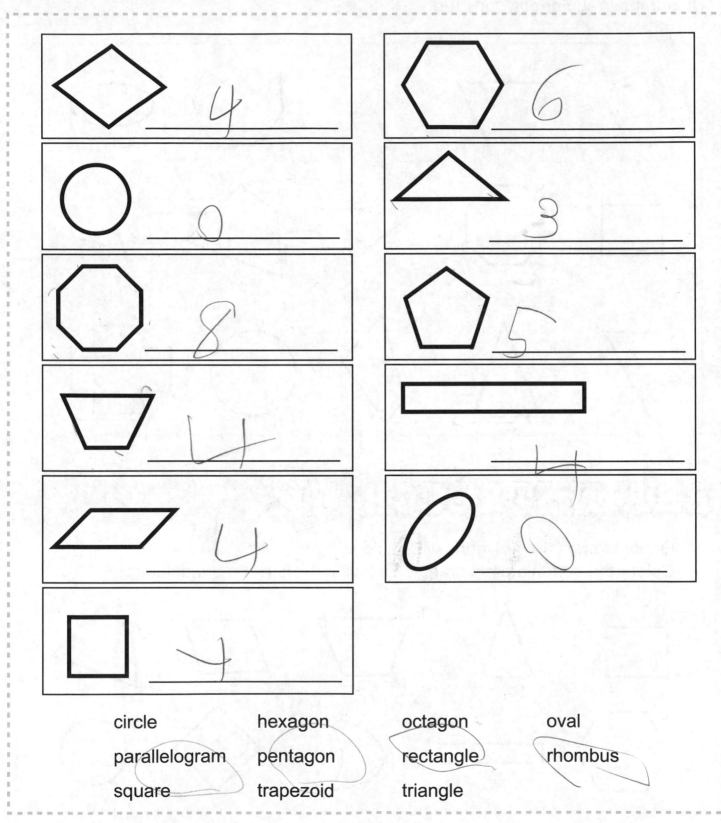

circle   hexagon   octagon   oval

parallelogram   pentagon   rectangle   rhombus

square   trapezoid   triangle

Sorting 2D Shapes

1. Read the rule. Colour the shapes that follow the rule.

Shapes with more than 4 vertices.

Shapes that are quadrilaterals.

Shapes with less than 5 sides.

Shapes with square corners.

Shapes that are irregular polygons.

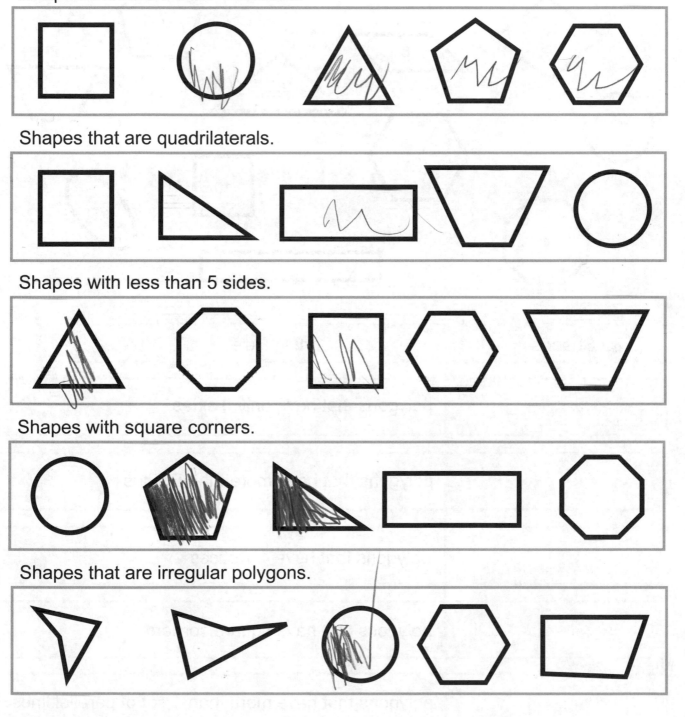

Sorting 2D Shapes (continued)

2. Sort the 2D shapes into groups.

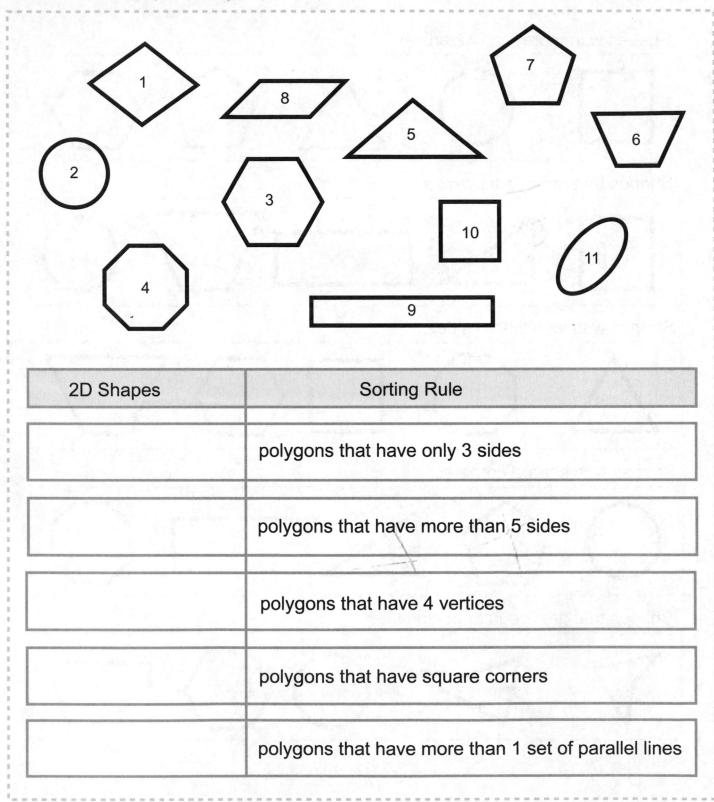

2D Shapes	Sorting Rule
	polygons that have only 3 sides
	polygons that have more than 5 sides
	polygons that have 4 vertices
	polygons that have square corners
	polygons that have more than 1 set of parallel lines

Identifying 3D Objects

1. Match the 3D object with its name.

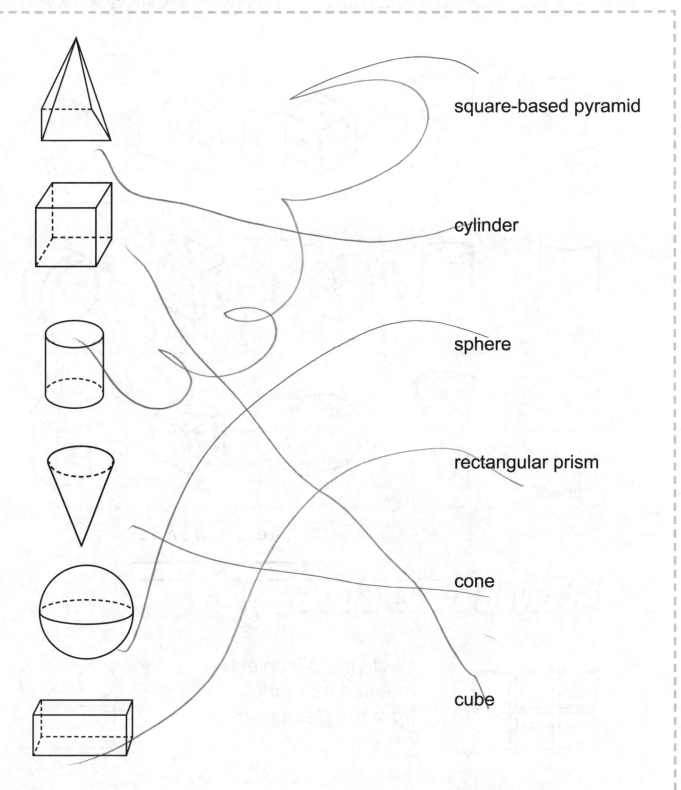

square-based pyramid

cylinder

sphere

rectangular prism

cone

cube

2. Match the name of the 3D object with an item it looks like. Circle the answer.

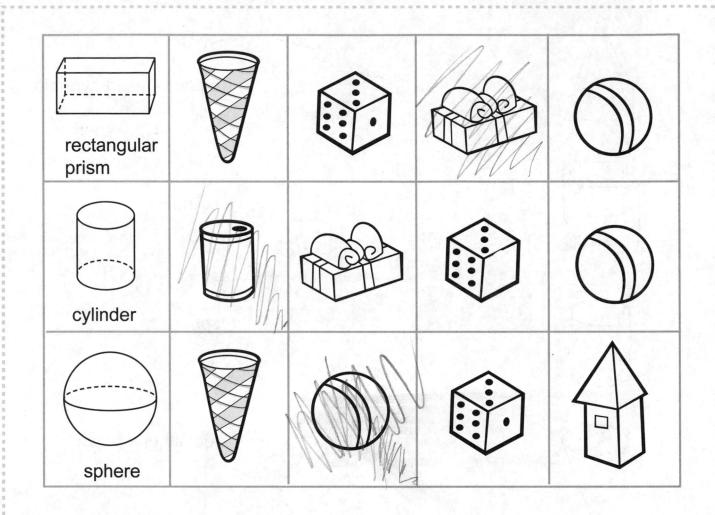

BRAIN STRETCH

a)

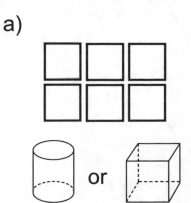

Circle the 3D object that can be made from the pieces.

b)

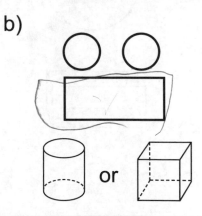

Attributes of 3D Objects

1. Use the words below to complete the chart. A **face** is any **flat side** of a shape. An **edge** is where **any two flat faces** of a shape meet.

cone   cylinder   square-based pyramid   cube

triangular prism   sphere   rectangular prism

	3D Object	Name of 3D Object	Number of Faces	Number of Edges	Number of Vertices
A.		Sphere			
B.		Cylinder			
C.		rectangular			
D.					
E.					
F.		Square base pyramid			
G.		triangular prism			

Attributes of 3D Objects (continued)

2. Circle the name of the 3D object that you can make from the pieces.

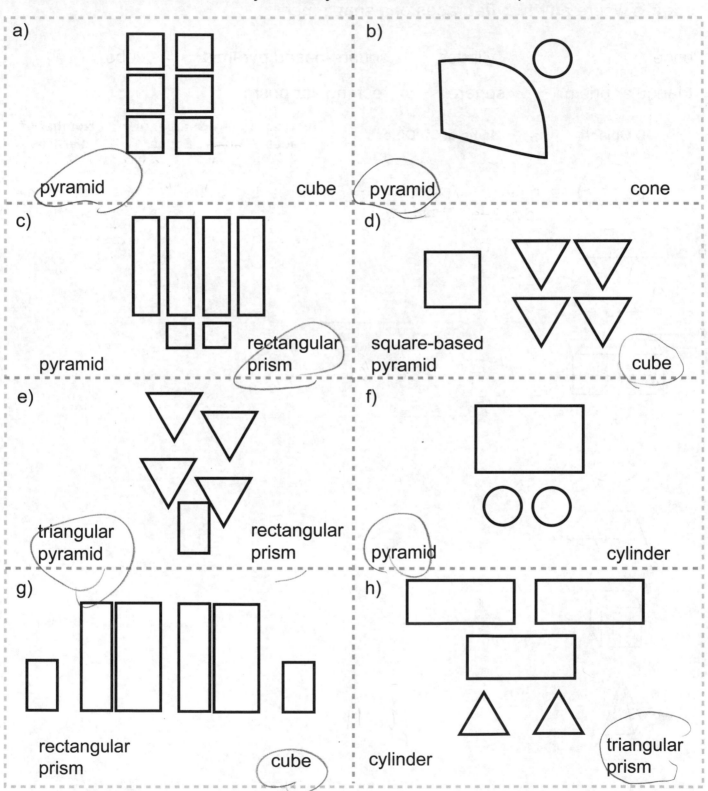

a)

~~pyramid~~   cube

b)

~~pyramid~~   cone

c)

pyramid   rectangular prism

d)

square-based pyramid   cube

e)

triangular pyramid   rectangular prism

f)

pyramid   cylinder

g)

rectangular prism   cube

h)

cylinder   triangular prism

Exploring Symmetry

A line of symmetry divides a figure into 2 parts that are the exact same size and shape. Some figures have more than 1 line of symmetry. Some figures have no lines of symmetry.

V — 1 line of symmetry

C — 1 line of symmetry

F — 0 lines of symmetry

1. Examine each letter. Draw a line of symmetry on the letters that have symmetry. Hint: Some letters have two. Circle the letters that do **not** have a line of symmetry.

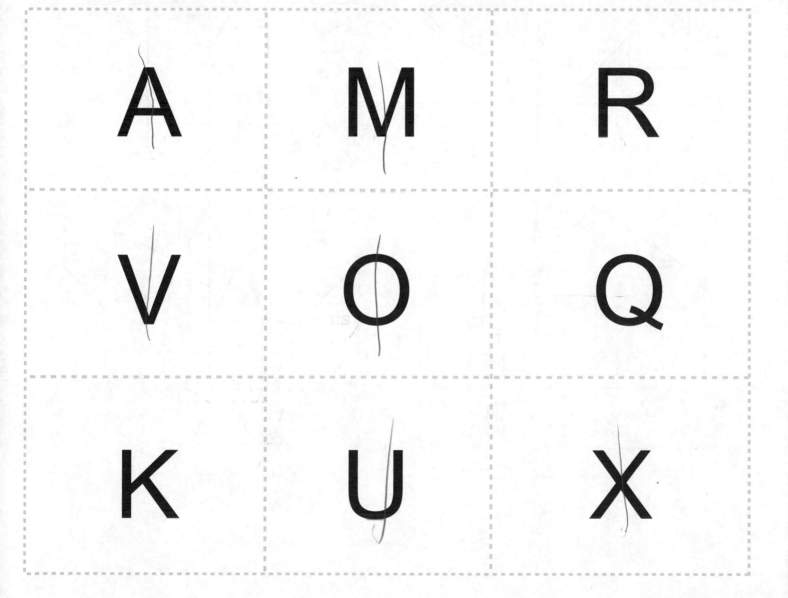

A   M   R

V   O   Q

K   U   X

Symmetry Fun

1. Each figure is half of a symmetrical shape. Complete each figure by using the dashed line of symmetry.

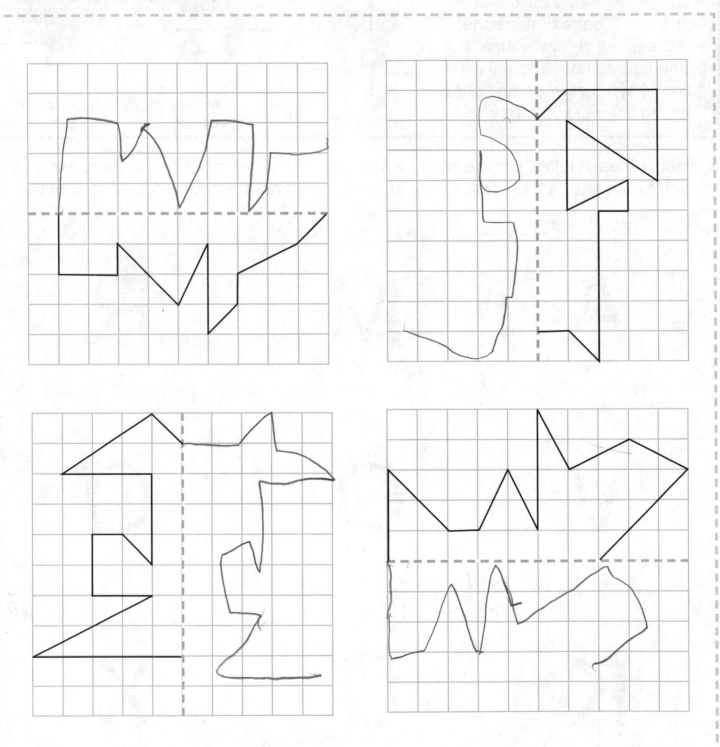

Congruent Figures

Congruent figures have the exact same shape and size.

1. Draw a line connecting the congruent shapes.

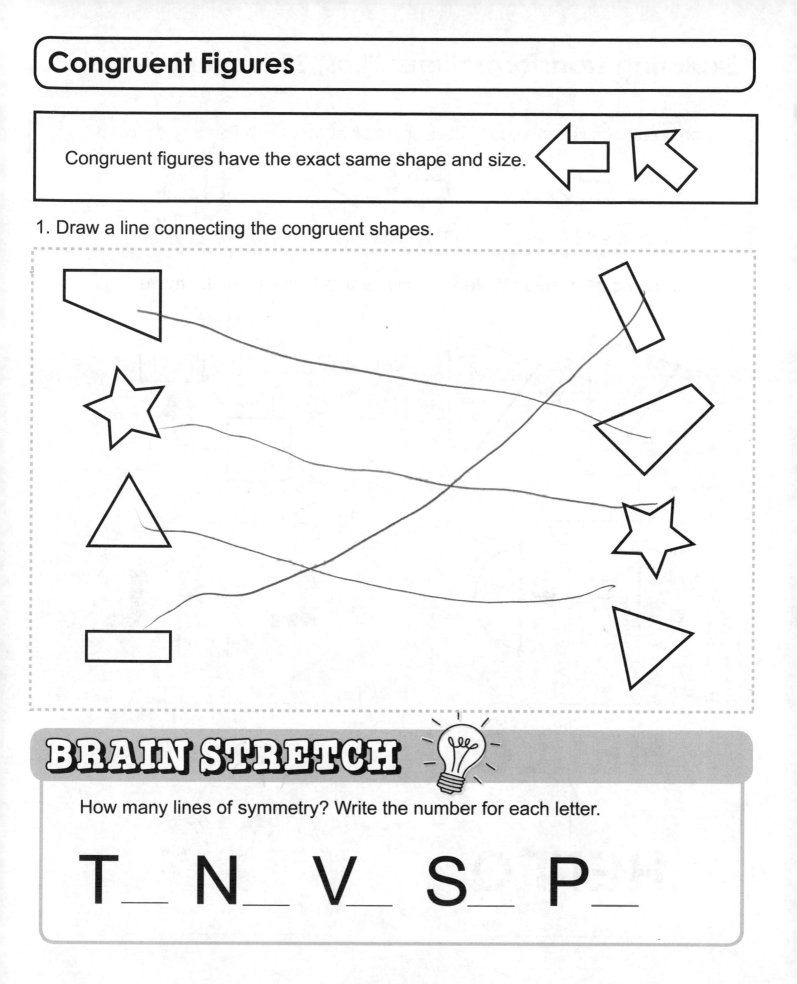

BRAIN STRETCH

How many lines of symmetry? Write the number for each letter.

T_ N_ V_ S_ P_

Exploring Transformations: Flips, Slides, and Turns

A transformation is a change in position. Look at how each figure has moved.

This is a flip.   This is a slide.   This is a turn.

1. How is the figure moved? Write slide, flip, or turn to tell about the move.

a) _____

b) _____

c) _____

d) _____

e) _____

f) _____

Exploring Pictographs

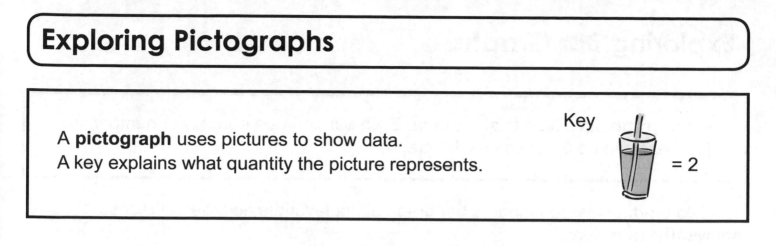

A **pictograph** uses pictures to show data.
A key explains what quantity the picture represents.

Key = 2

Here are the results of a survey about favourite drinks.
Use the pictograph to answer the questions about the results.

Favourite Drinks

Lemonade	
Milk	
Orange Juice	

Key = 2 people

1. How many people were surveyed? _____

2. Which drink did the fewest people choose? _____

3. Which two drinks were chosen by the same number of people?

   _____

4. How many more people chose milk than chose orange juice? _____

Exploring Bar Graphs

A **bar graph** uses bars to show data. Each bar shows a quantity or number. The bars can go up or across the graph.

The two grade 3 classes made a bar graph about favourite activities at recess. Answer the questions.

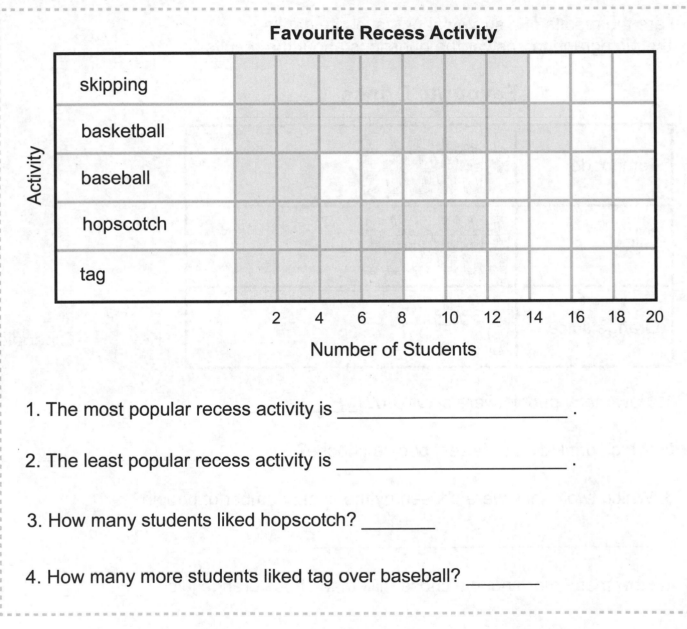

Favourite Recess Activity

1. The most popular recess activity is _____ .

2. The least popular recess activity is _____ .

3. How many students liked hopscotch? _____

4. How many more students liked tag over baseball? _____

Favourite Pizza Toppings Bar Graph

Ms. Gibson's grade 3 class did a survey about students' favourite pizza toppings.

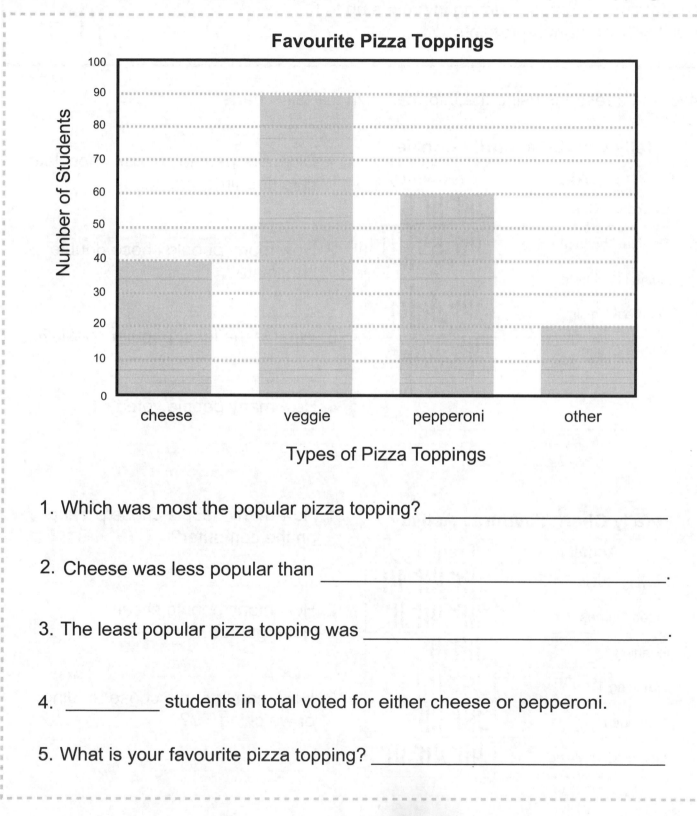

Favourite Pizza Toppings

1. Which was most the popular pizza topping? _____

2. Cheese was less popular than _____.

3. The least popular pizza topping was _____.

4. _____ students in total voted for either cheese or pepperoni.

5. What is your favourite pizza topping? _____

Reading Tally Charts

A **tally** chart records counting in groups up to 5.
Each tally or mark represents 1.

| = 1 ||||| = 5

Answer the questions using the information in the tally charts.

Tally Chart: Favourite Cookie

Cookie	Frequency
Chocolate Chip	||||| |||
Double Chocolate	||||| ||||| |||
Animal Crackers	||
Oatmeal Raisin	||||| ||||| ||
Vanilla Cream	||||| ||||

1. Did more people choose chocolate chip or animal crackers?

_____

2. How many people chose double chocolate?

_____

3. What is the least popular cookie?

_____

4. How many people voted?

_____

Tally Chart: Favourite Activity

Activity	Frequency
Playing Outside	||||| ||||| |||
Video Games	||||| ||||| |||
Reading	||||| ||
Watching TV	||||| ||||
Computer	||||| ||||
Listening to Music	||||| ||||| |||

1. How many people chose playing on the computer?

_____

2. How many people chose video games?

_____

3. How many people chose reading or watching TV?

_____

Favourite Snacks Bar Graph

Use the data from the tally chart to complete the bar graph. Answer the questions.

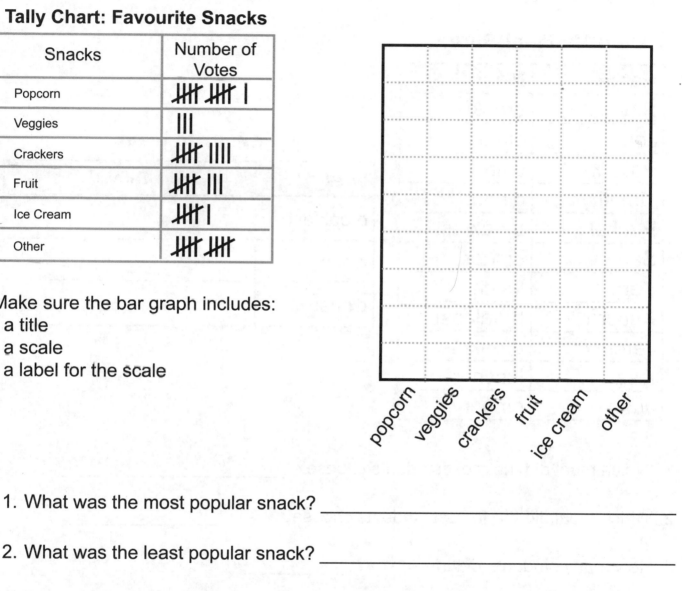

Tally Chart: Favourite Snacks

Snacks	Number of Votes
Popcorn	卌 卌 I
Veggies	III
Crackers	卌 IIII
Fruit	卌 III
Ice Cream	卌 I
Other	卌 卌

Make sure the bar graph includes:
• a title
• a scale
• a label for the scale

1. What was the most popular snack? _____

2. What was the least popular snack? _____

3. How many more students voted for crackers instead of fruit? _____

4. If 6 more students voted for ice cream, how
   many votes would there be for ice cream? _____

5. How many students voted in the survey? _____

Favourite Meal Survey Tally Chart

Iris surveyed her classmates about their favourite meal. Use the information from Iris's survey to complete the tally chart.

Favourite Meal Survey

Name	Meal
Roy	breakfast
Jody	dinner
Patrick	dinner
Timothy	dinner
Rachel	breakfast
Sam	dinner
Kara	lunch
Kendra	breakfast
Jeremy	breakfast
Lisa	lunch
Juan	dinner

Favourite Meal

Meal	Tally
breakfast	
lunch	
dinner	

1. Which meal did the most students choose? _____

2. Which meal did the fewest students choose? _____

3. How many students did Iris survey? _____

4. How many students chose breakfast? _____

5. How many students chose lunch? _____

6. How many students chose dinner? _____

Favourite Recess Activity Bar Graph

Michael surveyed the children in two grade 3 classes about their favourite recess activity.

1. Skipping got 12 votes, baseball got 11 votes, and basketball got 14 votes. Create a tally chart to show the information from the survey.

Skipping	Baseball	Basketball

2. Complete the **horizontal** bar graph to show the information from Michael. Make sure you use labels.

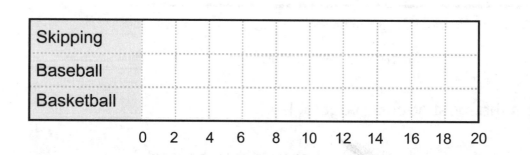

3. What was the most popular activity? _____

4. What was the least popular activity? _____

5. How many students voted in the survey? _____

6. How many students did not vote for basketball? _____

Favourite Vegetable Bar Graph

Mr. Clark's class took a survey of favourite vegetables.
Use the data from the frequency table to complete the bar graph.

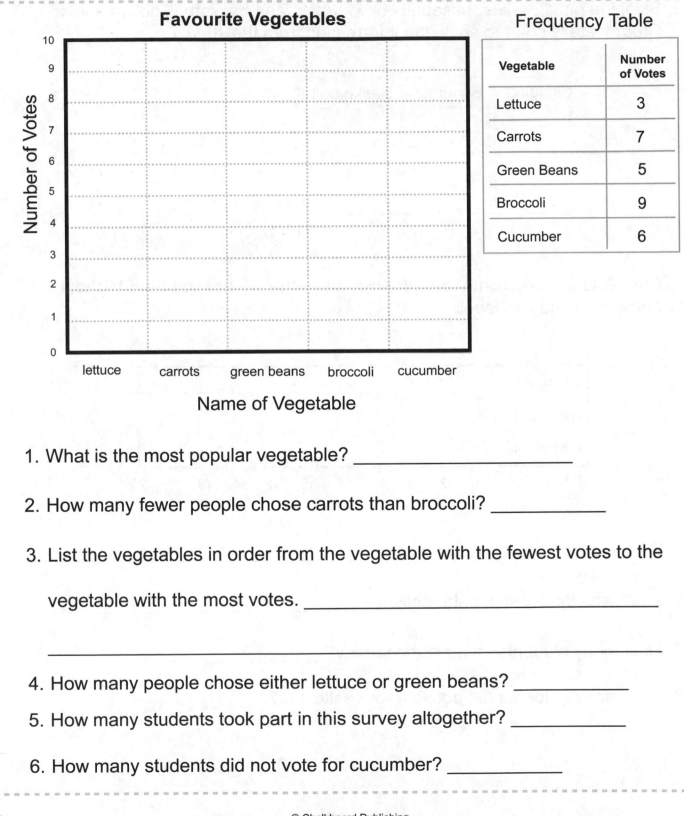

Favourite Vegetables

Number of Votes (y-axis: 0–10)

Name of Vegetable (x-axis: lettuce, carrots, green beans, broccoli, cucumber)

Frequency Table

Vegetable	Number of Votes
Lettuce	3
Carrots	7
Green Beans	5
Broccoli	9
Cucumber	6

1. What is the most popular vegetable? _____

2. How many fewer people chose carrots than broccoli? _____

3. List the vegetables in order from the vegetable with the fewest votes to the vegetable with the most votes. _____

_____

4. How many people chose either lettuce or green beans? _____

5. How many students took part in this survey altogether? _____

6. How many students did not vote for cucumber? _____

Exploring Ordered Pairs

An **ordered pair** describes a point on a grid. It has 2 numbers in a certain order.
• The first number tells how many units to count to the right.
• The second number tells how many units to count up.
Hint: Always start counting at the bottom left corner, at 0.

Count 1 unit right. Go up 3 units. The ordered pair is (1, 3).

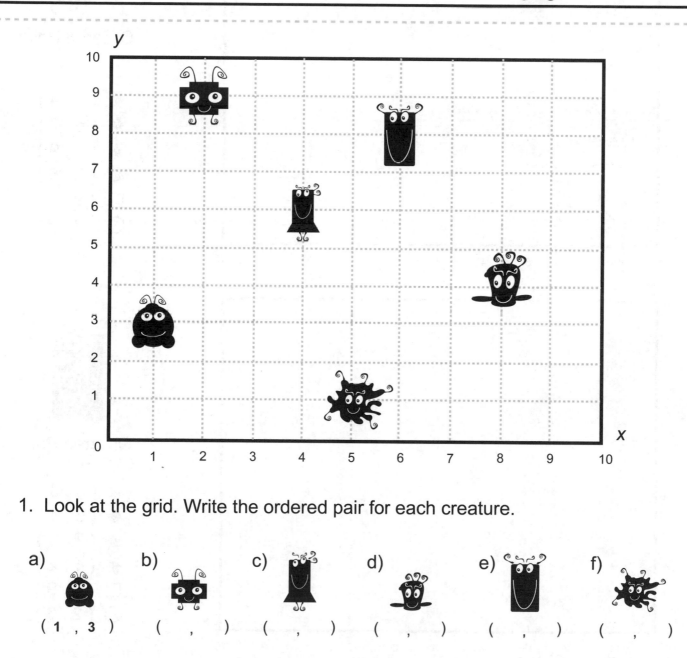

1. Look at the grid. Write the ordered pair for each creature.

a) (**1** , **3**)   b) (,)   c) (,)   d) (,)   e) (,)   f) (,)

Exploring Ordered Pairs (continued)

2. Draw the shapes on the grid at the locations given by the ordered pairs.

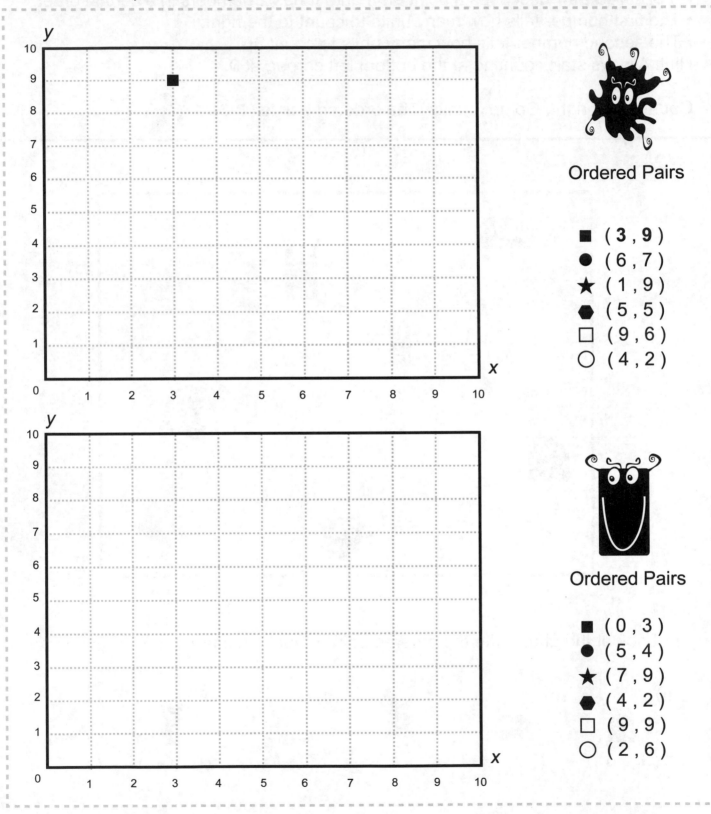

Ordered Pairs

■ (**3** , **9**)
● (6 , 7)
★ (1 , 9)
⬣ (5 , 5)
□ (9 , 6)
○ (4 , 2)

Ordered Pairs

■ (0 , 3)
● (5 , 4)
★ (7 , 9)
⬣ (4 , 2)
□ (9 , 9)
○ (2 , 6)

Exploring Measurement

1. What would be the best unit of measure for the following?

kilometres   **metres**   **centimetres**

The length of a classroom.	
The width of a stamp.	
The distance between two cities.	
The length of a book.	
The length of your arm.	
The length of a bus.	

2. Match the best measurement tool to measure each of the following:

The amount of sugar
in a cake recipe   ruler

The weight of 3 bunches
of bananas   thermometer

The temperature
on a hot day   measuring cup

The length of
a caterpillar   scale

Exploring Perimeter

The perimeter is the distance around a figure.
To find the distance around, add the sides.

5 m + 5 m + 3 m + 3 m = 16 m

The distance around is 16 metres.

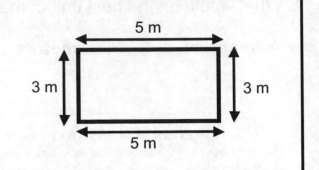

What is the distance around each shape? Use **m** for metres.

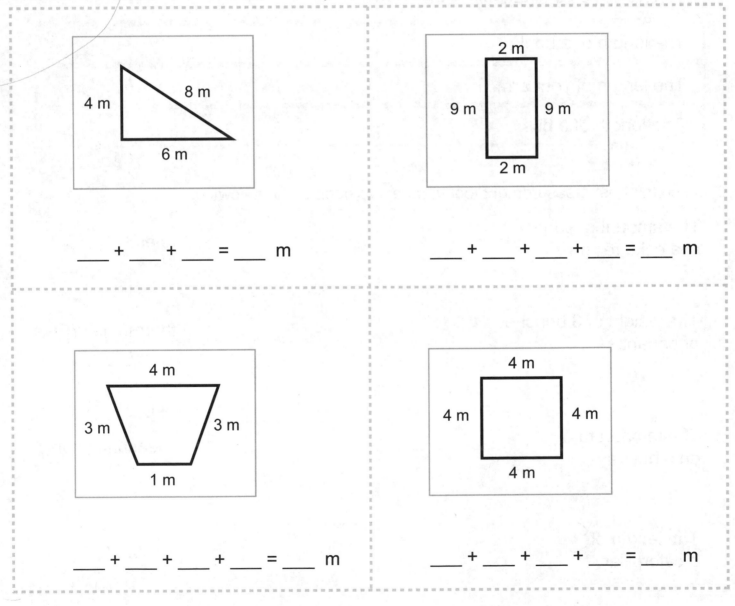

___ + ___ + ___ = ___ m

___ + ___ + ___ + ___ = ___ m

___ + ___ + ___ + ___ = ___ m

___ + ___ + ___ + ___ = ___ m

Exploring Perimeter (continued)

The **perimeter** is the distance around a figure. Find the perimeter of each figure by counting the units around each figure.

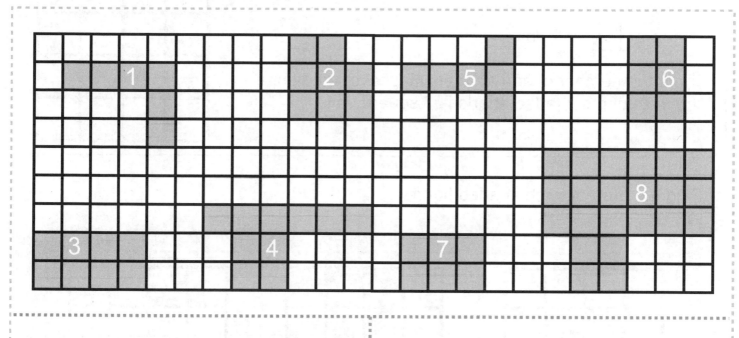

1. The perimeter of figure 1 is ___ units.

2. The perimeter of figure 2 is ___ units.

3. The perimeter of figure 3 is ___ units.

4. The perimeter of figure 4 is ___ units.

5. The perimeter of figure 5 is ___ units.

6. The perimeter of figure 6 is ___ units.

7. The perimeter of figure 7 is ___ units.

8. The perimeter of figure 8 is ___ units.

BRAIN STRETCH

Both of these figures have 12 squares.
Circle the figure with the shortest perimeter.

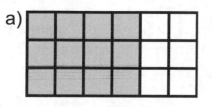

a)

b)

Exploring Area

Area is the number of units that covers a figure.

1 square [image] = 1 unit.

Count the number of square units that cover the figure.
The area of the shaded shape is 7 square units.

1. Find the area of each shaded figure.

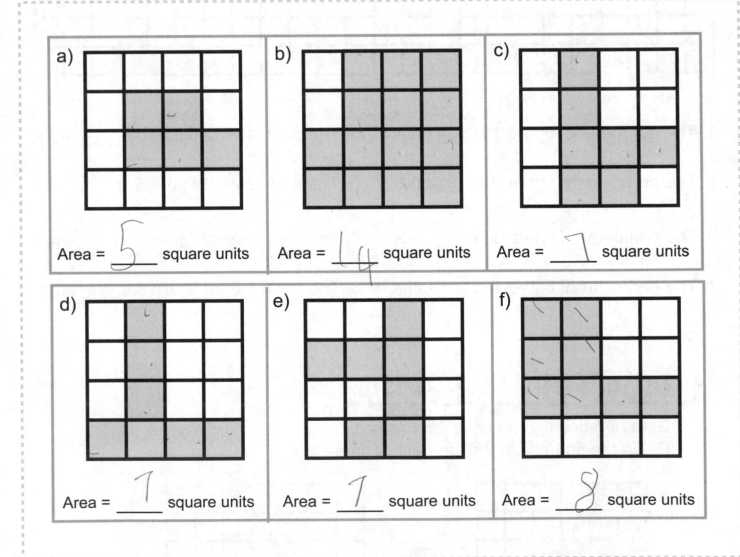

a)

Area = 5 square units

b)

Area = 4 square units

c)

Area = 7 square units

d)

Area = 7 square units

e)

Area = 7 square units

f)

Area = 8 square units

© Chalkboard Publishing

Exploring Area (continued)

2. Find the area of each figure.

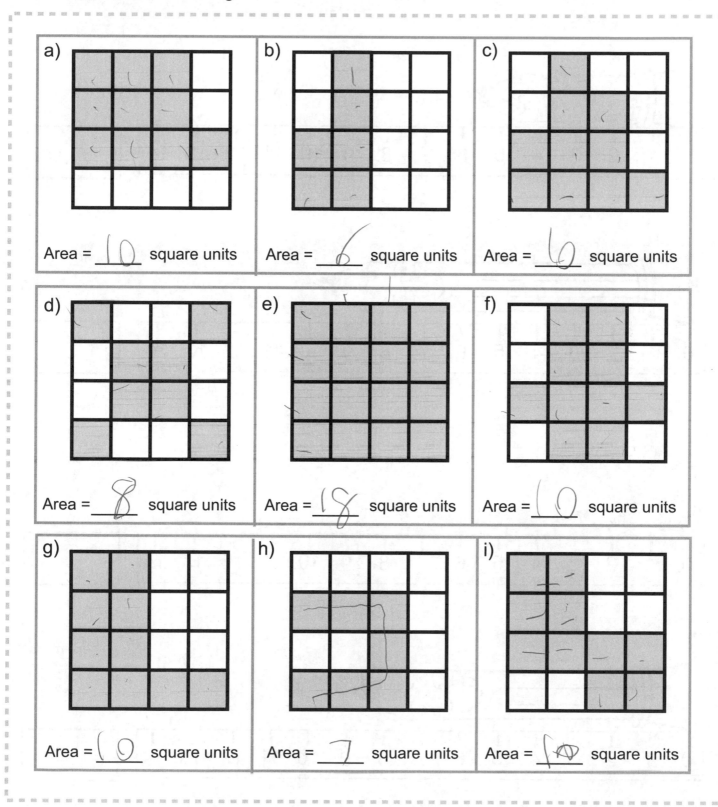

a) Area = 10 square units

b) Area = 6 square units

c) Area = 6 square units

d) Area = 8 square units

e) Area = 18 square units

f) Area = 10 square units

g) Area = 10 square units

h) Area = 7 square units

i) Area = 10 square units

Exploring Length

Write the length in centimetres. Write **cm** for centimetres.

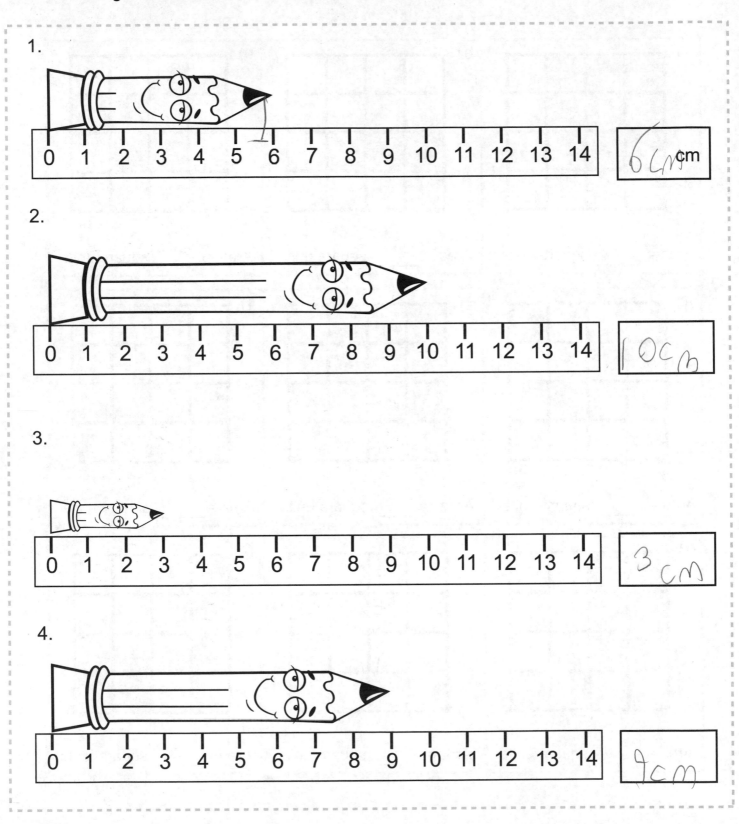

1.

6 cm

2.

10 cm

3.

3 cm

4.

9 cm

What Time Is It?

A clock shows time using numbers and hands. The face of a clock shows the numbers 1 to 12. It takes 5 minutes for the long minute hand to move from one number to the next.

The time is 2:40.

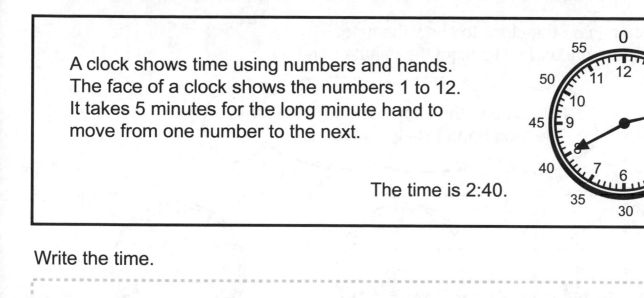

Write the time.

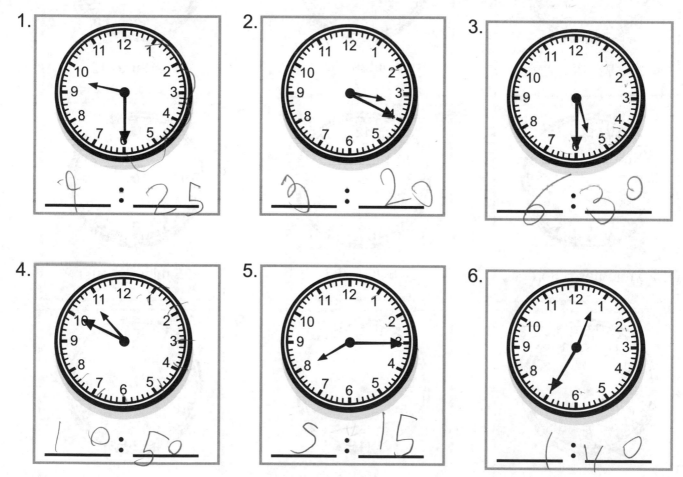

1. _____ : _____   (handwritten: 9 : 25)

2. _____ : _____   (handwritten: 3 : 20)

3. _____ : _____   (handwritten: 6 : 30)

4. _____ : _____   (handwritten: 10 : 50)

5. _____ : _____   (handwritten: 5 : 15)

6. _____ : _____   (handwritten: 1 : 40)

Drawing the Hands

Draw the two hands on the clock to show the time.
Highlight the hour hand blue. Highlight the minute hand red.

Remember, the short hand tells the hour.
The long hand tells the minutes.

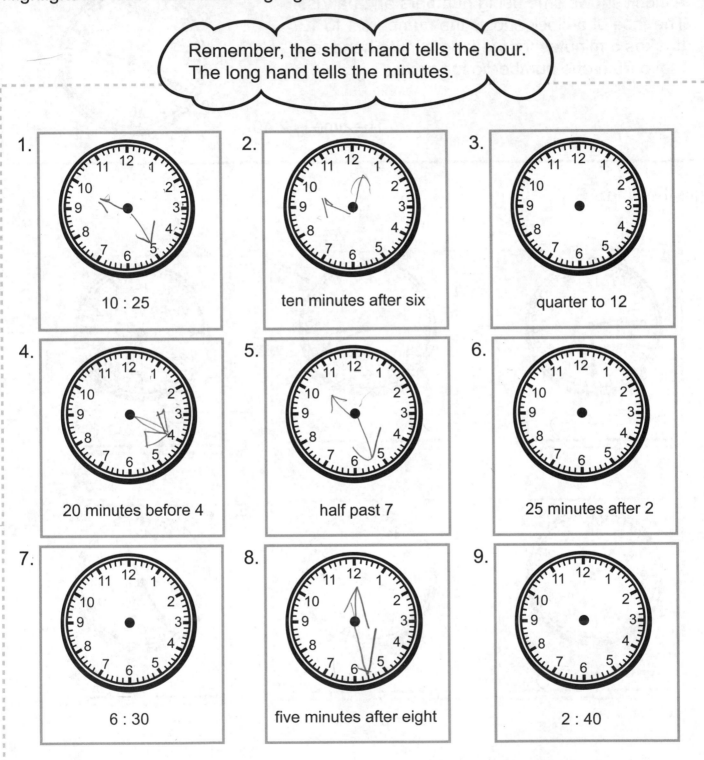

1. 10 : 25

2. ten minutes after six

3. quarter to 12

4. 20 minutes before 4

5. half past 7

6. 25 minutes after 2

7. 6 : 30

8. five minutes after eight

9. 2 : 40

Elapsed Time

Elapsed time is the amount of time that has passed from the start of a time period to the end of a time period.

25 minutes have elapsed.

Start Time

End Time

3:30 p.m.

3:55 p.m.

Write the start time and the end time.

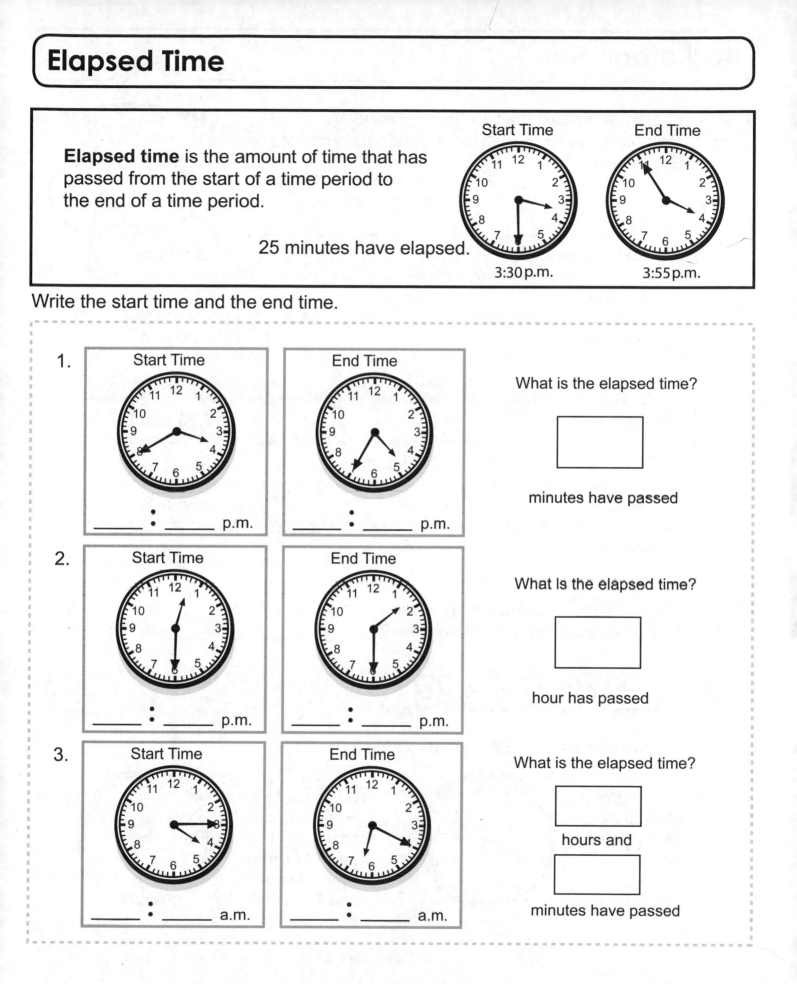

1.

Start Time

End Time

_____ : _____ p.m.

_____ : _____ p.m.

What is the elapsed time?

minutes have passed

2.

Start Time

End Time

_____ : _____ p.m.

_____ : _____ p.m.

What Is the elapsed time?

hour has passed

3.

Start Time

End Time

_____ : _____ a.m.

_____ : _____ a.m.

What is the elapsed time?

hours and

minutes have passed

Basketball Fun

1. Michael practises basketball for 25 minutes every night. Complete the chart to show his start and end time for each practice.

a.m. refers to before noon
p.m. refers to after noon

Day of the week	Start Time	Finish Time
Sunday	5:45 p.m.	
Monday		6:20 p.m.
Tuesday	5:35 p.m.	
Wednesday		7:25 p.m.
Thursday	5:40 p.m.	
Friday		4:55 p.m.
Saturday	5:05 p.m.	

2. How many minutes did Michael practise shooting basketballs for the whole week? _____

BRAIN STRETCH

Fill in the correct time. Be sure to include a.m. or p.m.

a) This afternoon, Megan started her homework at:

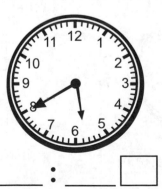

_____ : _____ ☐

b) Megan did her homework after school for 1 hour and 10 minutes. What time did she finish her homework?

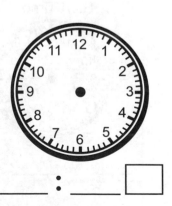

_____ : _____ ☐

Reading a Calendar

Use the calendar to answer the questions.

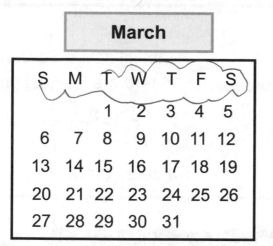

March

S	M	T	W	T	F	S
		1	2	3	4	5
6	7	8	9	10	11	12
13	14	15	16	17	18	19
20	21	22	23	24	25	26
27	28	29	30	31		

June

S	M	T	W	T	F	S
			1	2	3	4
5	6	7	8	9	10	11
12	13	14	15	16	17	18
19	20	21	22	23	24	25
26	27	28	29	30		

1. What day of the week is March 14?

_____

2. How many Wednesdays are there in March?

_____

3. What is the date 1 week and 2 days after March 3?

_____

4. What is the date of the first Tuesday in March?

_____

5. On what day of the week will the next month begin?

_____

6. What is the date of the third Monday?

_____

1. Katherine will have a birthday party in 4 days. Today is June 6. What is the date of her birthday?

_____

2. Jamil's karate tournament is in two weeks. Today is June 11. What date is the karate tournament?

_____

3. Jane will go on a trip in 6 days. Today is June 10. On what date will Jane go on her trip?

_____

4. Carolyn leaves for New York in 9 days. Today is June 17. What date will she leave?

_____

Addition and Multiplication

1. Write the addition sentence and the multiplication sentence.

Look at the groups of 3.

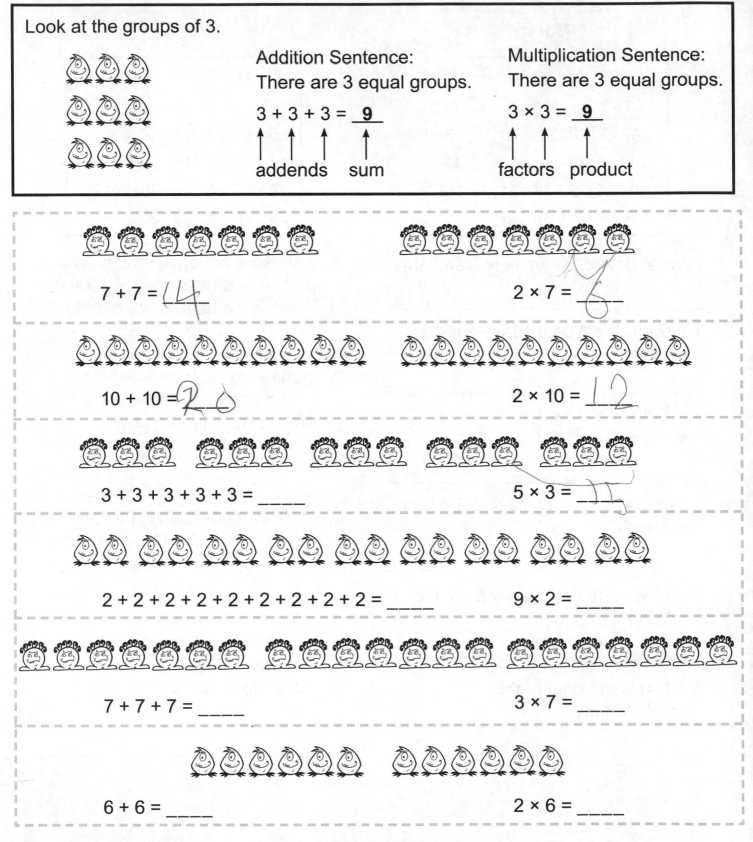

Addition Sentence:
There are 3 equal groups.

$3 + 3 + 3 = $ __9__

addends   sum

Multiplication Sentence:
There are 3 equal groups.

$3 \times 3 = $ __9__

factors   product

$7 + 7 = $ _14_

$2 \times 7 = $ ___

$10 + 10 = $ _20_

$2 \times 10 = $ _12_

$3 + 3 + 3 + 3 + 3 = $ _____

$5 \times 3 = $ _____

$2 + 2 + 2 + 2 + 2 + 2 + 2 + 2 + 2 = $ _____

$9 \times 2 = $ _____

$7 + 7 + 7 = $ _____

$3 \times 7 = $ _____

$6 + 6 = $ _____

$2 \times 6 = $ _____

Multiplying by Skip Counting

When you multiply two numbers, the answer is called the **product**.
Skip count on the number line to multiply. Write the product.

3 × 4 =

$$4 \quad + \quad 4 \quad + \quad 4 \quad = \underline{\mathbf{12}}$$

0 1 2 3 4 5 6 7 8 9 10 11 12 13 14 15 16 17 18 19 20

3 × 4 = **12**

4 × 4 =   = _____

0 1 2 3 4 5 6 7 8 9 10 11 12 13 14 15 16 17 18 19 20

4 × 4 = 18

5 × 2 =   = _____

0 1 2 3 4 5 6 7 8 9 10 11 12 13 14 15 16 17 18 19 20

5 × 2 = _____

2 × 7 =   = _____

0 1 2 3 4 5 6 7 8 9 10 11 12 13 14 15 16 17 18 19 20

2 × 7 = _____

Using Arrays to Help You Multiply

In the **array**, there are 2 rows with 4 blocks in each row.
Skip count by 4s to count the blocks.
The multiplication statement is 2 × 4 = 8.

2 × 4 = 8
factors ⟶ product

1. Write a multiplication statement for each array.

<u> 2 </u> rows and <u> 3 </u> blocks in each row <u> 2 × 3 = 6 </u>

a) ___ rows and ___ blocks in each row _____

b) ___ rows and ___ blocks in each row _____

c) ___ rows and ___ blocks in each row _____

d) ___ rows and ___ blocks in each row _____

e) ___ rows and ___ blocks in each row _____

f) ___ rows and ___ blocks in each row _____

2. Write a multiplication statement for each array.

a) _____

b) _____

c) _____

d) _____

e) _____

f) _____

g) _____

i) _____

3. Draw an array for each. Write the multiplication statement.

a) 7 × 3 = 21

b) 6 × 5 = 31

c) 1 × 7 = 7

d) 6 × 6 = 36

e) 4 × 4 = 16

f) 5 × 5 = 25

g) 4 × 7 = 28

h) 5 × 8 = 40

i) 2 × 9 = 18

j) 10 × 4 = 40

k) 9 × 2 = 18

l) 8 × 3 = 24

Multiplication Table for 0 to 10

The numbers on the dark borders are the **factors**.

The numbers inside the table are the **products**.

Try it! To find the product of 6 × 9, for example, find 6 in the left border and put your finger on it.

Then find 9 in the top border and put your finger on it.

Slide your finger on the 6 to the right across the row.

Slide your finger on the 9 down the column. Keep sliding your fingers until they meet.

The number in the square where the row and column meet is the product of the two numbers.

So 6 × 9 = 54.

×	0	1	2	3	4	5	6	7	8	9	10
0	0	0	0	0	0	0	0	0	0	0	0
1	0	1	2	3	4	5	6	7	8	9	10
2	0	2	4	6	8	10	12	14	16	18	20
3	0	3	6	9	12	15	18	21	24	27	30
4	0	4	8	12	16	20	24	28	32	36	40
5	0	5	10	15	20	25	30	35	40	45	50
6	0	6	12	18	24	30	36	42	48	54	60
7	0	7	14	21	28	35	42	49	56	63	70
8	0	8	16	24	32	40	48	56	64	72	80
9	0	9	18	27	36	45	54	63	72	81	90
10	0	10	20	30	40	50	60	70	80	90	100

Multiplying by 0 and 1

The product is always the same as the greater factor when any number is multiplied by 1.	The product is always 0 when any factor is multiplied by 0.
For example, $10 \times 1 = 10$.	For example, $0 \times 4 = 0$.

Multiply.

$0 \times 12 = \underline{12}$ $11 \times 1 = \underline{11}$ $8 \times 0 = \underline{0}$ $1 \times 3 = \underline{3}$

$5 \times 1 = \underline{5}$ $7 \times 1 = \underline{7}$ $3 \times 0 = \underline{0}$ $0 \times 6 = \underline{0}$

$6 \times 1 = \underline{6}$ $10 \times 1 = \underline{10}$ $1 \times 8 = \underline{8}$ $1 \times 0 = \underline{0}$

$0 \times 7 = \underline{0}$ $4 \times 1 = \underline{4}$ $9 \times 1 = \underline{9}$ $0 \times 10 = \underline{0}$

Using Doubles to Multiply

What is the double of 13?

13 = 10 + 3
The double of 10 is 20.
The double of 3 is 6.
20 + 6 = 26
The double of 13 is 26.

1. Draw a model. Then double the number.

What is the double of 14?

14 = 10 + ___

The double of 10 is ___.

The double of ___ is ___.

___ + ___ = ___

The double of 14 is ___.

What is the double of 11?

11 = 10 + ___

The double of 10 is ___.

The double of ___ is ___.

___ + ___ = ___

The double of 11 is ____.

What is the double of 19?

19 = 10 + ___

The double of 10 is ___.

The double of ___ is ___.

___ + ___ = ___

The double of 19 is ___.

What is the double of 23?

23 = 20 + ___

The double of 20 is ___.

The double of ___ is ___.

___ + ___ = ___

The double of 23 is ___.

Using Doubles to Multiply (continued)

If you know 2 times a number, you can double it to find 4 times the number.

For 4 × 6, you know:
$$2 × 6 = 12$$
Double the 2 to get 4:
$$4 × 6 = 24$$
You double the product to get 24.

$$2 × 6 = 12$$

$$4 × 6 = 24$$

2. Use doubles to multiply. Draw an array to help you multiply.

a) 3 × 5 = 15

So, 6 × 5 = 31

b) 2 × 9 = 18

So, 4 × 9 = 36

c) 2 × 6 = 12

So, 4 × 6 = 24

d) 2 × 8 = 16

So, 4 × 8 = 32

e) 2 × 5 = 10

So, 4 × 5 = 20

f) 3 × 7 = 21

So, 6 × 7 = 42

Matching Multiplication to Addition: Facts for 2

Complete the multiplication facts for 2. Use a multiplication table to help you. Then write the sums. Underline each matching sum and product. Use a different colour for each pair.

$1 \times 2 = $ _____ $2 + 2 + 2 + 2 + 2 + 2 + 2 + 2 = $ _____

$2 \times 2 = $ _____ $2 + 0 = $ _____

$3 \times 2 = $ _____ $2 + 2 + 2 + 2 + 2 + 2 + 2 + 2 + 2 = $ _____

$4 \times 2 = $ _____ $2 + 2 + 2 + 2 + 2 + 2 + 2 = $ _____

$5 \times 2 = $ _____ $2 + 2 + 2 = $ _____

$6 \times 2 = $ _____ $2 + 2 + 2 + 2 + 2 = $ _____

$7 \times 2 = $ _____ $2 + 2 + 2 + 2 = $ _____

$8 \times 2 = $ _____ $2 + 2 + 2 + 2 + 2 + 2 = $ _____

$9 \times 2 = $ _____ $2 + 2 + 2 + 2 + 2 + 2 + 2 + 2 + 2 + 2 = $ _____

$10 \times 2 = $ _____ $2 + 2 = $ _____

Two Times Table

1. Multiply. Colour the odd products yellow. Colour the even products pink.

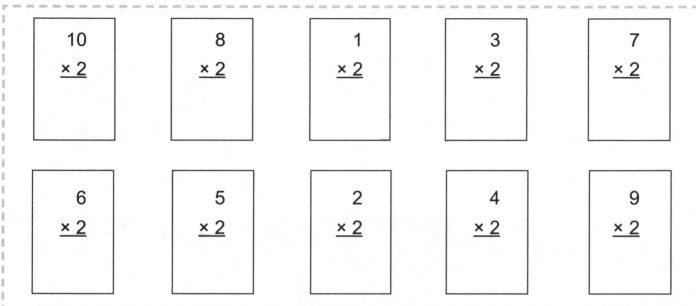

| 10
× 2 | 8
× 2 | 1
× 2 | 3
× 2 | 7
× 2 |
| 6
× 2 | 5
× 2 | 2
× 2 | 4
× 2 | 9
× 2 |

2. Multiply.

2 × _____ = 16	2 × _____ = 2	2 × _____ = 4	2 × _____ = 20
2 × _____ = 8	2 × _____ = 14	2 × _____ = 12	2 × _____ = 18
2 × _____ = 6	2 × _____ = 10		

Tip for Multiplying by 2
Double the number!
For example, 4 × 2.
Think: 4 + 4 = 8. So, 4 × 2 = 8.

Remember to practise skip counting by 2s!

Matching Multiplication to Addition: Facts for 3

Complete the multiplication facts for 3. Use a multiplication table to help you. Then write the sums. Underline each matching sum and product. Use a different colour for each pair.

$1 \times 3 =$ _3_

$3 + 3 + 3 + 3 + 3 + 3 + 3 + 3 + 3 =$ ____

$2 \times 3 =$ _6_

$3 + 3 =$ _6_

$3 \times 3 =$ _7_

$3 + 3 + 3 + 3 =$ _15_

$4 \times 3 =$ _12_

$3 + 3 + 3 + 3 + 3 =$ ____

$5 \times 3 =$ _15_

$3 + 0 =$ _3_

$6 \times 3 =$ _18_

$3 + 3 + 3 + 3 + 3 + 3 =$ _18_

$7 \times 3 =$ _21_

$3 + 3 + 3 + 3 + 3 + 3 + 3 + 3 =$ ____

$8 \times 3 =$ _24_

$3 + 3 + 3 + 3 + 3 + 3 + 3 + 3 + 3 + 3 =$ ____

$9 \times 3 =$ _17_

$3 + 3 + 3 =$ ____

$10 \times 3 =$ ____

$3 + 3 + 3 + 3 + 3 + 3 + 3 =$ ____

Three Times Table

1. Multiply. Colour the odd products yellow. Colour the even products pink.

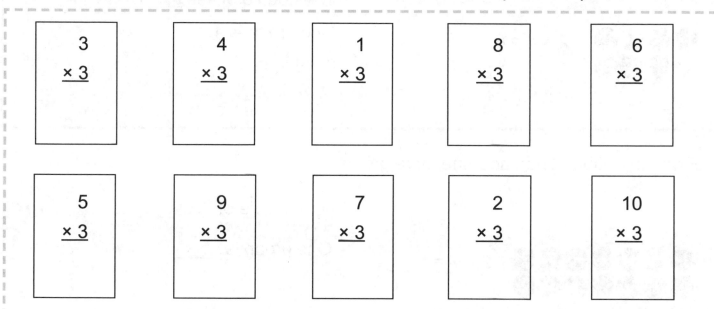

3 × 3	4 × 3	1 × 3	8 × 3	6 × 3
5 × 3	9 × 3	7 × 3	2 × 3	10 × 3

2. Multiply.

3 × _____ = 24	3 × _____ = 3	3 × _____ = 6	3 × _____ = 30
3 × _____ = 12	3 × _____ = 21	3 × _____ = 18	3 × _____ = 27
3 × _____ = 9	3 × _____ = 15		

Tip for Multiplying by 3
Double the number, and add one more!
For example, 3 × 5.
Think: 2 × 5 = 10.
Then add one more 5: 10 + 5 = 15.
So, 3 × 5 = 15.

Remember to practise skip counting by 3s!

Double, Plus One More Group

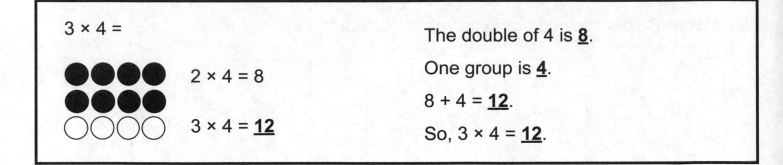

3 × 4 =

2 × 4 = 8

3 × 4 = **12**

The double of 4 is **8**.

One group is **4**.

8 + 4 = **12**.

So, 3 × 4 = **12**.

1. Find the double. Then add one more group.

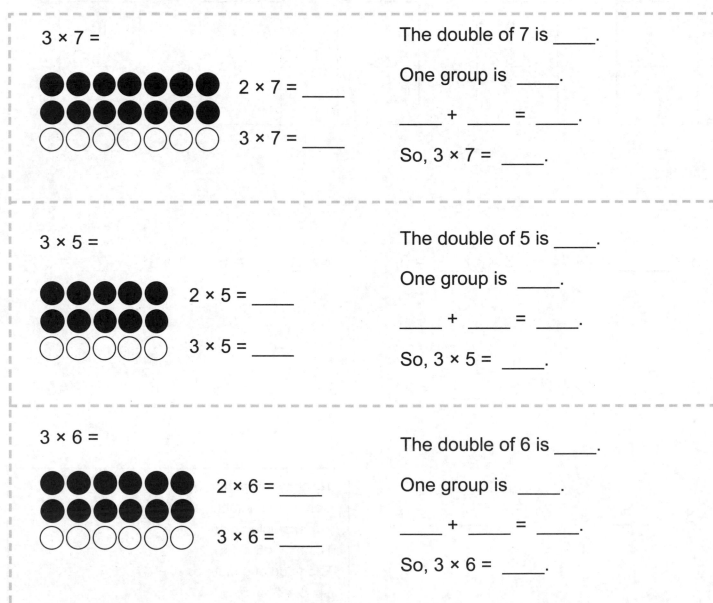

3 × 7 =

2 × 7 = ____

3 × 7 = ____

The double of 7 is ____.

One group is ____.

____ + ____ = ____.

So, 3 × 7 = ____.

3 × 5 =

2 × 5 = ____

3 × 5 = ____

The double of 5 is ____.

One group is ____.

____ + ____ = ____.

So, 3 × 5 = ____.

3 × 6 =

2 × 6 = ____

3 × 6 = ____

The double of 6 is ____.

One group is ____.

____ + ____ = ____.

So, 3 × 6 = ____.

Matching Multiplication to Addition: Facts for 4

Complete the multiplication facts for 4. Use a multiplication table to help you. Then write the sums. Underline each matching sum and product. Use a different colour for each pair.

$1 \times 4 =$ _____ $4 + 4 + 4 + 4 + 4 + 4 + 4 =$ _____

$2 \times 4 =$ _____ $4 + 4 + 4 + 4 + 4 + 4 + 4 + 4 + 4 + 4 =$ _____

$3 \times 4 =$ _____ $4 + 4 =$ _____

$4 \times 4 =$ _____ $4 + 4 + 4 + 4 + 4 + 4 =$ _____

$5 \times 4 =$ _____ $4 + 4 + 4 + 4 =$ _____

$6 \times 4 =$ _____ $4 + 4 + 4 =$ _____

$7 \times 4 =$ _____ $4 + 4 + 4 + 4 + 4 + 4 + 4 + 4 + 4 =$ _____

$8 \times 4 =$ _____ $4 + 4 + 4 + 4 + 4 =$ _____

$9 \times 4 =$ _____ $4 + 4 + 4 + 4 + 4 + 4 + 4 + 4 =$ _____

$10 \times 4 =$ _____ $4 + 0 =$ _____

Four Times Table

1. Multiply. Colour the odd products yellow. Colour the even products pink.

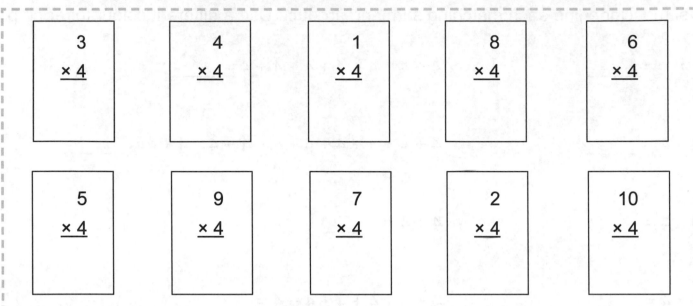

3 × 4	4 × 4	1 × 4	8 × 4	6 × 4
5 × 4	9 × 4	7 × 4	2 × 4	10 × 4

2. Multiply.

4 × _____ = 32   4 × _____ = 4   4 × _____ = 8   4 × _____ = 40

4 × _____ = 16   4 × _____ = 28   4 × _____ = 24   4 × _____ = 36

4 × _____ = 12   4 × _____ = 20

Tip for Multiplying by 4

2 × 2 = 4, so double the number, then double the answer you get.

For example, 5 × 4.

Think: 5 × 2 = 10.

Then 10 × 2 = 20. So, 5 × 4 = 20.

Remember to practise skip counting by 4s!

Matching Multiplication to Addition: Facts for 5

Complete the multiplication facts for 5. Use a multiplication table to help you. Then write the sums. Underline each matching sum and product. Use a different colour for each pair.

$1 \times 5 =$ _____ $5 + 5 + 5 + 5 =$ _____

$2 \times 5 =$ _____ $5 + 5 =$ _____

$3 \times 5 =$ _____ $5 + 5 + 5 + 5 + 5 + 5 =$ _____

$4 \times 5 =$ _____ $5 + 5 + 5 =$ _____

$5 \times 5 =$ _____ $5 + 5 + 5 + 5 + 5 + 5 + 5 + 5 + 5 =$ _____

$6 \times 5 =$ _____ $5 + 5 + 5 + 5 + 5 =$ _____

$7 \times 5 =$ _____ $5 + 5 + 5 + 5 + 5 + 5 + 5 + 5 + 5 + 5 =$ _____

$8 \times 5 =$ _____ $5 + 5 + 5 + 5 + 5 + 5 + 5 + 5 =$ _____

$9 \times 5 =$ _____ $5 + 0 =$ _____

$10 \times 5 =$ _____ $5 + 5 + 5 + 5 + 5 + 5 + 5 =$ _____

Five Times Table

1. Multiply. Colour the odd products yellow. Colour the even products pink.

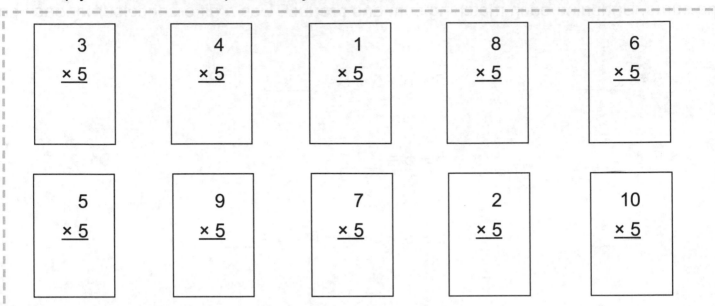

3 × 5	4 × 5	1 × 5	8 × 5	6 × 5
5 × 5	9 × 5	7 × 5	2 × 5	10 × 5

2. Multiply.

5 × _____ = 40   5 × _____ = 5   5 × _____ = 10   5 × _____ = 50

5 × _____ = 30   5 × _____ = 35   5 × _____ = 20   5 × _____ = 45

5 × _____ = 15   5 × _____ = 25

Tip for Multiplying by 5

The answer always ends in 5 or 0.

The product is half the number times 10.

For example, for 5 × 6, half of 6 is 3.

10 × 3 = 30. So, 5 × 6 = 30.

Remember to practice skip counting by 5s!

Matching Multiplication to Addition: Facts for 6

Complete the multiplication facts for 6. Use a multiplication table to help you. Then write the sums. Underline each matching sum and product. Use a different colour for each pair.

1 × 6 = _____   6 + 6 = _____

2 × 6 = _____   6 + 0 = _____

3 × 6 = _____   6 + 6 + 6 + 6 + 6 + 6 + 6 + 6 = _____

4 × 6 = _____   6 + 6 + 6 = _____

5 × 6 = _____   6 + 6 + 6 + 6 + 6 + 6 + 6 = _____

6 × 6 = _____   6 + 6 + 6 + 6 + 6 + 6 = _____

7 × 6 = _____   6 + 6 + 6 + 6 + 6 + 6 + 6 + 6 + 6 + 6 = _____

8 × 6 = _____   6 + 6 + 6 + 6 + 6 + 6 + 6 + 6 + 6 = _____

9 × 6 = _____   6 + 6 + 6 + 6 + 6 = _____

10 × 6 = _____   6 + 6 + 6 + 6 = _____

Six Times Table

1. Multiply. Colour the odd products yellow. Colour the even products pink.

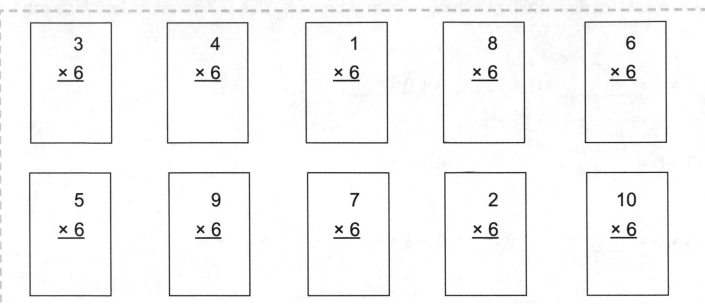

3 × 6	4 × 6	1 × 6	8 × 6	6 × 6
5 × 6	9 × 6	7 × 6	2 × 6	10 × 6

2. Multiply.

6 × _____ = 48   6 × _____ = 6   6 × _____ = 12   6 × _____ = 60

6 × _____ = 24   6 × _____ = 42   6 × _____ = 36   6 × _____ = 54

6 × _____ = 18   6 × _____ = 30

Tip for Multiplying by 6

When multiplying 6 by an even number, the answer always ends in the same number you multiplied 6 by.

For example, 6 × **2** = 1**2**.

In the answer, the tens column is always half the ones column. For example, 6 × 6 = **36**.

Remember to practise skip counting by 6s!

Matching Multiplication to Addition: Facts for 7

Complete the multiplication facts for 7. Use a multiplication table to help you. Then write the sums. Underline each matching sum and product. Use a different colour for each pair.

1 × 7 = _____   7 + 7 + 7 + 7 + 7 + 7 + 7 + 7 + 7 = _____

2 × 7 = _____   7 + 7 + 7 = _____

3 × 7 = _____   7 + 7 + 7 + 7 + 7 + 7 + 7 + 7 = _____

4 × 7 = _____   7 + 7 + 7 + 7 + 7 + 7 = _____

5 × 7 = _____   7 + 7 + 7 + 7 + 7 = _____

6 × 7 = _____   7 + 0 = _____

7 × 7 = _____   7 + 7 + 7 + 7 + 7 + 7 + 7 + 7 + 7 + 7 = _____

8 × 7 = _____   7 + 7 + 7 + 7 = _____

9 × 7 = _____   7 + 7 + 7 + 7 + 7 + 7 + 7 = _____

10 × 7 = _____   7 + 7 = _____

Seven Times Table

1. Multiply. Colour the odd products yellow. Colour the even products pink.

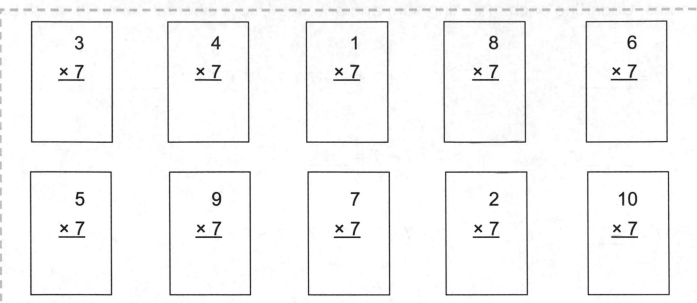

3 × 7	4 × 7	1 × 7	8 × 7	6 × 7
5 × 7	9 × 7	7 × 7	2 × 7	10 × 7

2. Multiply.

7 × _____ = 56	7 × _____ = 7	7 × _____ = 14	7 × _____ = 70
7 × _____ = 28	7 × _____ = 49	7 × _____ = 42	7 × _____ = 63
7 × _____ = 21	7 × _____ = 35		

Tip for Multiplying by 7

Multiply 7 by a number that you know close to the number. For $7 \times 7 =$, you know $5 \times 7 = 35$.

Then $7 - 5 = 2$ more 7s. Multiply the remaining 7s and add them to your answer.

Think: $5 \times 7 = 35$, and $2 \times 7 = 14$.

$35 + 14 = 49$. So, $7 \times 7 = 49$.

Remember to practise skip counting by 7s!

Matching Multiplication to Addition: Facts for 8

Complete the multiplication facts for 8. Use a multiplication table to help you. Then write the sums. Underline each matching sum and product. Use a different colour for each pair.

$1 \times 8 =$ _____ $8 + 8 + 8 + 8 + 8 =$ _____

$2 \times 8 =$ _____ $8 + 8 + 8 + 8 + 8 + 8 =$ _____

$3 \times 8 =$ _____ $8 + 8 + 8 =$ _____

$4 \times 8 =$ _____ $8 + 8 + 8 + 8 =$ _____

$5 \times 8 =$ _____ $8 + 8 + 8 + 8 + 8 + 8 + 8 =$ _____

$6 \times 8 =$ _____ $8 + 8 + 8 + 8 + 8 + 8 + 8 + 8 =$ _____

$7 \times 8 =$ _____ $8 + 8 =$ _____

$8 \times 8 =$ _____ $8 + 8 + 8 + 8 + 8 + 8 + 8 + 8 + 8 + 8 =$ _____

$9 \times 8 =$ _____ $8 + 8 + 8 + 8 + 8 + 8 + 8 + 8 + 8 =$ _____

$10 \times 8 =$ _____ $8 + 0 =$ _____

Eight Times Table

1. Multiply. Colour the odd products yellow. Colour the even products pink.

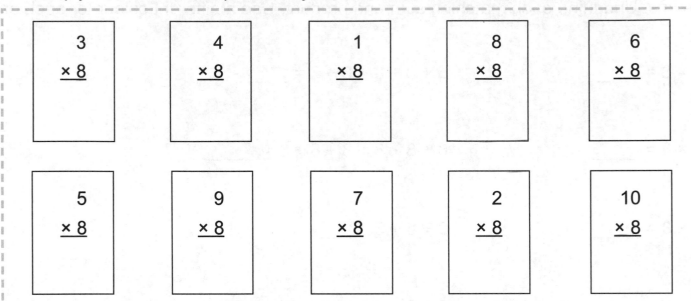

| 3 × 8 | 4 × 8 | 1 × 8 | 8 × 8 | 6 × 8 |
| 5 × 8 | 9 × 8 | 7 × 8 | 2 × 8 | 10 × 8 |

2. Multiply.

8 × _____ = 64   8 × _____ = 8   8 × _____ = 16   8 × _____ = 80

8 × _____ = 32   8 × _____ = 56   8 × _____ = 48   8 × _____ = 72

8 × _____ = 24   8 × _____ = 40

Tip for Multiplying by 8
Doubling 4 gives you 8, so double the number you multiply by 4 to get the multiple for 8!
For 8 × 8 =, you know that 4 × 8 = 32.
Next, double the 32: 32 × 2 = 64. So, 8 × 8 = 64.

Remember to practise skip counting by 8s!

Matching Multiplication to Addition: Facts for 9

Complete the multiplication facts for 9. Use a multiplication table to help you. Then write the sums. Underline each matching sum and product. Use a different colour for each pair.

$1 \times 9 =$ _____ $9 + 9 + 9 + 9 + 9 =$ _____

$2 \times 9 =$ _____ $9 + 9 =$ _____

$3 \times 9 =$ _____ $9 + 9 + 9 + 9 + 9 + 9 + 9 =$ _____

$4 \times 9 =$ _____ $9 + 9 + 9 + 9 + 9 + 9 + 9 + 9 + 9 + 9 =$ _____

$5 \times 9 =$ _____ $9 + 9 + 9 + 9 =$ _____

$6 \times 9 =$ _____ $9 + 9 + 9 + 9 + 9 + 9 =$ _____

$7 \times 9 =$ _____ $9 + 9 + 9 + 9 + 9 + 9 + 9 + 9 + 9 =$ _____

$8 \times 9 =$ _____ $9 + 0 =$ _____

$9 \times 9 =$ _____ $9 + 9 + 9 =$ _____

$10 \times 9 =$ _____ $9 + 9 + 9 + 9 + 9 + 9 + 9 + 9 =$ _____

Nine Times Table

1. Multiply. Colour the odd products yellow. Colour the even products pink.

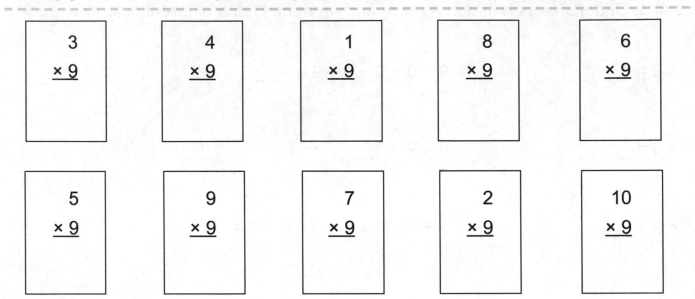

| 3 | 4 | 1 | 8 | 6 |
| × 9 | × 9 | × 9 | × 9 | × 9 |

| 5 | 9 | 7 | 2 | 10 |
| × 9 | × 9 | × 9 | × 9 | × 9 |

2. Multiply.

9 × _____ = 72   9 × _____ = 9   9 × _____ = 18   9 × _____ = 90

9 × _____ = 36   9 × _____ = 63   9 × _____ = 54   9 × _____ = 81

9 × _____ = 27   9 × _____ = 45

Tip for Multiplying by 9
Multiply the number by 10, then subtract one of that number from the answer.
For 7 × 9 =
Think: 7 × 10 = 70. 70 − 7 = 63. So, 7 × 9 = 63.

Remember to practise skip counting by 9s!

Using Patterns to Multiply by 9

Use the ten facts to help you multiply by 9. $9 \times 6 =$	You know that 10×6 is one more group of sixes than 9×6. $10 \times 6 = 60$ Now take away one group of 6. $60 - 6 = 54$ So, $9 \times 6 = 54$.

1. Use the ten facts to help you multiply by 9. Show your work.

a) $9 \times 7 = \quad 10 \times 7 = 70$
$70 - 7 = 63$
So, $9 \times 7 = 63$.

b) $9 \times 3 = \quad 10 \times 3 = 30$
$30 - 3 = 27$
So, $9 \times 3 = 27$.

2. a) Use the pattern in the tens and ones digits to help you learn the nine facts.

$1 \times 9 = \underline{\quad} \underline{\quad 9}$

$2 \times 9 = \underline{\quad 1} \underline{\quad 8}$

$3 \times 9 = \underline{\quad 2} \underline{\quad 7}$

$4 \times 9 = \underline{\quad} \underline{\quad}$

$5 \times 9 = \underline{\quad} \underline{\quad}$

$6 \times 9 = \underline{\quad} \underline{\quad}$

$7 \times 9 = \underline{\quad} \underline{\quad}$

$8 \times 9 = \underline{\quad} \underline{\quad}$

$9 \times 9 = \underline{\quad} \underline{\quad}$

$10 \times 9 = \underline{\quad} \underline{\quad}$

b) What pattern do you notice about the nine facts?

_____

_____

_____

_____

_____

_____

Matching Multiplication to Addition: Facts for 10

Complete the multiplication facts for 10. Use a multiplication table to help you. Then write the sums. Underline each matching sum and product. Use a different colour for each pair.

1 × 10 = _____   10 + 10 + 10 + 10 + 10 + 10 + 10 + 10 + 10 = _____

2 × 10 = _____   10 + 10 = _____

3 × 10 = _____   10 + 10 + 10 + 10 + 10 + 10 + 10 + 10 + 10 + 10 = _____

4 × 10 = _____   10 + 10 + 10 + 10 + 10 + 10 + 10 + 10 = _____

5 × 10 = _____   10 + 10 + 10 = _____

6 × 10 = _____   10 + 10 + 10 + 10 + 10 = _____

7 × 10 = _____   10 + 10 + 10 + 10 + 10 + 10 + 10 = _____

8 × 10 = _____   10 + 10 + 10 + 10 = _____

9 × 10 = _____   10 + 10 + 10 + 10 + 10 + 10 = _____

10 × 10 = _____   10 + 0 = _____

Ten Times Table

1. Multiply. Colour the odd products yellow. Colour the even products pink.

3 × 10	4 × 10	1 × 10	8 × 10	6 × 10
5 × 10	9 × 10	7 × 10	2 × 10	10 × 10

2. Multiply.

10 × _____ = 80	10 × _____ = 10	10 × _____ = 20	10 × _____ = 100
10 × _____ = 60	10 × _____ = 70	10 × _____ = 40	10 × _____ = 90
10 × _____ = 30	10 × _____ = 50		

Tip for Multiplying by 10
When multiplying by 10, just add 0!
For example, 6 × 10 = 60.

Remember to practise skip counting by 10s!

Introducing Division

12 creatures are divided into groups of 4.

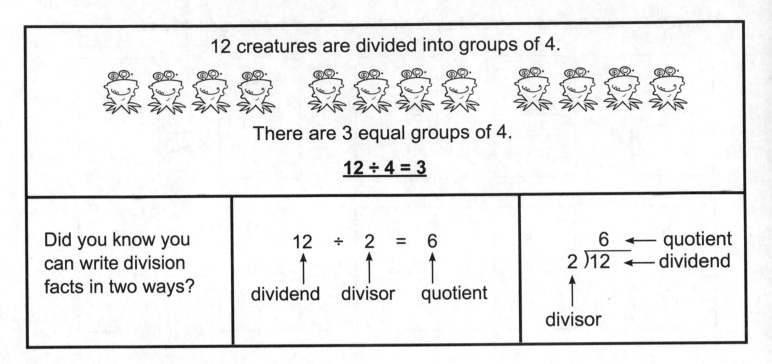

There are 3 equal groups of 4.

12 ÷ 4 = 3

Did you know you can write division facts in two ways?	12 ÷ 2 = 6 ↑ ↑ ↑ dividend divisor quotient	$\begin{array}{r} 6 \\ 2\overline{)12} \end{array}$ ← quotient ← dividend ↑ divisor

1. Write the division sentence.

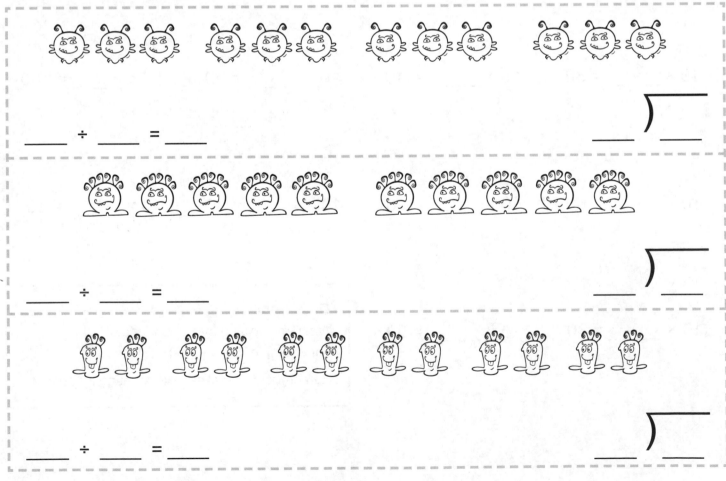

____ ÷ ____ = ____

____ ÷ ____ = ____

____ ÷ ____ = ____

Introducing Division (continued)

2. Write the division sentence.

____ ÷ ____ = ____

____ ÷ ____ = ____

____ ÷ ____ = ____

____ ÷ ____ = ____

____ ÷ ____ = ____

Introducing Division (continued)

3. Use a circle to divide into groups. Complete the division sentence.

Divide 10 creatures into groups of 2.

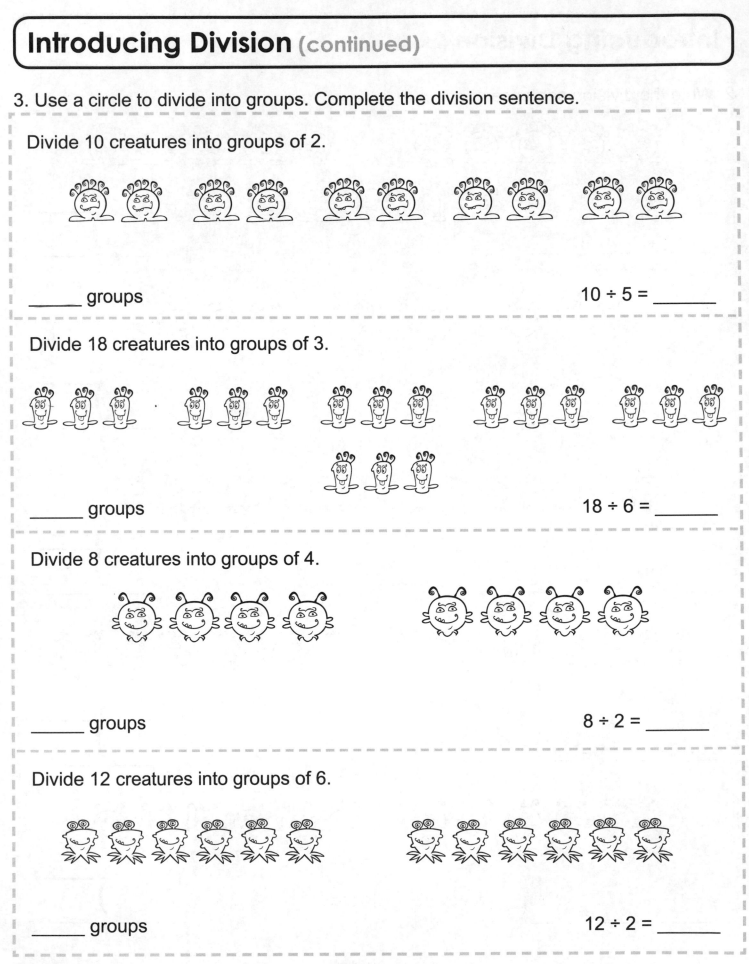

_____ groups

$10 \div 5 =$ _____

Divide 18 creatures into groups of 3.

_____ groups

$18 \div 6 =$ _____

Divide 8 creatures into groups of 4.

_____ groups

$8 \div 2 =$ _____

Divide 12 creatures into groups of 6.

_____ groups

$12 \div 2 =$ _____

Dividing by Skip Counting

$18 \div 3 =$

$$3 \;+\; 3 \;+\; 3 \;+\; 3 \;+\; 3 \;+\; 3 \;=\; 18$$

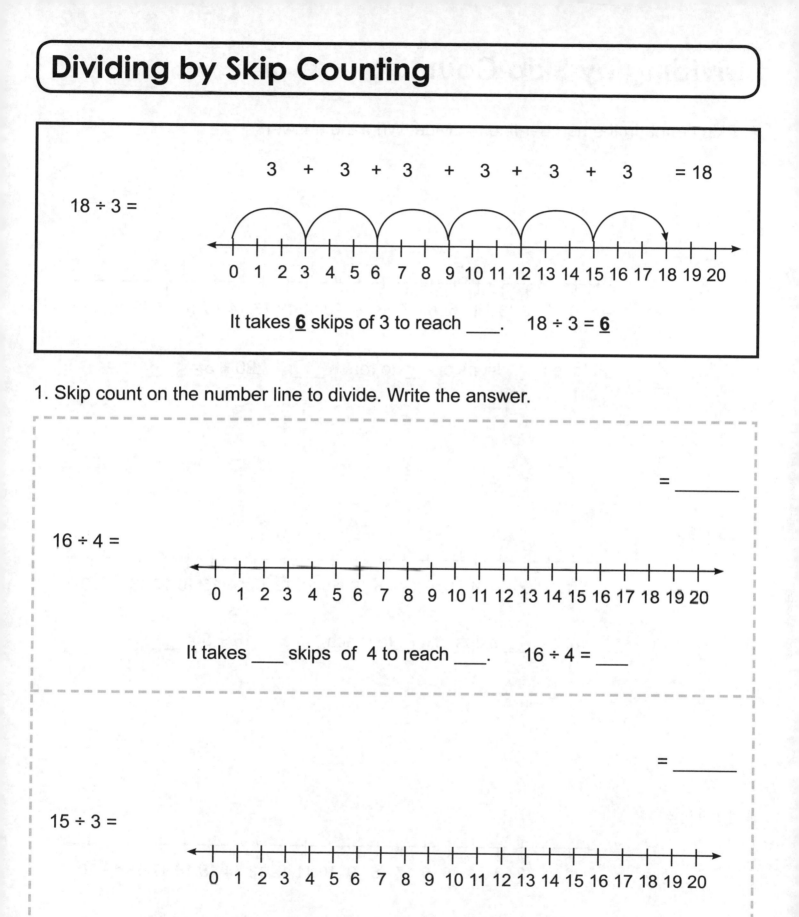

0 1 2 3 4 5 6 7 8 9 10 11 12 13 14 15 16 17 18 19 20

It takes **6** skips of 3 to reach ___. $18 \div 3 =$ **6**

1. Skip count on the number line to divide. Write the answer.

$= \underline{\hspace{3em}}$

$16 \div 4 =$

0 1 2 3 4 5 6 7 8 9 10 11 12 13 14 15 16 17 18 19 20

It takes ___ skips of 4 to reach ___. $16 \div 4 =$ ___

$= \underline{\hspace{3em}}$

$15 \div 3 =$

0 1 2 3 4 5 6 7 8 9 10 11 12 13 14 15 16 17 18 19 20

It takes ___ skips of ___ to reach ___. $15 \div 3 =$ ___

Dividing by Skip Counting (continued)

2. Skip count on the number line to divide. Write the answer.

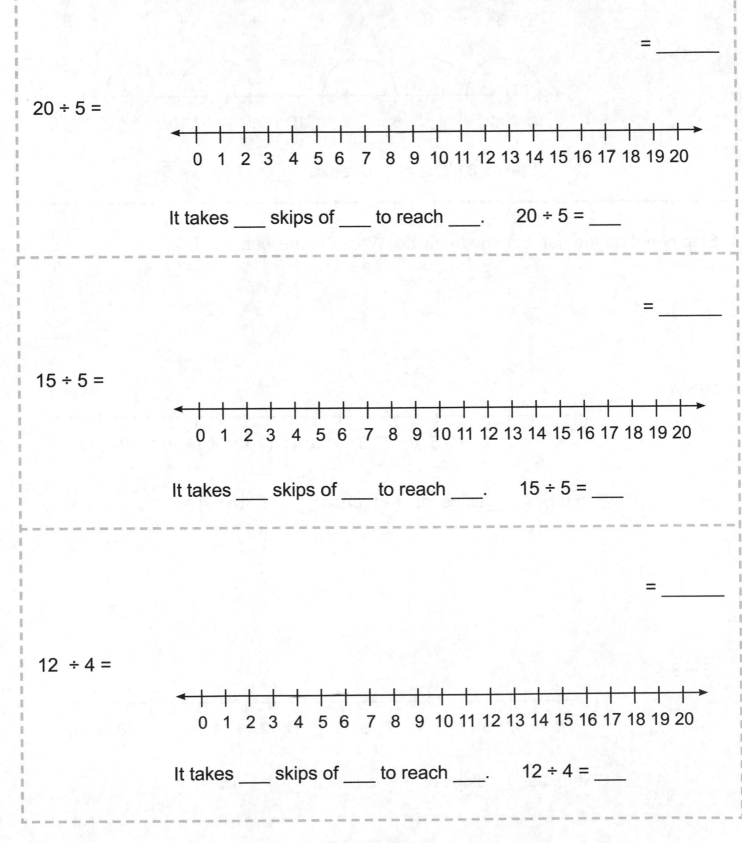

= _____

20 ÷ 5 =

0 1 2 3 4 5 6 7 8 9 10 11 12 13 14 15 16 17 18 19 20

It takes ___ skips of ___ to reach ___.   20 ÷ 5 = ___

= _____

15 ÷ 5 =

0 1 2 3 4 5 6 7 8 9 10 11 12 13 14 15 16 17 18 19 20

It takes ___ skips of ___ to reach ___.   15 ÷ 5 = ___

= _____

12 ÷ 4 =

0 1 2 3 4 5 6 7 8 9 10 11 12 13 14 15 16 17 18 19 20

It takes ___ skips of ___ to reach ___.   12 ÷ 4 = ___

Relating Multiplication to Division

1. Use the array to complete each number sentence.

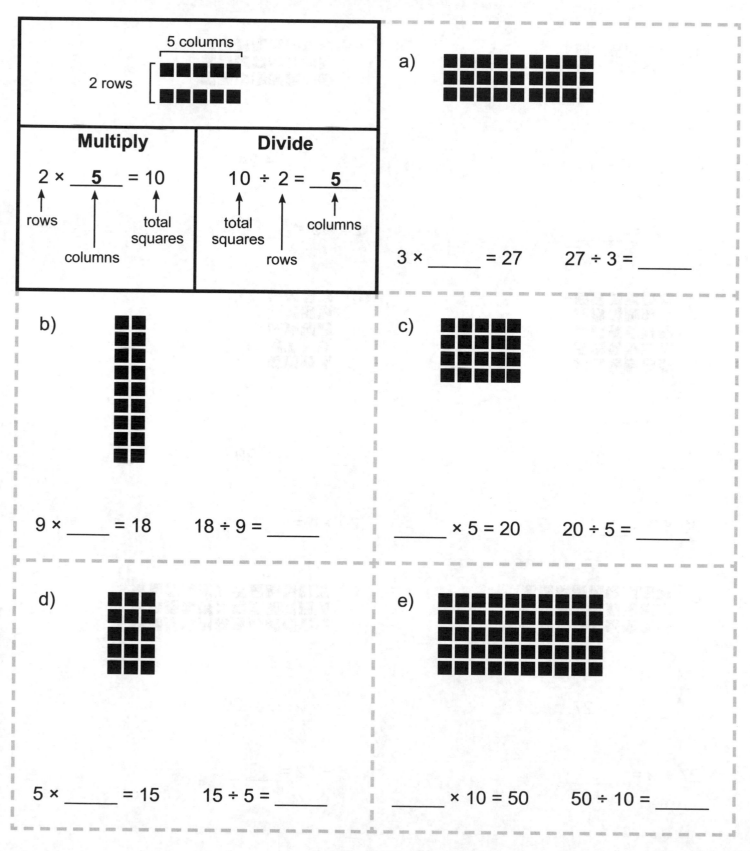

	5 columns
2 rows	(array of squares)

Multiply	**Divide**
2 × **5** = 10	10 ÷ 2 = **5**
rows columns total squares	total squares rows columns

a)

$3 \times$ _____ = 27 $27 \div 3 =$ _____

b)

$9 \times$ _____ = 18 $18 \div 9 =$ _____

c)

_____ $\times 5 = 20$ $20 \div 5 =$ _____

d)

$5 \times$ _____ = 15 $15 \div 5 =$ _____

e)

_____ $\times 10 = 50$ $50 \div 10 =$ _____

Relating Multiplication to Division (continued)

2. Use the array to complete each number sentence.

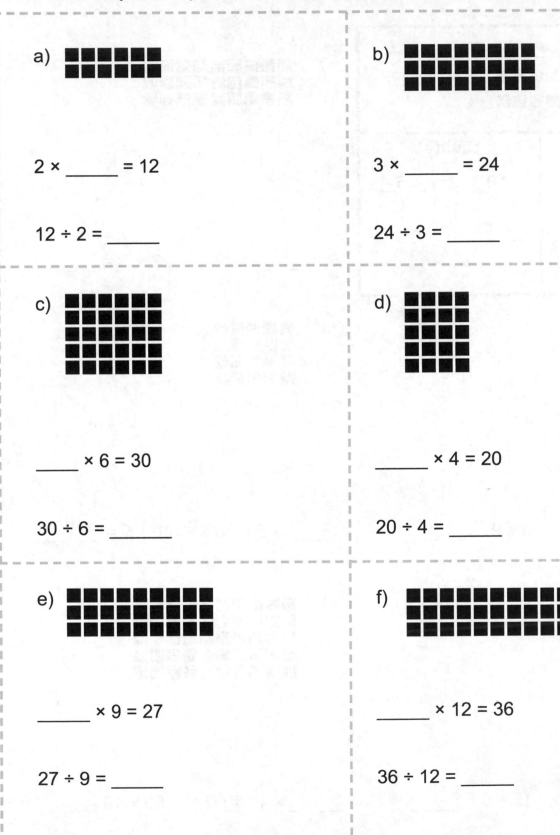

a)

$2 \times$ _____ $= 12$

$12 \div 2 =$ _____

b)

$3 \times$ _____ $= 24$

$24 \div 3 =$ _____

c)

_____ $\times 6 = 30$

$30 \div 6 =$ _____

d)

_____ $\times 4 = 20$

$20 \div 4 =$ _____

e)

_____ $\times 9 = 27$

$27 \div 9 =$ _____

f)

_____ $\times 12 = 36$

$36 \div 12 =$ _____

Using an Array to Find a Quotient

1. Draw an array to help you find the quotient.

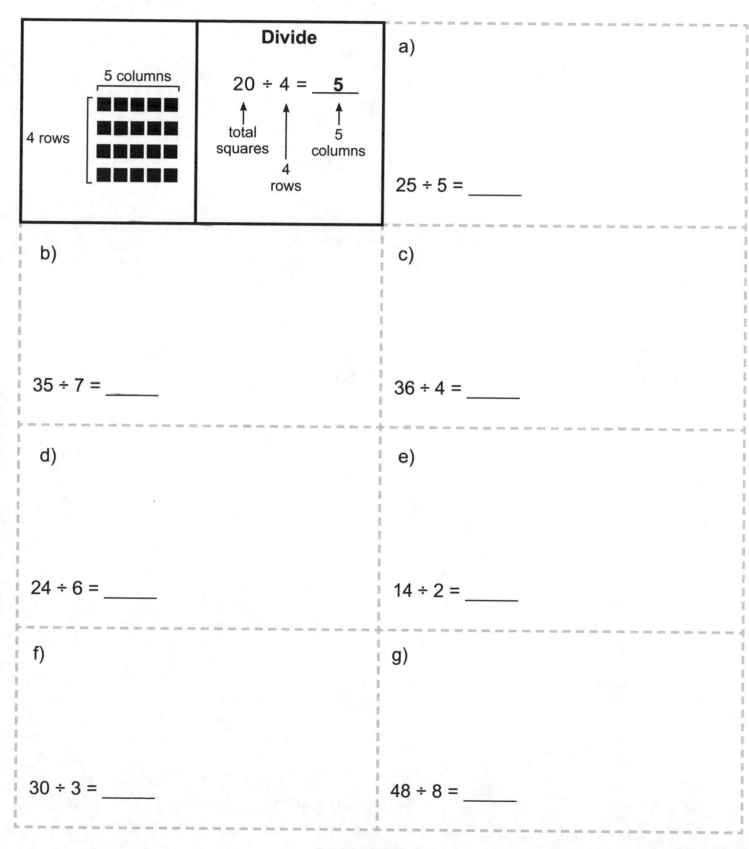

	Divide
5 columns	$20 \div 4 = \underline{\textbf{5}}$
4 rows	total squares 5 columns 4 rows

a)

$25 \div 5 = \underline{\hphantom{xxx}}$

b)

$35 \div 7 = \underline{\hphantom{xxx}}$

c)

$36 \div 4 = \underline{\hphantom{xxx}}$

d)

$24 \div 6 = \underline{\hphantom{xxx}}$

e)

$14 \div 2 = \underline{\hphantom{xxx}}$

f)

$30 \div 3 = \underline{\hphantom{xxx}}$

g)

$48 \div 8 = \underline{\hphantom{xxx}}$

Using an Array to Find a Quotient (continued)

2. Draw an array to help you find the quotient.

a)

$35 \div 5 =$ ____

b)

$48 \div 6 =$ ____

c)

$60 \div 10 =$ ____

d)

$50 \div 5 =$ ____

e)

$18 \div 2 =$ ____

f)

$27 \div 3 =$ ____

g)

$64 \div 8 =$ ____

h)

$40 \div 10 =$ ____

Relating Multiplication to Division

1. Use the multiplication fact to find the quotient.

a) $10 \times 2 = 20$

$20 \div 10 = $ _____

b) $7 \times 8 = 56$

$56 \div 8 = $ _____

c) $4 \times 6 = 24$

$24 \div 4 = $ _____

d) $10 \times 7 = 70$

$70 \div 7 = $ _____

e) $3 \times 9 = 27$

$27 \div 3 = $ _____

f) $8 \times 2 = 16$

$16 \div 2 = $ _____

g) $9 \times 9 = 81$

$81 \div 9 = $ _____

h) $10 \times 7 = 70$

$70 \div 7 = $ _____

i) $8 \times 9 = 72$

$72 \div 8 = $ _____

j) $5 \times 8 = 40$

$40 \div 8 = $ _____

k) $9 \times 6 = 54$

$54 \div 9 = $ _____

l) $6 \times 5 = 30$

$30 \div 5 = $ _____

Using Related Multiplication Facts to Divide by 0 and 1

The quotient is always 1 when any number other than 0 is divided by itself.

For example, $5 \div 5 = 1$.

Think of a related multiplication fact.

$5 \times 1 = 5$, so $5 \div 5 = 1$

The quotient is always the same as the dividend when any number is divided by 1.

For example, $8 \div 1 = 8$.

Think of a related multiplication fact.

$8 \times 1 = 8$, so $8 \div 1 = 8$

The quotient is always 0 when 0 is divided by any number other than 0.

For example, $0 \div 3 = 0$.

Think of a related multiplication fact.

$3 \times 0 = 0$, so $0 \div 3 = 0$

You cannot divide any number by 0.

Divide.

$0 \div 2 =$ _____	$11 \div 1 =$ _____	$9 \div 1 =$ _____	$0 \div 1 =$ _____
$3 \div 3 =$ _____	$0 \div 9 =$ _____	$5 \div 1 =$ _____	$6 \div 1 =$ _____
$0 \div 6 =$ _____	$12 \div 12 =$ _____	$0 \div 7 =$ _____	$8 \div 8 =$ _____
$7 \div 7 =$ _____	$0 \div 4 =$ _____	$10 \div 1 =$ _____	$0 \div 8 =$ _____

Dividing by 2

Match the division sentence with the correct quotient. Hint: Practise skip counting by 2s.

0 ÷ 2 = ___	2
2 ÷ 2 = ___	5
4 ÷ 2 = ___	0
6 ÷ 2 = ___	12
8 ÷ 2 = ___	1
10 ÷ 2 = ___	7
12 ÷ 2 = ___	10
14 ÷ 2 = ___	3
16 ÷ 2 = ___	11
18 ÷ 2 = ___	8
20 ÷ 2 = ___	6
22 ÷ 2 = ___	9
24 ÷ 2 = ___	4

Math Riddle: Dividing by 2

What is a polar bear's favourite food?

___ ___ ___ / ___ ___ ___ ___ ___ ___ ___ !
4 8 11   1 2 7 0 11 7 6

Watch out! Some letters are not used in the riddle!

1. Find the quotient.

A	B	C
$18 \div 2 = $ ___	$2 \div 2 = $ ___	$16 \div 2 = $ ___
E	**F**	**G**
$22 \div 2 = $ ___	$6 \div 2 = $ ___	$0 \div 2 = $ ___
I	**M**	**N**
$8 \div 2 = $ ___	$10 \div 2 = $ ___	$24 \div 2 = $ ___
R	**S**	**U**
$14 \div 2 = $ ___	$12 \div 2 = $ ___	$4 \div 2 = $ ___

2. Find the missing dividend.

___ $\div 2 = 0$	___ $\div 2 = 12$	___ $\div 2 = 6$	___ $\div 2 = 11$
___ $\div 2 = 1$	___ $\div 2 = 10$	___ $\div 2 = 8$	___ $\div 2 = 2$

Dividing by 3

Match the division sentence with the correct quotient. Hint: Practise skip counting by 3s.

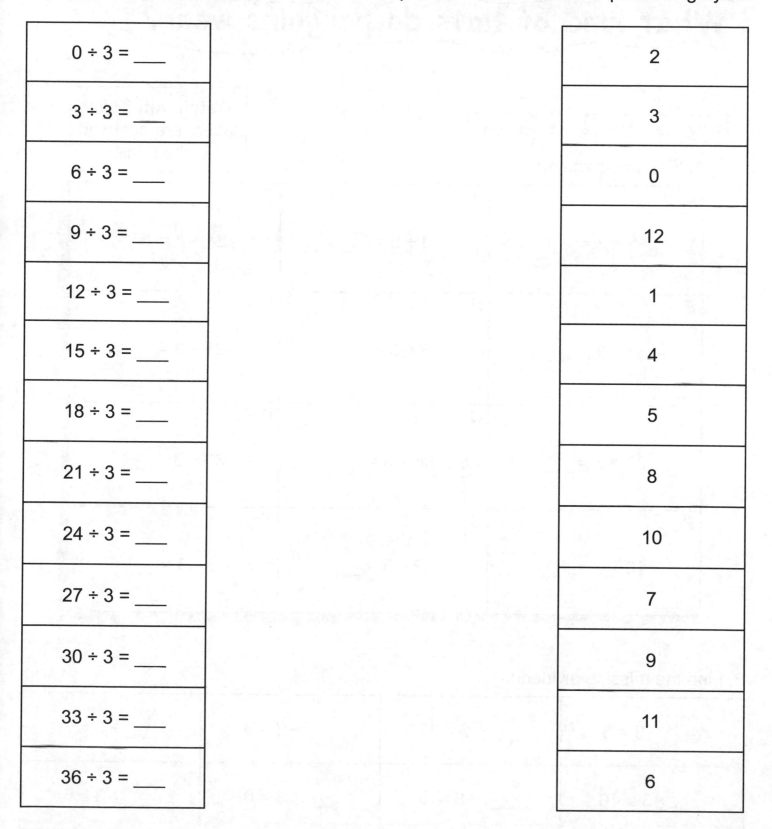

0 ÷ 3 = ___	2
3 ÷ 3 = ___	3
6 ÷ 3 = ___	0
9 ÷ 3 = ___	12
12 ÷ 3 = ___	1
15 ÷ 3 = ___	4
18 ÷ 3 = ___	5
21 ÷ 3 = ___	8
24 ÷ 3 = ___	10
27 ÷ 3 = ___	7
30 ÷ 3 = ___	9
33 ÷ 3 = ___	11
36 ÷ 3 = ___	6

Math Riddle: Dividing by 3

What kind of hats do penguins wear?

___ ___ ___ / ___ ___ ___ ___ !
7 8 11   8 5 6 4

Watch out! Some letters are not used in the riddle!

1. Find the quotient.

A	B	C
$15 \div 3 =$ ___	$3 \div 3 =$ ___	$24 \div 3 =$ ___
E $33 \div 3 =$ ___	**H** $6 \div 3 =$ ___	**I** $21 \div 3 =$ ___
M $27 \div 3 =$ ___	**N** $36 \div 3 =$ ___	**O** $30 \div 3 =$ ___
P $18 \div 3 =$ ___	**S** $12 \div 3 =$ ___	**T** $9 \div 3 =$ ___

2. Find the missing dividend.

___ $\div 3 = 3$	___ $\div 3 = 12$	___ $\div 3 = 9$	___ $\div 3 = 7$
___ $\div 3 = 10$	___ $\div 3 = 5$	___ $\div 3 = 8$	___ $\div 3 = 6$

Dividing by 1, 2, and 3

1. Use long division to find the quotient.

a) $1\overline{)4}$

b) $2\overline{)4}$

c) $2\overline{)16}$

d) $1\overline{)6}$

e) $3\overline{)27}$

f) $2\overline{)12}$

g) $1\overline{)8}$

h) $3\overline{)24}$

i) $3\overline{)3}$

j) $2\overline{)8}$

k) $3\overline{)21}$

l) $2\overline{)14}$

m) $2\overline{)10}$

n) $3\overline{)30}$

o) $1\overline{)5}$

p) $2\overline{)18}$

Dividing by 4

Match the division sentence with the correct quotient. Hint: Practise skip counting by 4s.

0 ÷ 4 = ___	2
4 ÷ 4 = ___	5
8 ÷ 4 = ___	8
12 ÷ 4 = ___	11
16 ÷ 4 = ___	1
20 ÷ 4 = ___	10
24 ÷ 4 = ___	7
28 ÷ 4 = ___	3
32 ÷ 4 = ___	12
36 ÷ 4 = ___	0
40 ÷ 4 = ___	6
44 ÷ 4 = ___	4
48 ÷ 4 = ___	9

Math Riddle: Dividing by 4

Which building has the most storeys?

$$\overline{}_{11}\ \overline{}_{1}\ \overline{}_{5}\ /\ \overline{}_{10}\ \overline{}_{4}\ \overline{}_{12}\ \overline{}_{7}\ \overline{}_{2}\ \overline{}_{7}\ \overline{}_{8}\ !$$

Watch out! Some letters are not used in the riddle!

1. Find the quotient.

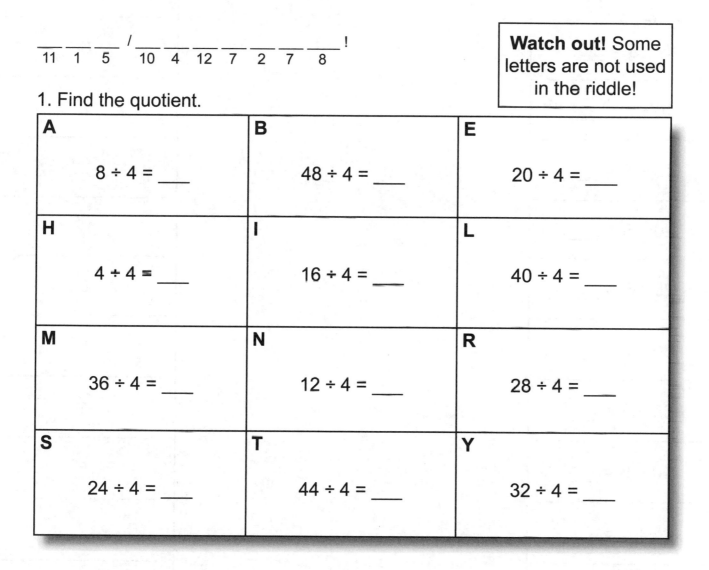

A	B	E
8 ÷ 4 = ___	48 ÷ 4 = ___	20 ÷ 4 = ___
H	**I**	**L**
4 ÷ 4 = ___	16 ÷ 4 = ___	40 ÷ 4 = ___
M	**N**	**R**
36 ÷ 4 = ___	12 ÷ 4 = ___	28 ÷ 4 = ___
S	**T**	**Y**
24 ÷ 4 = ___	44 ÷ 4 = ___	32 ÷ 4 = ___

2. Find the missing dividend.

___ ÷ 4 = 5	___ ÷ 4 = 1	___ ÷ 4 = 7	___ ÷ 4 = 10
___ ÷ 4 = 9	___ ÷ 4 = 3	___ ÷ 4 = 4	___ ÷ 4 = 2

Dividing by 5

Match the division sentence with the correct quotient. Hint: Practise skip counting by 5s.

0 ÷ 5 = ___	10
5 ÷ 5 = ___	6
10 ÷ 5 = ___	2
15 ÷ 5 = ___	3
20 ÷ 5 = ___	12
25 ÷ 5 = ___	0
30 ÷ 5 = ___	9
35 ÷ 5 = ___	1
40 ÷ 5 = ___	5
45 ÷ 5 = ___	7
50 ÷ 5 = ___	8
55 ÷ 5 = ___	11
60 ÷ 5 = ___	4

Math Riddle: Dividing by 5

What belongs to you but is used more by other people?

___ ___ ___ ___ / ___ ___ ___ ___ !
6 12 10 4   1 2 7 5

Watch out! Some letters are not used in the riddle!

1. Find the quotient.

A $10 \div 5 =$ ___	**C** $40 \div 5 =$ ___	**E** $25 \div 5 =$ ___
G $45 \div 5 =$ ___	**M** $35 \div 5 =$ ___	**N** $5 \div 5 =$ ___
O $60 \div 5 =$ ___	**R** $20 \div 5 =$ ___	**S** $55 \div 5 =$ ___
U $50 \div 5 =$ ___	**W** $15 \div 5 =$ ___	**Y** $30 \div 5 =$ ___

2. Find the missing dividend.

___ $\div 5 = 1$	___ $\div 5 = 9$	___ $\div 5 = 7$	___ $\div 5 = 3$
___ $\div 5 = 6$	___ $\div 5 = 10$	___ $\div 5 = 12$	___ $\div 5 = 8$

Dividing by 6

Match the division sentence with the correct quotient. Hint: Practise skip counting by 6s.

0 ÷ 6 = ___	2
6 ÷ 6 = ___	7
12 ÷ 6 = ___	0
18 ÷ 6 = ___	4
24 ÷ 6 = ___	10
30 ÷ 6 = ___	3
36 ÷ 6 = ___	12
42 ÷ 6 = ___	1
48 ÷ 6 = ___	11
54 ÷ 6 = ___	5
60 ÷ 6 = ___	6
66 ÷ 6 = ___	9
72 ÷ 6 = ___	8

Math Riddle: Dividing by 6

What did the tornado say to the sports car?

$$\overline{}_{7} \ \overline{}_{8} \ \overline{}_{10} \ , \ \overline{}_{11} \ / \ \overline{}_{6} \ \overline{}_{9} \ / \ \overline{}_{12} \ \overline{}_{9} \ \overline{}_{4} \ / \ \overline{}_{3} \ / \ \overline{}_{11} \ \overline{}_{5} \ \overline{}_{2} \ \overline{}_{1} \ !$$

Watch out! Some letters are not used in the riddle!

1. Find the quotient.

A	E	F
$18 \div 6 = \underline{}$	$48 \div 6 = \underline{}$	$72 \div 6 = \underline{}$
G	**I**	**L**
$36 \div 6 = \underline{}$	$12 \div 6 = \underline{}$	$42 \div 6 = \underline{}$
N	**O**	**P**
$6 \div 6 = \underline{}$	$54 \div 6 = \underline{}$	$30 \div 6 = \underline{}$
R	**S**	**T**
$24 \div 6 = \underline{}$	$66 \div 6 = \underline{}$	$60 \div 6 = \underline{}$

2. Find the missing dividend.

$\underline{} \div 6 = 3$	$\underline{} \div 6 = 7$	$\underline{} \div 6 = 6$	$\underline{} \div 6 = 9$
$\underline{} \div 6 = 4$	$\underline{} \div 6 = 5$	$\underline{} \div 6 = 10$	$\underline{} \div 6 = 8$

Dividing by 4, 5, and 6

1. Use long division to find the quotient.

a) $4\overline{)12}$

b) $4\overline{)4}$

c) $6\overline{)60}$

d) $4\overline{)40}$

e) $6\overline{)18}$

f) $4\overline{)12}$

g) $5\overline{)35}$

h) $6\overline{)42}$

i) $5\overline{)10}$

j) $6\overline{)30}$

k) $5\overline{)5}$

l) $5\overline{)40}$

m) $6\overline{)66}$

n) $4\overline{)20}$

o) $4\overline{)28}$

p) $5\overline{)20}$

Dividing by 7

Match the division sentence with the correct quotient. Hint: Practise skip counting by 7s.

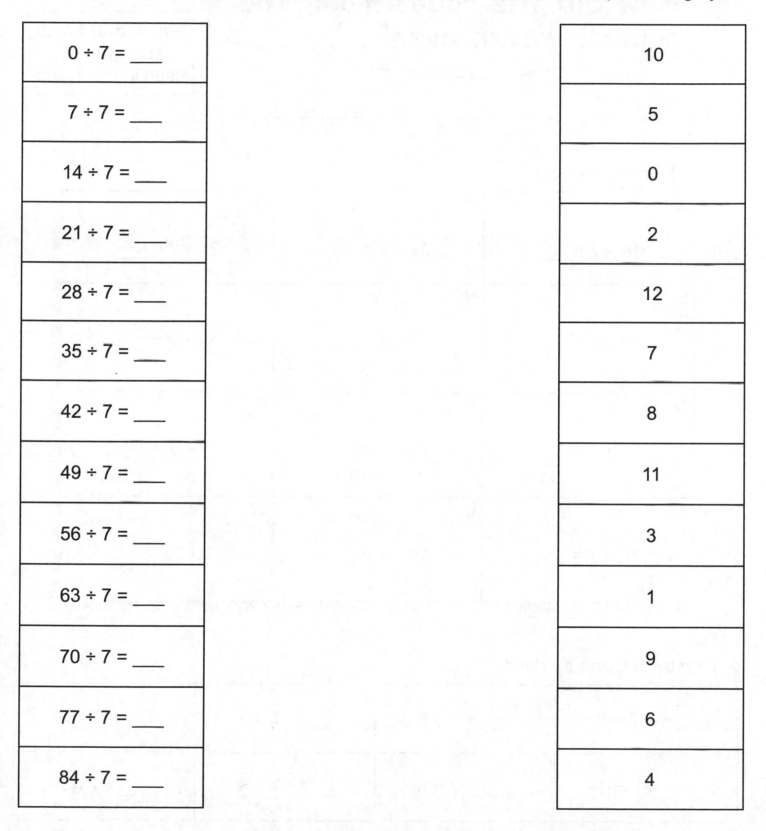

0 ÷ 7 = ___	10
7 ÷ 7 = ___	5
14 ÷ 7 = ___	0
21 ÷ 7 = ___	2
28 ÷ 7 = ___	12
35 ÷ 7 = ___	7
42 ÷ 7 = ___	8
49 ÷ 7 = ___	11
56 ÷ 7 = ___	3
63 ÷ 7 = ___	1
70 ÷ 7 = ___	9
77 ÷ 7 = ___	6
84 ÷ 7 = ___	4

Math Riddle: Dividing by 7

How did the robot make the number seven even?

Watch out! Some letters are not used in the riddle!

___ ___ ___ / ___ ___ ___ ___ / ___ ___ ___ / ___ ___ ___ / ___ !
11　9　7　　10　5　5　6　　5　4　10　　10　9　7　　11

1. Find the quotient.

A	C	D
14 ÷ 7 = ___	84 ÷ 7 = ___	21 ÷ 7 = ___
E	**H**	**K**
49 ÷ 7 = ___	63 ÷ 7 = ___	42 ÷ 7 = ___
O	**P**	**S**
35 ÷ 7 = ___	56 ÷ 7 = ___	77 ÷ 7 = ___
T	**U**	**W**
70 ÷ 7 = ___	28 ÷ 7 = ___	7 ÷ 7 = ___

2. Find the missing dividend.

___ ÷ 7 = 3	___ ÷ 7 = 6	___ ÷ 7 = 1	___ ÷ 7 = 10
___ ÷ 7 = 4	___ ÷ 7 = 5	___ ÷ 7 = 8	___ ÷ 7 = 2

Dividing by 8

Match the division sentence with the correct quotient. Hint: Practise skip counting by 8s.

0 ÷ 8 = ___	2
8 ÷ 8 = ___	5
16 ÷ 8 = ___	10
24 ÷ 8 = ___	1
32 ÷ 8 = ___	7
40 ÷ 8 = ___	12
48 ÷ 8 = ___	3
56 ÷ 8 = ___	11
64 ÷ 8 = ___	8
72 ÷ 8 = ___	0
80 ÷ 8 = ___	6
88 ÷ 8 = ___	9
96 ÷ 8 = ___	4

Math Riddle: Dividing by 8

What has four legs but cannot walk?

___ / ___ ___ ___ ___ ___ !
 3   9   2   3   5   8

1. Find the quotient.

Watch out! Some letters are not used in the riddle!

A	B	C
24 ÷ 8 = ___	48 ÷ 8 = ___	72 ÷ 8 = ___
E	**H**	**I**
32 ÷ 8 = ___	16 ÷ 8 = ___	40 ÷ 8 = ___
J	**K**	**L**
96 ÷ 8 = ___	56 ÷ 8 = ___	80 ÷ 8 = ___
P	**Q**	**R**
88 ÷ 8 = ___	8 ÷ 8 = ___	64 ÷ 8 = ___

2. Find the missing dividend.

___ ÷ 8 = 9	___ ÷ 8 = 5	___ ÷ 8 = 3	___ ÷ 8 = 10
___ ÷ 8 = 4	___ ÷ 8 = 8	___ ÷ 8 = 2	___ ÷ 8 = 6

Dividing by 9

Match the division sentence with the correct quotient. Hint: Practise skip counting by 9s.

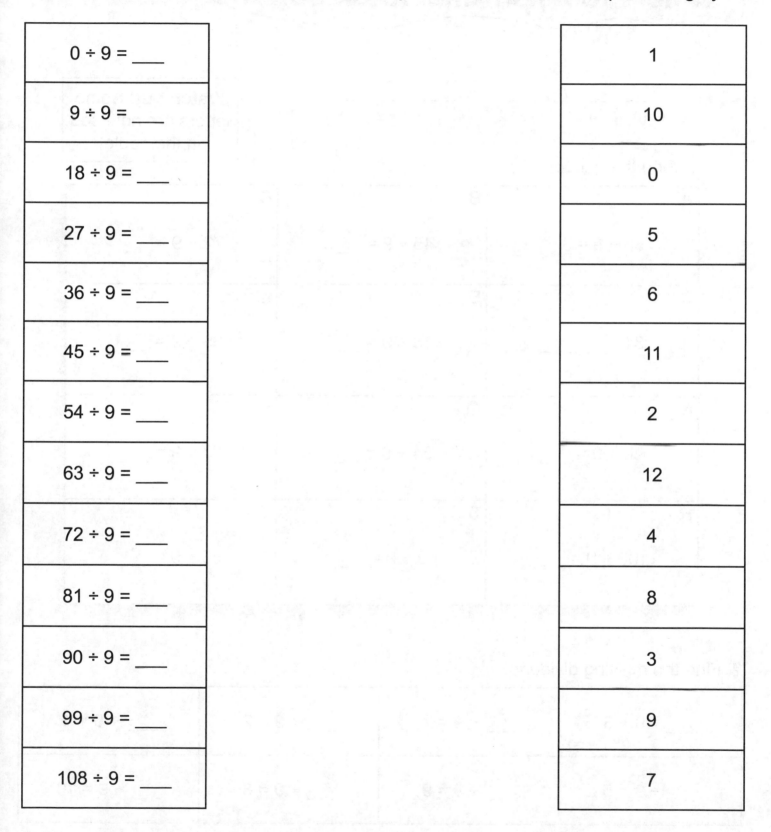

$0 \div 9 =$ ___	1
$9 \div 9 =$ ___	10
$18 \div 9 =$ ___	0
$27 \div 9 =$ ___	5
$36 \div 9 =$ ___	6
$45 \div 9 =$ ___	11
$54 \div 9 =$ ___	2
$63 \div 9 =$ ___	12
$72 \div 9 =$ ___	4
$81 \div 9 =$ ___	8
$90 \div 9 =$ ___	3
$99 \div 9 =$ ___	9
$108 \div 9 =$ ___	7

Math Riddle: Dividing by 9

Where do fish like to sleep?

___ ___ / ___ / ___ ___ ___ ___ ___ ___ !
6   10   4   1   2   4   5   2   9

Watch out! Some letters are not used in the riddle!

1. Find the quotient.

A	B	C
$36 \div 9 =$ ___	$45 \div 9 =$ ___	$72 \div 9 =$ ___
D	**E**	**M**
$81 \div 9 =$ ___	$18 \div 9 =$ ___	$99 \div 9 =$ ___
N	**O**	**P**
$90 \div 9 =$ ___	$54 \div 9 =$ ___	$27 \div 9 =$ ___
R	**S**	**T**
$108 \div 9 =$ ___	$9 \div 9 =$ ___	$63 \div 9 =$ ___

2. Find the missing dividend.

___ $\div 9 = 3$	___ $\div 9 = 7$	___ $\div 9 = 2$	___ $\div 9 = 4$
___ $\div 9 = 5$	___ $\div 9 = 9$	___ $\div 9 = 8$	___ $\div 9 = 10$

Dividing by 7, 8, and 9

1. Use long division to find the quotient.

a) $8\overline{)40}$ b) $9\overline{)81}$ c) $7\overline{)56}$ d) $8\overline{)64}$

e) $9\overline{)18}$ f) $9\overline{)90}$ g) $8\overline{)24}$ h) $7\overline{)49}$

i) $9\overline{)27}$ j) $8\overline{)48}$ k) $7\overline{)42}$ l) $9\overline{)54}$

m) $7\overline{)70}$ n) $9\overline{)90}$ o) $8\overline{)56}$ p) $7\overline{)63}$

Dividing by 10

Match the division sentence with the correct quotient. Hint: Practise skip counting by 10s.

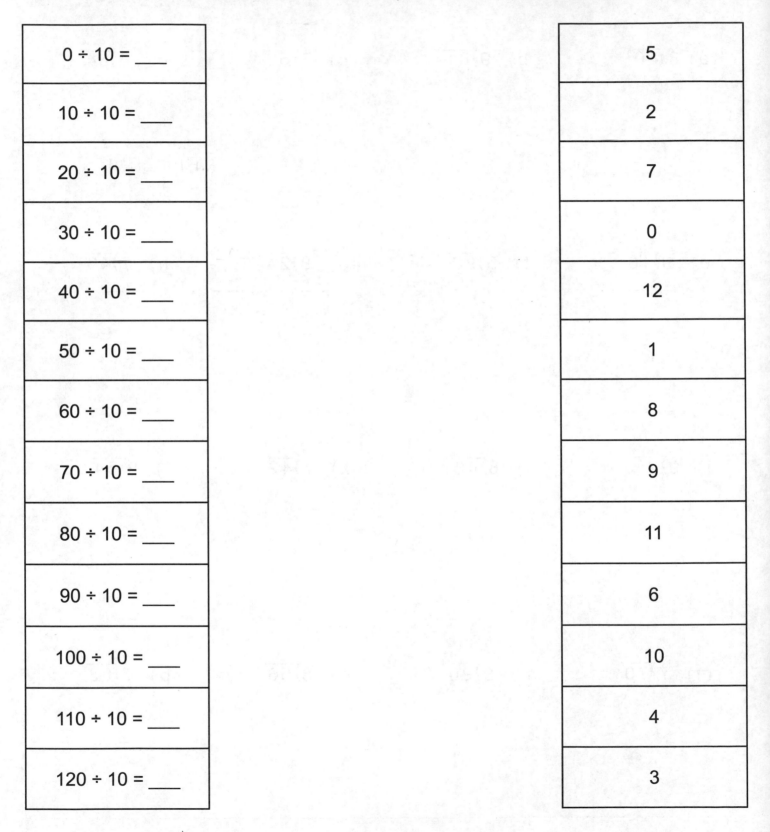

0 ÷ 10 = ___	5
10 ÷ 10 = ___	2
20 ÷ 10 = ___	7
30 ÷ 10 = ___	0
40 ÷ 10 = ___	12
50 ÷ 10 = ___	1
60 ÷ 10 = ___	8
70 ÷ 10 = ___	9
80 ÷ 10 = ___	11
90 ÷ 10 = ___	6
100 ÷ 10 = ___	10
110 ÷ 10 = ___	4
120 ÷ 10 = ___	3

Math Riddle: Dividing by 10

What do you call a famous fish?

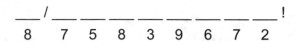

___ / ___ ___ ___ ___ ___ ___ ___ ___ !
8   7   5   8   3   9   6   7   2

Watch out! Some letters are not used in the riddle!

1. Find the quotient.

A	B	E
80 ÷ 10 = __	40 ÷ 10 = ___	120 ÷ 10 = ___
F	**G**	**H**
90 ÷ 10 = ___	110 ÷ 10 = ___	20 ÷ 10 = ___
I	**J**	**R**
60 ÷ 10 = ___	100 ÷ 10 = ___	30 ÷ 10 = ___
S	**T**	**Y**
70 ÷ 10 = ___	50 ÷ 10 = ___	10 ÷ 10 = ___

2. Find the missing dividend.

___ ÷ 10 = 6	___ ÷ 10 = 7	___ ÷ 10 = 4	___ ÷ 10 = 9
___ ÷ 10 = 10	___ ÷ 10 = 3	___ ÷ 10 = 8	___ ÷ 10 = 5

Test 1—Multiplying by 1, 2, and 3

5	4	6	8	4	2	1
× 2	× 3	× 1	× 2	× 1	× 3	× 2
10	*12*	*6*	*16*	*4*	*6*	*2*

3	5	2	4	8	7	9
× 1	× 3	× 2	× 2	× 3	× 1	× 2
3	*15*	*4*		*24*	*7*	*18*

8	6	3	1	5	6
× 1	× 3	× 2	× 1	× 1	× 2
8	*18*	*6*	*1*	*5*	*12*

Number Correct

20 / 20

Test 2—Multiplying by 1, 2, and 3

2	5	3	4	5	7	4
× 1	× 2	× 3	× 2	× 3	× 2	× 1
2	*10*	*9*	*8*	*15*		

2	1	5	8	9	6	4
× 3	× 1	× 1	× 3	× 2	× 1	× 3

1	7	3	3	6	10
× 2	× 3	× 1	× 2	× 2	× 3

Number Correct

/ 20

Test 3—Multiplying by 1, 2, and 3

2	5	4	3	1	8	3
× 2	× 3	× 1	× 1	× 2	× 3	× 2
4	15	4	3	2	24	6

4	8	2	4	3	9	6
× 3	× 2	× 1	× 2	× 3	× 1	× 3
12	16	2	8	9	9	18

7	1	5	9	8	6
× 1	× 3	× 1	× 3	× 1	× 2
7	3	5	27	8	12

Number Correct

20 / 20

Test 4—Multiplying by 1, 2, and 3

4	5	3	1	3	2	3
× 1	× 3	× 2	× 1	× 3	× 2	× 1
4	15	6	1	9	4	3

9	2	5	10	8	2	9
× 3	× 1	× 2	× 1	× 2	× 3	× 1
27	2	10	10	16		9

4	7	6	1	9	8
× 3	× 2	× 1	× 3	× 2	× 1
12	14	6	3	18	8

Number Correct

20 / 20

Test 5—Multiplying by 1, 2, and 3

$$\begin{array}{r}5\\\times\ 3\\\hline 5\end{array}\qquad\begin{array}{r}3\\\times\ 2\\\hline 6\end{array}\qquad\begin{array}{r}4\\\times\ 1\\\hline 4\end{array}\qquad\begin{array}{r}2\\\times\ 1\\\hline 2\end{array}\qquad\begin{array}{r}1\\\times\ 3\\\hline 3\end{array}\qquad\begin{array}{r}9\\\times\ 2\\\hline 16\end{array}\qquad\begin{array}{r}6\\\times\ 3\\\hline 8\end{array}$$

$$\begin{array}{r}7\\\times\ 1\\\hline 7\end{array}\qquad\begin{array}{r}3\\\times\ 3\\\hline 9\end{array}\qquad\begin{array}{r}6\\\times\ 1\\\hline 6\end{array}\qquad\begin{array}{r}4\\\times\ 2\\\hline 8\end{array}\qquad\begin{array}{r}9\\\times\ 3\\\hline 21\end{array}\qquad\begin{array}{r}1\\\times\ 1\\\hline 1\end{array}\qquad\begin{array}{r}5\\\times\ 2\\\hline 10\end{array}$$

$$\begin{array}{r}5\\\times\ 1\\\hline 5\end{array}\qquad\begin{array}{r}1\\\times\ 2\\\hline 2\end{array}\qquad\begin{array}{r}3\\\times\ 1\\\hline 3\end{array}\qquad\begin{array}{r}2\\\times\ 3\\\hline 6\end{array}\qquad\begin{array}{r}8\\\times\ 1\\\hline 8\end{array}\qquad\begin{array}{r}4\\\times\ 3\\\hline 12\end{array}$$

Number Correct

____
20

Test 6—Multiplying by 1, 2, and 3

$$\begin{array}{r}4\\\times\ 1\\\hline 4\end{array}\qquad\begin{array}{r}5\\\times\ 3\\\hline 15\end{array}\qquad\begin{array}{r}2\\\times\ 2\\\hline 4\end{array}\qquad\begin{array}{r}5\\\times\ 1\\\hline 5\end{array}\qquad\begin{array}{r}4\\\times\ 3\\\hline 12\end{array}\qquad\begin{array}{r}1\\\times\ 2\\\hline 2\end{array}\qquad\begin{array}{r}3\\\times\ 1\\\hline 3\end{array}$$

$$\begin{array}{r}4\\\times\ 2\\\hline 8\end{array}\qquad\begin{array}{r}8\\\times\ 1\\\hline 8\end{array}\qquad\begin{array}{r}5\\\times\ 2\\\hline 10\end{array}\qquad\begin{array}{r}3\\\times\ 3\\\hline 9\end{array}\qquad\begin{array}{r}7\\\times\ 2\\\hline\end{array}\qquad\begin{array}{r}1\\\times\ 1\\\hline 1\end{array}\qquad\begin{array}{r}6\\\times\ 3\\\hline 18\end{array}$$

$$\begin{array}{r}9\\\times\ 3\\\hline\end{array}\qquad\begin{array}{r}3\\\times\ 2\\\hline\end{array}\qquad\begin{array}{r}9\\\times\ 1\\\hline\end{array}\qquad\begin{array}{r}8\\\times\ 3\\\hline\end{array}\qquad\begin{array}{r}6\\\times\ 2\\\hline\end{array}\qquad\begin{array}{r}2\\\times\ 1\\\hline\end{array}$$

Number Correct

____
20

Test 7—Multiplying by 1, 2, and 3

4	3	5	3	2	4	1
× 2	× 3	× 1	× 2	× 1	× 3	× 2

6	2	7	5	2	1	6
× 1	× 2	× 3	× 2	× 3	× 1	× 2

7	5	9	1	8	10
× 2	× 3	× 1	× 3	× 2	× 1

Number Correct

____

20

Test 8—Multiplying by 1, 2, and 3

4	5	3	1	5	2	3
× 1	× 3	× 2	× 3	× 1	× 2	× 1

6	2	8	4	3	7	5
× 3	× 1	× 2	× 2	× 3	× 1	× 2

4	1	1	6	9	7
× 3	× 1	× 2	× 1	× 3	× 2

Number Correct

____

20

Test 9—Multiplying by 1, 2, and 3

3	4	5	2	1	5	4
× 3	× 2	× 1	× 1	× 3	× 2	× 1

7	5	9	8	4	1	3
× 2	× 3	× 1	× 2	× 3	× 1	× 2

8	3	9	8	2	6
× 1	× 1	× 2	× 3	× 2	× 3

Number Correct

―――
20

Test 10—Multiplying by 1, 2, and 3

10	4	3	2	1	3	5
× 2	× 1	× 3	× 2	× 1	× 2	× 3

4	2	8	3	2	10	6
× 2	× 1	× 3	× 1	× 3	× 1	× 2

1	7	4	2	5	9
× 2	× 1	× 3	× 7	× 2	× 3

Number Correct

―――
20

148

Test 1—Multiplying by 4, 5, and 6

10	8	6	7	10	9	4
× 4	× 6	× 5	× 4	× 6	× 5	× 4

7	10	9	6	8	2	3
× 6	× 5	× 4	× 6	× 5	× 4	× 6

3	8	4	9	7	5
× 5	× 4	× 6	× 6	× 5	× 4

Number Correct

―――
20

Test 2—Multiplying by 4, 5, and 6

10	8	9	7	10	6	8
× 5	× 4	× 6	× 5	× 4	× 6	× 5

6	7	3	10	9	6	4
× 4	× 6	× 5	× 6	× 4	× 5	× 6

8	4	7	5	2	3
× 6	× 5	× 4	× 6	× 5	× 4

Number Correct

―――
20

Test 3—Multiplying by 4, 5, and 6

9	7	10	8	6	9	7
× 4	× 5	× 6	× 4	× 5	× 6	× 4

8	10	5	6	3	8	2
× 6	× 4	× 5	× 6	× 4	× 5	× 6

3	6	1	9	5	2
× 5	× 4	× 6	× 5	× 6	× 4

Number Correct

_____
20

Test 4—Multiplying by 4, 5, and 6

1	10	7	6	8	3	9
× 4	× 6	× 4	× 5	× 4	× 6	× 5

1	5	7	4	6	2	10
× 5	× 4	× 6	× 5	× 4	× 6	× 5

9	5	1	2	8	4
× 4	× 5	× 6	× 5	× 6	× 4

Number Correct

_____
20

Test 5—Multiplying by 4, 5, and 6

7	6	8	10	9	6	4
× 6	× 4	× 5	× 4	× 5	× 6	× 5

10	5	9	6	7	10	2
× 6	× 5	× 4	× 5	× 4	× 5	× 6

1	3	7	2	8	1
× 4	× 6	× 5	× 4	× 6	× 5

Number Correct

_____
20

Test 6—Multiplying by 4, 5, and 6

3	4	8	4	7	10	9
× 4	× 6	× 5	× 5	× 4	× 6	× 5

5	2	4	3	9	1	7
× 6	× 5	× 4	× 5	× 4	× 6	× 5

6	3	5	6	8	9
× 4	× 6	× 4	× 6	× 4	× 6

Number Correct

_____
20

Test 7—Multiplying by 4, 5, and 6

8	7	6	10	3	6	9
× 5	× 4	× 5	× 6	× 4	× 6	× 5

7	6	8	3	1	9	2
× 5	× 4	× 6	× 5	× 4	× 6	× 5

7	9	2	1	5	10
× 6	× 4	× 6	× 5	× 6	× 4

Number Correct

_____
20

Test 8—Multiplying by 4, 5, and 6

6	8	7	10	7	9	6
× 6	× 4	× 5	× 6	× 4	× 6	× 5

3	8	10	2	1	5	4
× 4	× 6	× 5	× 6	× 4	× 5	× 4

10	8	7	4	3	9
× 4	× 5	× 6	× 6	× 5	× 4

Number Correct

_____
20

Test 9—Multiplying by 4, 5, and 6

10	7	9	8	6	10	2
× 4	× 6	× 5	× 4	× 5	× 6	× 4

4	3	6	1	5	2	4
× 5	× 6	× 4	× 6	× 4	× 5	× 4

8	3	7	4	1	10
× 6	× 5	× 4	× 6	× 4	× 5

Number Correct

___
20

Test 10—Multiplying by 4, 5, and 6

1	2	6	9	8	3	9
× 5	× 4	× 5	× 6	× 4	× 6	× 5

5	7	2	8	9	10	7
× 4	× 5	× 6	× 5	× 4	× 6	× 4

10	2	6	3	10	8
× 4	× 5	× 6	× 4	× 5	× 6

Number Correct

___
20

Test 1—Multiplying by 7, 8, and 9

10	4	9	5	8	2	7
× 7	× 8	× 9	× 7	× 8	× 7	× 9

6	9	8	4	7	10	5
× 8	× 7	× 9	× 7	× 8	× 9	× 8

4	1	3	2	7	2
× 9	× 8	× 7	× 9	× 7	× 8

Number Correct

——
20

Test 2—Multiplying by 7, 8, and 9

10	7	5	3	9	6	8
× 8	× 7	× 9	× 7	× 8	× 9	× 8

5	4	9	6	3	8	3
× 8	× 9	× 7	× 8	× 9	× 7	× 8

10	6	4	1	2	7
× 9	× 7	× 8	× 9	× 7	× 8

Number Correct

——
20

Test 3—Multiplying by 7, 8, and 9

9	4	10	5	8	3	6
× 7	× 8	× 9	× 8	× 7	× 9	× 7

9	5	6	8	4	10	7
× 8	× 7	× 8	× 9	× 7	× 8	× 7

4	10	7	6	1	2	Number Correct
× 9	× 7	× 8	× 9	× 7	× 8	

$$\frac{}{20}$$

Test 4—Multiplying by 7, 8, and 9

9	5	4	6	3	8	7
× 7	× 8	× 9	× 8	× 7	× 8	× 9

3	5	8	2	10	9	4
× 8	× 7	× 9	× 7	× 8	× 9	× 8

10	2	7	5	6	1	Number Correct
× 7	× 9	× 8	× 9	× 7	× 8	

$$\frac{}{20}$$

Test 5—Multiplying by 7, 8, and 9

10 × 9	4 × 7	9 × 8	5 × 9	5 × 7	2 × 8	7 × 9
3 × 8	1 × 9	8 × 7	1 × 8	8 × 9	1 × 7	8 × 8
3 × 7	10 × 8	6 × 9	7 × 7	4 × 8	9 × 9	

Number Correct

___
20

Test 6—Multiplying by 7, 8, and 9

2 × 8	7 × 9	5 × 7	3 × 9	9 × 7	6 × 8	8 × 9
3 × 7	4 × 8	9 × 9	8 × 7	10 × 8	5 × 9	2 × 7
10 × 9	1 × 7	8 × 8	3 × 8	2 × 9	6 × 7	

Number Correct

___
20

Test 7—Multiplying by 7, 8, and 9

7	4	9	5	8	2	6
× 9	× 8	× 7	× 9	× 7	× 8	× 9

1	5	2	9	6	10	3
× 8	× 7	× 9	× 8	× 7	× 9	× 8

4	1	7	10	5	2
× 7	× 9	× 8	× 7	× 8	× 7

Number Correct

_____
20

Test 8—Multiplying by 7, 8, and 9

9	8	4	5	3	7	6
× 8	× 7	× 9	× 7	× 8	× 9	× 7

6	5	7	3	1	2	4
× 9	× 8	× 7	× 9	× 7	× 8	× 8

10	2	8	1	9	4
× 7	× 9	× 8	× 8	× 9	× 7

Number Correct

_____
20

Test 9—Multiplying by 7, 8, and 9

10	4	9	5	8	2	7
× 7	× 8	× 9	× 7	× 8	× 9	× 7
70	72	81	30			

3	1	7	4	6	9	5
× 9	× 7	× 8	× 9	× 7	× 8	× 9
					72	

6	10	3	2	7	2
× 8	× 9	× 7	× 8	× 9	× 7
48					

Number Correct

___
20

Test 10—Multiplying by 7, 8, and 9

1	7	4	6	9	3	8
× 9	× 7	× 8	× 9	× 7	× 8	× 9
					24	

5	4	2	10	5	3	6
× 8	× 9	× 7	× 8	× 9	× 7	× 8

10	8	3	4	7	9
× 7	× 8	× 9	× 7	× 8	× 9

Number Correct

___
20

158

How Am I Doing?

Tests—Multiplying by 1, 2, and 3

Number correct	Test 1	Test 2	Test 3	Test 4	Test 5	Test 6	Test 7	Test 8	Test 9	Test 10
20										
19										
18										
17										
16										
15										
14										
13										
12										
11										
10										
9										
8										
7										
6										
5										
4										
3										
2										
1										

Tests—Multiplying by 4, 5, and 6

Number correct	Test 1	Test 2	Test 3	Test 4	Test 5	Test 6	Test 7	Test 8	Test 9	Test 10
20										
19										
18										
17										
16										
15										
14										
13										
12										
11										
10										
9										
8										
7										
6										
5										
4										
3										
2										
1										

How Am I Doing?

Tests—Multiplying by 7, 8, and 9

Number correct	Test 1	Test 2	Test 3	Test 4	Test 5	Test 6	Test 7	Test 8	Test 9	Test 10
20										
19										
18										
17										
16										
15										
14										
13										
12										
11										
10										
9										
8										
7										
6										
5										
4										
3										
2										
1										

Test 1—Dividing by 1, 2, and 3

$2\overline{)10}$ $3\overline{)12}$ $1\overline{)6}$ $2\overline{)16}$ $1\overline{)4}$ $3\overline{)18}$ $2\overline{)2}$

$1\overline{)3}$ $3\overline{)15}$ $2\overline{)4}$ $2\overline{)8}$ $3\overline{)24}$ $1\overline{)7}$ $2\overline{)18}$

$1\overline{)8}$ $2\overline{)20}$ $2\overline{)6}$ $1\overline{)1}$ $1\overline{)5}$ $2\overline{)12}$

Number Correct

$\overline{20}$

Test 2—Dividing by 1, 2, and 3

$1\overline{)2}$ $2\overline{)10}$ $3\overline{)9}$ $2\overline{)8}$ $3\overline{)15}$ $2\overline{)14}$ $1\overline{)4}$

$3\overline{)21}$ $2\overline{)6}$ $1\overline{)5}$ $3\overline{)24}$ $2\overline{)18}$ $1\overline{)6}$ $3\overline{)12}$

$2\overline{)2}$ $3\overline{)6}$ $1\overline{)3}$ $1\overline{)1}$ $2\overline{)12}$ $3\overline{)30}$

Number Correct

$\overline{20}$

Test 3—Dividing by 1, 2, and 3

$2\overline{)\ 4}$ $3\overline{)\ 15}$ $1\overline{)\ 4}$ $1\overline{)\ 3}$ $2\overline{)\ 2}$ $3\overline{)\ 24}$ $2\overline{)\ 6}$

$3\overline{)\ 12}$ $2\overline{)\ 16}$ $1\overline{)\ 2}$ $2\overline{)\ 8}$ $3\overline{)\ 9}$ $1\overline{)\ 9}$ $3\overline{)\ 18}$

$1\overline{)\ 7}$ $3\overline{)\ 3}$ $2\overline{)\ 20}$ $3\overline{)\ 27}$ $1\overline{)\ 8}$ $2\overline{)\ 12}$

Number Correct

$\overline{}$
20

Test 4—Dividing by 1, 2, and 3

$1\overline{)\ 4}$ $1\overline{)\ 10}$ $2\overline{)\ 6}$ $1\overline{)\ 1}$ $3\overline{)\ 9}$ $2\overline{)\ 4}$ $3\overline{)\ 30}$

$3\overline{)\ 27}$ $1\overline{)\ 2}$ $2\overline{)\ 10}$ $3\overline{)\ 15}$ $2\overline{)\ 16}$ $3\overline{)\ 6}$ $1\overline{)\ 9}$

$3\overline{)\ 12}$ $2\overline{)\ 14}$ $1\overline{)\ 6}$ $3\overline{)\ 3}$ $2\overline{)\ 18}$ $1\overline{)\ 8}$

Number Correct

$\overline{}$
20

Test 5—Dividing by 1, 2, and 3

$3\overline{)15}$ $2\overline{)6}$ $1\overline{)4}$ $2\overline{)14}$ $3\overline{)3}$ $2\overline{)18}$ $1\overline{)6}$

$1\overline{)7}$ $3\overline{)9}$ $3\overline{)18}$ $2\overline{)8}$ $3\overline{)27}$ $1\overline{)1}$ $2\overline{)10}$

$1\overline{)5}$ $2\overline{)20}$ $1\overline{)3}$ $3\overline{)30}$ $1\overline{)8}$ $3\overline{)12}$

Number Correct

—

20

Test 6—Dividing by 1, 2, and 3

$1\overline{)4}$ $3\overline{)15}$ $2\overline{)4}$ $1\overline{)5}$ $3\overline{)12}$ $2\overline{)2}$ $1\overline{)3}$

$2\overline{)18}$ $1\overline{)8}$ $2\overline{)10}$ $3\overline{)9}$ $2\overline{)14}$ $1\overline{)1}$ $3\overline{)18}$

$3\overline{)27}$ $2\overline{)6}$ $1\overline{)9}$ $3\overline{)24}$ $2\overline{)12}$ $1\overline{)2}$

Number Correct

—

20

Test 7—Dividing by 1, 2, and 3

$2\overline{)8}$ $3\overline{)9}$ $1\overline{)5}$ $2\overline{)20}$ $1\overline{)2}$ $3\overline{)12}$ $2\overline{)2}$

$1\overline{)6}$ $2\overline{)4}$ $3\overline{)21}$ $2\overline{)10}$ $3\overline{)27}$ $1\overline{)1}$ $2\overline{)6}$

$2\overline{)14}$ $3\overline{)15}$ $1\overline{)9}$ $3\overline{)3}$ $2\overline{)16}$ $1\overline{)10}$

Number
Correct

———
20

Test 8—Dividing by 1, 2, and 3

$1\overline{)4}$ $3\overline{)15}$ $2\overline{)6}$ $3\overline{)30}$ $1\overline{)5}$ $2\overline{)4}$ $1\overline{)3}$

$3\overline{)18}$ $1\overline{)2}$ $2\overline{)16}$ $2\overline{)8}$ $3\overline{)9}$ $1\overline{)7}$ $2\overline{)12}$

$3\overline{)12}$ $1\overline{)1}$ $2\overline{)20}$ $1\overline{)6}$ $3\overline{)21}$ $2\overline{)10}$

Number
Correct

———
20

Test 9—Dividing by 1, 2, and 3

$3\overline{)9}$ $2\overline{)8}$ $1\overline{)5}$ $1\overline{)2}$ $3\overline{)21}$ $2\overline{)10}$ $1\overline{)4}$

$2\overline{)14}$ $3\overline{)15}$ $1\overline{)9}$ $2\overline{)16}$ $3\overline{)12}$ $1\overline{)1}$ $2\overline{)6}$

$1\overline{)8}$ $1\overline{)3}$ $2\overline{)18}$ $3\overline{)24}$ $2\overline{)4}$ $3\overline{)18}$

Number Correct

$\overline{}$
20

Test 10—Dividing by 1, 2, and 3

$2\overline{)20}$ $1\overline{)4}$ $3\overline{)9}$ $2\overline{)4}$ $1\overline{)1}$ $2\overline{)6}$ $3\overline{)15}$

$2\overline{)16}$ $1\overline{)2}$ $3\overline{)24}$ $1\overline{)3}$ $3\overline{)6}$ $1\overline{)10}$ $2\overline{)12}$

$2\overline{)2}$ $1\overline{)7}$ $3\overline{)12}$ $1\overline{)9}$ $2\overline{)10}$ $3\overline{)27}$

Number Correct

$\overline{}$
20

Test 1—Dividing by 4, 5, and 6

$4\overline{)40}$ $6\overline{)48}$ $5\overline{)30}$ $4\overline{)28}$ $6\overline{)60}$ $5\overline{)45}$ $4\overline{)16}$

$6\overline{)42}$ $5\overline{)50}$ $4\overline{)32}$ $6\overline{)36}$ $5\overline{)40}$ $4\overline{)8}$ $6\overline{)18}$

$5\overline{)15}$ $4\overline{)36}$ $6\overline{)24}$ $6\overline{)54}$ $5\overline{)35}$ $4\overline{)20}$

Number Correct

$\overline{}$
20

Test 2—Dividing by 4, 5, and 6

$5\overline{)50}$ $4\overline{)32}$ $6\overline{)54}$ $5\overline{)35}$ $4\overline{)40}$ $6\overline{)36}$ $5\overline{)40}$

$4\overline{)24}$ $6\overline{)42}$ $5\overline{)15}$ $6\overline{)60}$ $4\overline{)36}$ $5\overline{)30}$ $6\overline{)24}$

$6\overline{)48}$ $5\overline{)20}$ $4\overline{)28}$ $6\overline{)30}$ $5\overline{)10}$ $4\overline{)12}$

Number Correct

$\overline{}$
20

Test 3—Dividing by 4, 5, and 6

$4\overline{)36}$ $5\overline{)30}$ $6\overline{)60}$ $4\overline{)32}$ $5\overline{)30}$ $6\overline{)54}$ $4\overline{)28}$

$6\overline{)48}$ $4\overline{)40}$ $5\overline{)25}$ $6\overline{)36}$ $4\overline{)12}$ $5\overline{)40}$ $6\overline{)12}$

$5\overline{)15}$ $4\overline{)24}$ $6\overline{)6}$ $5\overline{)45}$ $6\overline{)30}$ $4\overline{)8}$

Number Correct

$\overline{20}$

Test 4—Dividing by 4, 5, and 6

$4\overline{)4}$ $6\overline{)60}$ $4\overline{)28}$ $5\overline{)30}$ $4\overline{)32}$ $6\overline{)18}$ $5\overline{)45}$

$5\overline{)5}$ $4\overline{)20}$ $6\overline{)42}$ $5\overline{)20}$ $4\overline{)24}$ $6\overline{)12}$ $5\overline{)50}$

$4\overline{)36}$ $5\overline{)25}$ $6\overline{)6}$ $5\overline{)10}$ $6\overline{)48}$ $4\overline{)16}$

Number Correct

$\overline{20}$

Test 5—Dividing by 4, 5, and 6

$6\overline{)42}$ $4\overline{)24}$ $5\overline{)40}$ $4\overline{)40}$ $5\overline{)45}$ $6\overline{)36}$ $5\overline{)20}$

$6\overline{)60}$ $5\overline{)25}$ $4\overline{)36}$ $5\overline{)30}$ $4\overline{)28}$ $5\overline{)50}$ $6\overline{)12}$

$4\overline{)\;4}$ $6\overline{)18}$ $5\overline{)35}$ $4\overline{)\;8}$ $6\overline{)48}$ $5\overline{)\;5}$

Number Correct

___

20

Test 6—Dividing by 4, 5, and 6

$4\overline{)12}$ $6\overline{)24}$ $5\overline{)40}$ $6\overline{)36}$ $4\overline{)28}$ $6\overline{)60}$ $5\overline{)45}$

$6\overline{)30}$ $5\overline{)10}$ $4\overline{)16}$ $5\overline{)20}$ $4\overline{)36}$ $6\overline{)\;6}$ $5\overline{)35}$

$4\overline{)24}$ $6\overline{)18}$ $4\overline{)20}$ $5\overline{)15}$ $4\overline{)32}$ $6\overline{)54}$

Number Correct

___

20

Test 7—Dividing by 4, 5, and 6

$5\overline{)40}$	$4\overline{)28}$	$5\overline{)30}$	$6\overline{)60}$	$4\overline{)12}$	$6\overline{)36}$	$5\overline{)45}$
$5\overline{)35}$	$4\overline{)24}$	$6\overline{)48}$	$5\overline{)15}$	$4\overline{)4}$	$6\overline{)54}$	$5\overline{)10}$
$6\overline{)42}$	$4\overline{)36}$	$6\overline{)12}$	$5\overline{)5}$	$6\overline{)30}$	$4\overline{)40}$	

Number Correct

———
20

Test 8—Dividing by 4, 5, and 6

$6\overline{)36}$	$4\overline{)32}$	$5\overline{)35}$	$6\overline{)60}$	$4\overline{)28}$	$6\overline{)54}$	$5\overline{)30}$
$4\overline{)12}$	$6\overline{)48}$	$5\overline{)50}$	$6\overline{)12}$	$4\overline{)4}$	$5\overline{)25}$	$4\overline{)16}$
$4\overline{)40}$	$5\overline{)40}$	$6\overline{)42}$	$6\overline{)24}$	$5\overline{)15}$	$4\overline{)36}$	

Number Correct

———
20

Test 9—Dividing by 4, 5, and 6

$4\overline{)40}$ $6\overline{)42}$ $5\overline{)45}$ $4\overline{)32}$ $5\overline{)30}$ $6\overline{)60}$ $4\overline{)8}$

$5\overline{)20}$ $6\overline{)18}$ $4\overline{)24}$ $6\overline{)6}$ $4\overline{)20}$ $5\overline{)10}$ $4\overline{)16}$

$6\overline{)48}$ $5\overline{)15}$ $4\overline{)28}$ $6\overline{)24}$ $4\overline{)4}$ $5\overline{)50}$

Number Correct

$\overline{20}$

Test 10—Dividing by 4, 5, and 6

$5\overline{)5}$ $4\overline{)8}$ $5\overline{)30}$ $6\overline{)54}$ $4\overline{)32}$ $6\overline{)18}$ $5\overline{)45}$

$4\overline{)20}$ $5\overline{)35}$ $6\overline{)12}$ $5\overline{)40}$ $4\overline{)36}$ $6\overline{)60}$ $4\overline{)32}$

$4\overline{)40}$ $5\overline{)10}$ $6\overline{)36}$ $4\overline{)12}$ $5\overline{)50}$ $6\overline{)48}$

Number Correct

$\overline{20}$

Test 1—Dividing by 7, 8, and 9

$7\overline{)70}$ $8\overline{)32}$ $9\overline{)81}$ $7\overline{)35}$ $8\overline{)64}$ $7\overline{)14}$ $9\overline{)63}$

$8\overline{)48}$ $7\overline{)63}$ $9\overline{)72}$ $7\overline{)28}$ $8\overline{)56}$ $9\overline{)90}$ $8\overline{)40}$

$9\overline{)36}$ $8\overline{)8}$ $7\overline{)21}$ $9\overline{)18}$ $7\overline{)49}$ $8\overline{)16}$

Number Correct

$\dfrac{}{20}$

Test 2—Dividing by 7, 8, and 9

$8\overline{)80}$ $7\overline{)49}$ $9\overline{)45}$ $7\overline{)21}$ $8\overline{)72}$ $9\overline{)54}$ $8\overline{)64}$

$8\overline{)40}$ $9\overline{)36}$ $7\overline{)63}$ $8\overline{)48}$ $9\overline{)27}$ $7\overline{)56}$ $8\overline{)24}$

$9\overline{)90}$ $7\overline{)42}$ $8\overline{)32}$ $9\overline{)9}$ $7\overline{)14}$ $8\overline{)56}$

Number Correct

$\dfrac{}{20}$

Test 3—Dividing by 7, 8, and 9

$7\overline{)63}$ $8\overline{)32}$ $9\overline{)90}$ $8\overline{)40}$ $7\overline{)56}$ $9\overline{)27}$ $7\overline{)42}$

$8\overline{)72}$ $7\overline{)35}$ $8\overline{)48}$ $9\overline{)72}$ $7\overline{)28}$ $8\overline{)80}$ $7\overline{)49}$

$9\overline{)36}$ $7\overline{)70}$ $8\overline{)56}$ $9\overline{)54}$ $7\overline{)7}$ $8\overline{)16}$

Number Correct

____
20

Test 4—Dividing by 7, 8, and 9

$7\overline{)63}$ $8\overline{)40}$ $9\overline{)36}$ $8\overline{)48}$ $7\overline{)21}$ $8\overline{)64}$ $9\overline{)63}$

$8\overline{)24}$ $7\overline{)35}$ $9\overline{)72}$ $7\overline{)14}$ $8\overline{)80}$ $9\overline{)81}$ $8\overline{)32}$

$7\overline{)70}$ $9\overline{)18}$ $8\overline{)56}$ $9\overline{)45}$ $7\overline{)42}$ $8\overline{)8}$

Number Correct

____
20

Test 5—Dividing by 7, 8, and 9

$9\overline{)90}$ $7\overline{)28}$ $8\overline{)72}$ $9\overline{)63}$ $7\overline{)35}$ $8\overline{)16}$ $9\overline{)72}$

$8\overline{)24}$ $9\overline{)9}$ $7\overline{)56}$ $8\overline{)8}$ $9\overline{)45}$ $7\overline{)7}$ $8\overline{)64}$

$7\overline{)21}$ $8\overline{)80}$ $9\overline{)54}$ $7\overline{)49}$ $8\overline{)32}$ $9\overline{)81}$

Number
Correct

———
20

Test 6—Dividing by 7, 8, and 9

$8\overline{)16}$ $9\overline{)63}$ $7\overline{)35}$ $9\overline{)72}$ $7\overline{)63}$ $8\overline{)48}$ $9\overline{)27}$

$7\overline{)21}$ $8\overline{)32}$ $9\overline{)81}$ $7\overline{)56}$ $8\overline{)80}$ $9\overline{)45}$ $7\overline{)14}$

$9\overline{)90}$ $7\overline{)7}$ $8\overline{)64}$ $8\overline{)24}$ $9\overline{)18}$ $7\overline{)42}$

Number
Correct

———
20

Test 7—Dividing by 7, 8, and 9

$9\overline{)63}$ $8\overline{)32}$ $7\overline{)63}$ $9\overline{)45}$ $7\overline{)56}$ $8\overline{)16}$ $9\overline{)54}$

$8\overline{)\,8}$ $7\overline{)35}$ $9\overline{)18}$ $8\overline{)72}$ $7\overline{)42}$ $9\overline{)90}$ $8\overline{)24}$

$7\overline{)28}$ $9\overline{)\,9}$ $8\overline{)56}$ $7\overline{)70}$ $8\overline{)40}$ $7\overline{)14}$

Number Correct

$\overline{20}$

Test 8—Dividing by 7, 8, and 9

$8\overline{)72}$ $7\overline{)56}$ $9\overline{)36}$ $7\overline{)35}$ $8\overline{)24}$ $9\overline{)63}$ $7\overline{)42}$

$9\overline{)54}$ $8\overline{)40}$ $7\overline{)49}$ $9\overline{)27}$ $7\overline{)\,7}$ $8\overline{)16}$ $8\overline{)32}$

$7\overline{)70}$ $9\overline{)18}$ $8\overline{)64}$ $8\overline{)\,8}$ $9\overline{)81}$ $7\overline{)28}$

Number Correct

$\overline{20}$

Test 9—Dividing by 7, 8, and 9

$7\overline{)21}$ $8\overline{)8}$ $9\overline{)27}$ $7\overline{)7}$ $8\overline{)24}$ $9\overline{)9}$ $7\overline{)35}$

$9\overline{)36}$ $7\overline{)49}$ $8\overline{)64}$ $9\overline{)18}$ $7\overline{)42}$ $8\overline{)32}$ $9\overline{)18}$

$8\overline{)40}$ $9\overline{)90}$ $7\overline{)35}$ $8\overline{)24}$ $9\overline{)54}$ $7\overline{)14}$

Number Correct

$\overline{20}$

Test 10—Dividing by 7, 8, and 9

$9\overline{)9}$ $7\overline{)49}$ $8\overline{)32}$ $9\overline{)54}$ $7\overline{)63}$ $8\overline{)24}$ $9\overline{)72}$

$8\overline{)40}$ $9\overline{)36}$ $7\overline{)14}$ $8\overline{)80}$ $9\overline{)45}$ $7\overline{)21}$ $8\overline{)48}$

$7\overline{)70}$ $8\overline{)64}$ $9\overline{)27}$ $7\overline{)28}$ $8\overline{)56}$ $9\overline{)81}$

Number Correct

$\overline{20}$

How Am I Doing?

Tests—Dividing by 1, 2, and 3

Number correct	Test 1	Test 2	Test 3	Test 4	Test 5	Test 6	Test 7	Test 8	Test 9	Test 10
20										
19										
18										
17										
16										
15										
14										
13										
12										
11										
10										
9										
8										
7										
6										
5										
4										
3										
2										
1										

Division Tests—Dividing by 4, 5, and 6

Number correct	Test 1	Test 2	Test 3	Test 4	Test 5	Test 6	Test 7	Test 8	Test 9	Test 10
20										
19										
18										
17										
16										
15										
14										
13										
12										
11										
10										
9										
8										
7										
6										
5										
4										
3										
2										
1										

How Am I Doing?

Tests—Dividing by 7, 8, and 9

Number correct	Test 1	Test 2	Test 3	Test 4	Test 5	Test 6	Test 7	Test 8	Test 9	Test 10
20										
19										
18										
17										
16										
15										
14										
13										
12										
11										
10										
9										
8										
7										
6										
5										
4										
3										
2										
1										

Trace and write. Circle your best *a* or *a* on each line.

a a a a a a a a

a a a a a a a a a

August

august *August*

a a a a a a a a a

a

a a a a a a a a aa

air

air air air

an

actor

alligator

Trace and write. Circle your best $\mathcal{B}$ or b on each line.

$\mathcal{B}$ $\mathcal{B}$ $\mathcal{B}$ $\mathcal{B}$ $\mathcal{B}$ $\mathcal{B}$ $\mathcal{B}$ $\mathcal{B}$

$\mathcal{B}$ $\mathcal{B}$

Bella

b b b b b b b b

b

four

bake

blue

buffalo

Trace and write. Circle your best *C* or *c* on each line.

C C C C C C C C C

C

Canada

c c c c c c c c c c

c

cat

cow

climb

cursive

Dd Trace and write. Circle your best $\mathcal{D}$ or d on each line.

$\mathcal{D}$ $\mathcal{D}$ $\mathcal{D}$ $\mathcal{D}$ $\mathcal{D}$ $\mathcal{D}$ $\mathcal{D}$

$\mathcal{D}$

December

d d d d d d d d

d

dad

dear

duck

dinosaur

Trace and write. Circle your best $\mathcal{E}$ or e on each line.

$\mathcal{E}$ $\mathcal{E}$ $\mathcal{E}$ $\mathcal{E}$ $\mathcal{E}$ $\mathcal{E}$ $\mathcal{E}$ $\mathcal{E}$ $\mathcal{E}$ $\mathcal{E}$ $\mathcal{E}$

$\mathcal{E}$

Ethan

e e e e e e e e e e e

e

eel

eat

egg

elephant

Trace and write. Circle your best *F* or *f* on each line.

$\mathcal{F}$ $\mathcal{F}$ $\mathcal{F}$ $\mathcal{F}$ $\mathcal{F}$ $\mathcal{F}$ $\mathcal{F}$ $\mathcal{F}$ $\mathcal{F}$

$\mathcal{F}$

February

f f f f f f f f

f

for

find

floss

friend

Trace and write. Circle your best $\mathscr{G}$ or g on each line.

$\mathscr{G}$ $\mathscr{G}$ $\mathscr{G}$ $\mathscr{G}$ $\mathscr{G}$ $\mathscr{G}$ $\mathscr{G}$ $\mathscr{G}$

$\mathscr{G}$

Grace

g g g g g g g g

g

get

glad

great

giraffe

Trace and write. Circle your best *H* or *h* on each line.

H H H H H H H H H H

H

Harold

h h h h h h h h h

h

hat

help

home

hiccup

Trace and write. Circle your best $\mathcal{I}$ or i on each line.

$\mathcal{I}$ $\mathcal{I}$ $\mathcal{I}$ $\mathcal{I}$ $\mathcal{I}$ $\mathcal{I}$ $\mathcal{I}$ $\mathcal{I}$

$\mathcal{I}$

Isaac

i i i i i i i i

i

if

ice

igloo

insect

Trace and write. Circle your best *J* or *j* on each line.

J   J   J   J   J   J   J   J   J

J

January

J   J   J   J   J   J   J   J   J

j

jar

jug

jolly

jaguar

Trace and write. Circle your best $\mathcal{K}$ or k on each line.

$\mathcal{K}$ $\mathcal{K}$ $\mathcal{K}$ $\mathcal{K}$ $\mathcal{K}$ $\mathcal{K}$ $\mathcal{K}$ $\mathcal{K}$ $\mathcal{K}$ $\mathcal{K}$

$\mathcal{K}$

Kevin

k k k k k k k k k k

k

key

kite

kayak

koala

Trace and write. Circle your best $\mathcal{L}$ or l on each line.

$\mathcal{L}$ $\mathcal{L}$ $\mathcal{L}$ $\mathcal{L}$ $\mathcal{L}$ $\mathcal{L}$ $\mathcal{L}$ $\mathcal{L}$

$\mathcal{L}$

$\mathcal{L}auren$

l l l l l l l l

l

lap

leg

$lion$

$lynn$

Trace and write. Circle your best *M* or *m* on each line.

M   M   M   M   M   M   M

M

March

m   m   m   m   m   m   m

m

mom

map

make

mouse

Trace and write. Circle your best *n* or *n* on each line.

n   n   n   n   n   n   n   n

n

November

m   m   m   m   m   m   m

m

met

mut

mine

nest

Trace and write. Circle your best O or o on each line.

O O O O O O O O O

O

October

o o o o o o o o

o

oat

one

open

octopus

Trace and write. Circle your best $\mathcal{P}$ or p on each line.

$\mathcal{P}$ $\mathcal{P}$ $\mathcal{P}$ $\mathcal{P}$ $\mathcal{P}$ $\mathcal{P}$ $\mathcal{P}$ $\mathcal{P}$

$\mathcal{P}$

Peter

p p p p p p p

p

pet

pat

purple

penguin

Qq Trace and write. Circle your best _Q_ or _q_ on each line.

Q Q Q Q Q Q Q Q Q

Q

Quebec

q q q q q q q q

q

quiet

quack

quick

quail

© Chalkboard Publishing

Trace and write. Circle your best *R* or *r* on each line.

R R R R R R R R

R

Ryan

r r r r r r r r

r

rat

roll

river

rabbit

Trace and write. Circle your best $\mathcal{S}$ or s on each line.

September

sea

stop

sheep

squirrel

Trace and write. Circle your best $\mathcal{T}$ or t on each line.

$\mathcal{T}$ $\mathcal{T}$ $\mathcal{T}$ $\mathcal{T}$ $\mathcal{T}$ $\mathcal{T}$ $\mathcal{T}$ $\mathcal{T}$ $\mathcal{T}$

$\mathcal{T}$

Taylor

t t t t t t t t

t

top

try

tape

turkey

Trace and write. Circle your best $\mathcal{U}$ or u on each line.

Uncle

up

under

unicorn

umbrella

Trace and write. Circle your best $\mathcal{V}$ or $\mathcal{v}$ on each line.

$\mathcal{V}$ $\mathcal{V}$ $\mathcal{V}$ $\mathcal{V}$ $\mathcal{V}$ $\mathcal{V}$ $\mathcal{V}$ $\mathcal{V}$ $\mathcal{V}$ $\mathcal{V}$

$\mathcal{V}$

Victoria

$\mathcal{v}$ $\mathcal{v}$ $\mathcal{v}$ $\mathcal{v}$ $\mathcal{v}$ $\mathcal{v}$ $\mathcal{v}$ $\mathcal{v}$ $\mathcal{v}$ $\mathcal{v}$

$\mathcal{v}$

van

violin

vulture

victory

Trace and write. Circle your best _W_ or _w_ on each line.

W W W W W W W W W

W

Whitney

w w w w w w w w w

w

wet

wall

where

wolf

Trace and write. Circle your best $\mathcal{X}$ or x on each line.

$\mathcal{X}$ $\mathcal{X}$ $\mathcal{X}$ $\mathcal{X}$ $\mathcal{X}$ $\mathcal{X}$ $\mathcal{X}$ $\mathcal{X}$ $\mathcal{X}$

$\mathcal{X}$

Xavier

x x x x x x x x x

x

axe

exit

x-ray

xylophone

Trace and write. Circle your best *Y* or *y* on each line.

Y Y Y Y Y Y Y Y Y Y

Y

Yukon

y y y y y y y y

y

you

yak

young

yellow

Trace and write. Circle your best *Z* or *z* on each line.

Z   Z   Z   Z   Z   Z   Z   Z   Z

Z

Zack

z   z   z   z   z   z   z   z

z

zoo

zap

zebra

zipper

Exploring Kinds of Sentences

A **telling** sentence ends with a **period**.

Example: Ken goes to the park.

An **asking** sentence ends with a **question mark**.

Example: Would you like to go to the park?

A sentence that shows strong feeling, such as excitement, joy, or anger, ends with an **exclamation mark**.

Examples: I love the park!   Ouch!   I can't wait!

A **command** sentence tells someone to do something.

It can end with a **period** or with an **exclamation mark**.

Examples: Take off your boots.   Watch out!

1. Write the correct punctuation at the end of each sentence.

a) Would you like a slice of pizza___

b) Put the basket on the table___

c) Hooray, we are going to the zoo___

d) Are you going to the library___

e) The girls are watching the parade___

f) Be careful___

g) What is your favourite season of the year___

2. Write two examples of each kind of sentence. Be sure to include the correct punctuation at the end of each sentence.

a) Telling sentence:

_____

_____

_____

b) Asking sentence:

_____

_____

_____

c) Sentence that shows strong feeling:

_____

_____

_____

d) Command sentence:

_____

_____

What Is a Noun?

A **noun** is a word that names a **person**, **place**, or **thing**.

1. Circle the nouns that name a **person**.

Tom   run   girl   pretty   man   Maria   grandfather   hide   doctor

2. Circle the nouns that name a **place**.

school   library   small   backyard   eat   falling   mall   beach   Canada

3. Circle the nouns that name a **thing**.

ask   lamp   pencil   walking   tell   grow   coat   car   tree

4. Circle all the **nouns** in the group of words. Remember that a noun names a **person, place, or thing**.

a) shoe   sing   carrot   basement   quickly

b) big   teacher   cried   bed   soft

c) baby   wanted   woman   strong   bedroom

5. Circle the **nouns** in the sentence.

a) The kitchen is very clean.

b) Carlos ran quickly down the street.

c) The truck drove past our house.

d) Mom painted the bathroom.

What Are Proper Nouns?

Nouns that always begin with a capital letter are called **proper nouns**.

The following kinds of nouns always begin with a capital letter:
- Specific places, such as a **country, province, city,** or **town.**
  Example: Canada
- Names of **holidays.** *Example: Canada Day*
- Names of **people** or **pets.** *Example: Fido*
- Names of the **days of the week** and the **months of the year.**
  Examples: Monday and June

1. Use proper nouns to complete the sentence.

   a) My cousin lives in the province of _____.

   b) My family likes to eat turkey on _____.

   c) Halifax and _____ are Canadian cities.

   d) My dog's name is _____.

   e) I go to school on _____.

2. Write eight examples of a proper noun.

   _____   _____

   _____   _____

   _____   _____

   _____   _____

What Are Pronouns?

A **pronoun** is a word that replaces a noun.

Here are examples of pronouns that replace a **singular noun**:
I, me, you, he, him, she, her, and *it.*

Here are examples of pronouns that replace a **plural noun**:
we, us, you, they, and *them.*

1. Choose the correct pronoun to fill in the blank.

a) This is my sister. _She_ is older than me. (She / He)

b) This is my toy. _Them_ is new. (It / Them)

c) Jess and Tom are my friends. _they_ are coming over to play.
(They / Them)

d) My family is going on a trip. _they_ are excited. (We / They)

e) I have a treat. I will share _it_ with my brother. (it / him)

f) My mom is great. I love _her_ a lot! (her / him)

g) My grandparents live far away. I called _them_ last night.
(they / them)

h) Will you tell _me_ how to get to the store? (I / me)

i) Jake is coming over. _He_ is bringing a movie. (She / He)

Making It Plural

To make many **nouns** plural, just add the letter **s**.

Examples: rock   rocks   window   windows   cat   cats   flower   flowers

For some nouns, you need to do something different. Watch for nouns like the ones below.

Nouns ending in...	To make the noun plural...
s, x, ch, or **sh**	Add **es** *Example: one fox – two foxes*
Consonant + **y**	Change the **y** to **i** and add **es** *Example: one fly — two flies*

1. Choose a **noun** from the list below. Make sure it makes sense. Write the **plural** of the noun in the sentence. Use each word only once.

   wish   berry   dish   match   penny   bus   push   bench   box   baby

   a) After dinner, I helped wash the _____. dishes

   b) I found two ___penny___ in my pocket. pennies

   c) My mother ___push___ my baby brother in the stroller.

   d) Pablo packed his books into two ___box___.

   e) In the fairy tale, the girl got to make three ___ba by___. babies

   f) When we were camping, we used ___matam___ to make a fire.

   g) There were two ___sbench___ for people to sit on.

   h) They rode on two ___bus___ to get to the mall.

2. Rewrite the sentence to make the underlined nouns plural. **Do not** use the words *a* or *an* before a plural noun.

   a) I got a <u>scratch</u> on my <u>arm</u>.

   _____

   b) I saw a <u>lady</u> wearing a <u>dress</u>.

   _____

Tricky Plurals

Making some nouns plural is tricky!
Be careful when making plurals from nouns that end in the letter **o**.
For some nouns that end in **o**, add the letters **es**.
For other nouns that end in **o**, just add the letter **s**.

Add es
hero – heroes
potato – potatoes
tomato – tomatoes
echo – echoes

Add s
patio – patios
photo – photos
piano – pianos
radio – radios

video – videos
zero – zeros

1. Complete the sentence by writing **plural nouns** from the lists above. In the sentence, use a word that makes sense.

   a) The restaurant has two ___patios___ where people eat outside.

   b) There are two ___zero___ in the number 100.

   c) We picked the ___tomatoes___ that were red and ripe.

   d) All ___patios___ have black keys and white keys.

2. Rewrite the sentence below to make the <u>underlined nouns</u> plural. **Do not** use the words *a* or *an* before a plural noun.

   a) On the <u>radio</u>, they told about a <u>hero</u>.

   ___On the radios they told about the heros___

   b) Larry sent me a <u>photo</u> of a <u>potato</u> from his garden.

   ___Larry sent me photos of potato's from his garden___

   c) In the <u>video</u>, people heard an <u>echo</u>.

   ___in the videos people heard echo___

Tricky Plurals (continued)

Watch out when making plurals from nouns that end with the letter **f**.
For most nouns that end in **f**, change the **f** to a **v** and add **es**.
For a few nouns that end in **f**, just add the letter **s**.

Change *f* to *v* and add *es*

elf – elves	scarf – scarves
half – halves	shelf – shelves
leaf – leaves	thief – thieves
loaf – loaves	wolf – wolves

Just add *s*

chef – chefs
cliff – cliffs
roof – roofs

3. Complete the sentence by writing **plural nouns** from the lists above. In each sentence, use a word that makes sense.

a) You can share an apple by cutting it into two ___halves___.

b) The ___thieves___ stole many bicycles.

c) Three ___wolves___ howled loudly during the night.

d) The library has many ___shelves___ full of books.

4. Rewrite these sentences to make the underlined nouns plural. **Do not** use the words *a* or *an* before a plural noun.

a) The <u>chef</u> made a <u>loaf</u> of bread.

___The chefs made loaves of bread___

b) A <u>leaf</u> blew onto the <u>roof</u>.

___leaves blew onto the roofs___

c) It is dangerous to play near a <u>cliff</u>.

___It is dangerous to play near cliffs___

d) A <u>thief</u> stole my <u>scarf</u>.

___thieves stole my scarf___

Tricky Plurals (continued)

Do not be tricked by tricky **plural nouns**!

For nouns ending with the letters **fe**, change the **f** to a **v** and add **s**.

Examples: knife   knives   life   lives   wife   wives

To make these nouns plural, do not change anything!

Examples: one fish   two fish   one sheep   six sheep   one deer   four deer

You will need to remember these tricky plurals.

Singular	Plural	Singular	Plural
child	children	mouse	mice
foot	feet	person	people
goose	geese	tooth	teeth
man	men	woman	women

5. Complete the sentence by writing a **plural noun** shown above.

   a) My father uses _____ to cut vegetables for dinner.

   b) When we went fishing, my sister caught three _____.

   c) I like to learn about the _____ of famous people.

   d) The three curly _____ said, "Baa!"

6. Rewrite these sentences to make the underlined nouns plural. **Do not** use the words **a** or **an** before a plural noun.

   a) The wife made lots of food for the party.

   _____

   b) A mouse ran over my foot!

   _____

   c) The child fed the goose.

   _____

   d) The woman saw a deer in the woods.

   _____

What Is a Verb?

A **verb** is a word that tells what someone or something is doing. In the sentences below, the verbs are underlined.

Karen <u>reaches</u> for the book.   *The glass <u>falls</u> to the floor.*

1. Circle the **verb** in the sentence.

   a) Justin jumps over the puddle.

   b) The bird flies far away.

   c) Eliza gives an apple to her sister.

   d) Lightning flashes across the sky.

   e) He forgets my name all the time.

   f) My grandmother sends me a birthday card every year.

   g) I see a nest in that tree!

   h) That door squeaks when you open it.

   i) Carla and Frank dance to the music.

   j) The happy sheep runs down the hill.

2. Circle all the **verbs** in each group of words.

   a) wood   rug   tells   spiders   cleans

   b) writes   pencil   erasers   penny   says

   c) builds   roads   explores   garbage   tea

   d) windows   sports   hears   hides   bush

   e) buys   medicine   rainbows   scarf   pours

   f) remembers   pillows   asks   scrubs   suitcase

   g) skips   sidewalk   decides   kittens   shoes

Spelling Present Tense Verbs

For most **present tense** verbs, add *s* if **he**, **she**, or **it** does the action.
But watch out for verbs that need tricky spelling changes!
For verbs that end in a **consonant + y**, change the *y* to *i* and add *es*.

Examples: I study   she studies   they carry   he carries

1. In the blank, write the correct **present tense** of the verb in brackets.

   a) She _copies_, the words from the board. (copy)

   b) The little boy _cries_ because he is scared. (cry)

   c) Max _buyss_ carrots and onions. (buy)

   d) The kite _flies_ in the wind. (fly)

   e) The raccoon _tries_ to climb over the fence. (try)

   f) Mrs. Alvarez _says_ we should work hard. (say)

   g) The woman _hurries_ down the street. (hurry)

   h) My cat _stays_ inside when it rains. (stay)

For verbs that end with **s**, **x**, **ch**, or **sh**, add *es*.
Examples: I kiss   she kisses   I fix   he fixes
          they pinch   it pinches   you wish   he wishes

2. In the blank, write the correct **present tense** of the verb in brackets.

   a) My brother _scraltes_ his mosquito bite. (scratch)

   b) Alice _pues_ the button on the elevator. (push)

   c) Marcus _passs_ the stack of papers. (pass)

   d) She _mixs_ the flour and fruit together. (mix)

   e) The bucket _cates_ the drops of water. (catch)

   f) The doctor _rues_ to help the sick man. (rush)

   g) Ramona _toes_ me the ball. (toss)

   h) Jay _waes_ his car to make it shine. (wax)

     © Chalkboard Publishing

Using the Correct Verb Tense

When you write **present tense** verbs, add **s** to the verb if **he**, **she**, or **it** does the action.

Examples: I jump   she jumps   you lift   he lifts

Remember that some verbs need a spelling change before you add **s**.

Examples: you copy   he copies   we brush   she brushes

1. Write the correct **present tense** verb in each sentence.

   a) Rick _walks_ to school with his sister. (walk walks)

   b) The dogs _bark_ when the cat runs through the yard. (bark barks)

   c) Many people _walks_ to the park on Saturday. (walk walks)

   d) An elephant _uses_ its trunk to pick up food. (use uses)

   e) They _decides_ to go to bed early tonight. (decide decides)

   f) The girls _wants_ to play hide and seek with us. (want wants)

   g) The kite _flies_ high above the trees. (fly flies)

   h) The woman with red hair _rush_ across the street. (rush rushes)

2. Some sentences below have an **incorrect** present tense verb.

   If the verb is **correct**, put a check mark at the end of the sentence.

   If the verb is **incorrect**, cross it out and write the correct verb above it.

   The clown slips on th
   a) The clown slips on the banana peel. ✓

   b) The police officers believes the man is telling the truth. ✗

   the man with two dogs wave to me
   c) The man with two dogs wave to me. ✗

   d) Marco and Hanna look for the pink scarf. ✓

   e) The girl with freckles play her guitar for us. ✗

   f) My grandparents jog around the block every day.

Past Tense Verbs

Past tense verbs tell what happened in the past. Look at these examples:

Verb	Present Tense	Past Tense
talk	Today, I talk.	Yesterday, I talked.
	Today, she talks.	Yesterday, she talked.

For many verbs, add *ed* to the verb to make the past tense.
If the verb already ends with *e*, just add *d*.

1. Write the **past tense** of the verbs below. Add *ed* or *d* to these verbs to make the past tense.

   a) invent ___Invented___   b) cough ___Coughed___

   c) share ___Shared___   d) work ___Worked___

   e) borrow ___borrowed___   f) escape ___escaped___

   g) agree ___agreed___   h) explode ___exploded___

2. Complete each sentence. Write the **past tense** of the verb in brackets to show that the action happened in the past.

   a) The dog ___chased___ the squirrel. (chase)

   b) Leon ___chewed___ his food slowly. (chew)

   c) Kelly ___filled___ the sink with water. (fill)

   d) We ___invited___ all our friends to the party. (invite)

   e) The children ___played___ in the backyard. (play)

3. Is the verb in each sentence **present tense** or **past tense**? Write *present* or *past* beside each sentence.

   a) Mom glued the pieces back together. ___past tense___

   b) We race along the path through the park. ___present___

   c) Jonathan rinses the shampoo out of his hair. ___past___

   d) Hernando searched for his cap. ___present___

Spelling Past Tense Verbs

For many verbs that end with **consonant + vowel + consonant**, double the final consonant before adding **ed**.

Examples: hop   hopped   clap   clapped   zip   zipped

1. Write the **past tense** of the verb in brackets. For these verbs, double the final consonant before adding **ed**.

   a) Aaron _tripped_ on a rock. (trip)

   b) The car _stopped_ at the red light. (stop)

   c) Dad made the soup and I _stirred_ it. (stir)

   d) Ella _dripped_ paint on the floor. (drip)

   e) Richard _stepped_ over the puddle. (step)

   f) The janitor _mopped_ the dirty floor. (mop)

   g) We _planned_ a trip to the Grand Canyon. (plan)

   h) Who _wrapped_ this gift? (wrap)

   i) The happy puppy _wagged_ its tail. (wag)

   j) My grandfather _hugged_ me. (hug)

For most verbs that end with **consonant + y**, change the **y** to an **i** and add **ed**.
Examples: study – studied   marry – married

2. Write the **past tense** of the verb in brackets.

   a) The baby _cried_ when he dropped his rattle. (cry)

   b) The movers _carried_ the heavy boxes. (carry)

   c) They _hurries_ to the party. (hurry)

   d) Danika _worries_ about her lost dog. (worry)

   e) The mouse _scurried_ under the leaves. (scurry)

Tricky Tense Verbs

The **past tense** of some verbs does not end with **ed**. Watch out for these tricky verbs when you write in the past tense!

Present Tense	Past Tense	Present Tense	Past Tense
come, comes	came	get, gets	got
drive, drives	drove	give, gives	gave
eat, eats	ate	have, has	had
fall, falls	fell	say, says	said

1. Write the **past tense** of the verb in brackets.

   a) Lisa _had_ a cold last week. (have)

   b) Yesterday, Jacob _said_ he wanted to visit us. (say)

   c) Who _ate_ all the snacks? (eat)

   d) The principal _came_ to our classroom. (come)

   e) I _gaive_ the flowers to Sandy. (give)

   f) Mr. Patel _drove_ to the train station. (drive)

   g) Karen _got_ a birthday card in the mail. (get)

   h) Nick hurt his foot when he _fell_. (fall)

2. Rewrite the sentence. Change the **past tense verb** to **present tense**.

   a) We drove to the grocery store.

   We drive to the grocery

   b) The squirrel ate all the nuts.

   The squirrel eats all the nuts

   c) I had two pencils in my desk.

   I have two pencis in my desk

   d) Carly came to my house every week.

   Carly come to my to my house every week

Tricky Tense Verbs (continued)

Watch out for these tricky verbs when you write in the **past tense**!

Present Tense	Past Tense	Present Tense	Past Tense
buy, buys	bought	know, knows	knew
draw, draws	drew	go, goes	went
drink, drinks	drank	take, takes	took
find, finds	found	think, thinks	thought

3. Write the **past tense** of the verb in brackets.

a) We _went_ along the path through the forest. (go)

b) Brendan _drank_ a glass of milk with his sandwich. (drink)

c) I _thought_ my answer was correct. (think)

d) Emily _boght_ some pretty flowers at the market. (buy)

e) The children _____ off their mittens. (take)

f) We _____ the baby bird under a tree. (find)

g) Matt _____ where Lee was hiding. (know)

h) My best friend _drew_ this picture of me. (draw)

4. Rewrite the sentence. Change the **past tense verb** to **present tense**.

a) We drank juice with our breakfast.

we drink juice with our breakfast

b) He bought a new toy for his grandson.

He buys a new toy for his grandson

c) Anna found lots of seashells at the beach.

Anna finds lots of seashells at the beach

d) I thought about my best friend.

I think about my best friend

Future Tense Verbs

Future tense verbs tell about things that will happen in the **future**.
To make future tense verbs, use the "helping verb" **will**.

One Person or Thing
I will walk
You will walk
He/She/It will walk

More Than One Person or Thing
We will walk
You will walk
They will walk

1. Complete the sentence. Write the **future tense** of the verb in brackets to show that the action will happen in the future.

   a) Tomorrow, they _____will_____ a horse. (ride)

   b) Next week, Sandy _____will swim_____ in the pool. (swim)

   c) This morning, the sun _____will shine_____. (shine)

   d) In ten minutes, Dad _____will dive_____ me home. (drive)

   e) Before long, you _____will grow_____ even taller. (grow)

2. Rewrite the sentence. Change the **past tense** verb to a **future tense** verb.

   a) Timothy planted a tree in the backyard.

   Timoth will plant a tree in the backyard

   b) Carlos and Mary talked about the movie.

   Carlos and mary will talked about the movie

   c) People laughed at all my silly jokes.

   people laughed at all my silly jokes

   d) Kim shared her raisins with Ken and Beth.

   _____

   e) Josh washed the car very carefully.

   _____

What Is an Adjective?

An **adjective** is a word that describes a noun. Read this sentence:

A big lion ran after me!

The word *big* is an adjective. It describes the noun *lion*.

1. Circle the **adjective** in the sentence. Underline the **noun** it describes.

   a) A brown mouse ran over the carpet.

   b) Mr. Tanaka gave me a large book.

   c) A scary dragon lived in the cave.

   d) The playful puppy ran after me.

   e) Please pass me the green mug.

   f) I fell on the slippery ice.

   g) The loud thunder woke me up.

   h) She watched an interesting movie with Jack.

   i) Rachel told me a funny joke.

   j) They put the presents on the round table.

   k) I want to climb a tall mountain.

   l) Bob washed the dirty dishes.

2. In each sentence below, write an **adjective** that makes sense. Underline the noun your adjective describes.

   a) I think I will wear the ____clean____ socks today.

   b) Pedro spoke in a ____loud____ voice.

   c) There were ____white____ clouds in the sky.

   d) The ____fast____ runner will win the race.

   e) Dad put the ____yellow____ flowers in a vase.

   f) The ____white____ cat chased a mouse.

Adjectives After Nouns

An **adjective** describes a noun. Sometimes an adjective comes **before** the noun it describes. Sometimes the adjective comes **after** the noun.

Before a noun: *We walked across the shiny floor.*

After a noun: *The floor was shiny.*

1. Circle the **adjective** in the sentence. Underline the **noun** it describes.

   a) The clown was funny.

   b) Do not cross the street when the light is red.

   c) The woman was angry when the dog ran away.

   d) Do you think the towels are dry?

   e) The video Ali watched was exciting.

   f) The pillow I sleep on is soft.

   g) The baby in the crib is cute.

   h) Mr. Rossi makes sandwiches that are delicious.

   i) I wear sunglasses when the sun is bright.

   j) We did not swim in the lake because the water was cold.

   k) Enzo was tired, so he did not want to play.

   l) Ms. Jones said the answer is correct.

2. Circle each **adjective** and underline each **noun**. Draw an arrow from each adjective to the noun it describes.

   Example: The old man wore a scarf that was yellow

   a) The huge dinosaur had teeth that were sharp.

   b) The children were happy when the colourful rainbow appeared.

   c) A woman who was tall fixed our leaky roof.

Adjectives Can Describe How Many

An **adjective** describes a noun. Some adjectives answer the question, "How many?" **Numbers** can be adjectives.

Example: I popped three balloons!

In this sentence, *three* is an **adjective** that describes the noun *balloons*. The adjective *three* answers the question "How many balloons?"

1. Circle the **adjectives** and underline **all** the **nouns**. Draw an arrow from each adjective to the noun it describes.

   a) Three apples fell from the tree.

   b) Raj found four pennies under the bed.

   c) Sandra watched two squirrels climb a tree.

   d) Eight frogs hopped into the pond.

Some **adjectives** answer the question "How many?" but they do not tell exactly how many.

Example: I have some questions for you.

In this sentence, *some* is an **adjective** that describes the noun *questions*. *Some* does not tell exactly how many questions, but it tells us there are more than one.

2. Circle each **adjective** that answers the question "How many?"

   a) I returned several books to the library.

   b) Many students are absent today.

   c) Few people keep snakes as pets.

   d) We watched some airplanes land at the airport.

   e) There were many cows on the farm, but I saw few horses.

   f) I have collected several seashells and many rocks.

Pronouns for People

A **pronoun** is a word that takes the place of one or more nouns.
Use these pronouns to take the place of nouns that name **people**.

I you he she we they him her them us

1. Use a **pronoun** to take the place of the underlined word or words.

   a) <u>Ralph</u> likes horses.

      _____he_____ likes horses.

   b) <u>The children</u> played hide and seek.

      _____they_____ played hide and seek.

   c) Emma shared the grapes with <u>Eva and Ravi</u>.

      Emma shared the grapes with _____them_____.

2. Rewrite the sentence. Change the underlined word or words to a **pronoun**.

   a) <u>Jack and Eva</u> played with the puppies.

   they played with the puppies

   b) <u>Lisa</u> showed the picture to <u>Mark</u>.

   she showed the picture to he

   c) The doctor and the nurse smiled at <u>my sister and me</u>.

   The doctor and the nurse smiled at us

   d) <u>Tara and I</u> waved goodbye to our aunt and uncle.

   we waved goodbye to our aunt and uncle

Pronouns for Things

A **pronoun** is a word that takes the place of one or more nouns.
Pronouns take the place of nouns that name **people, places,** or **things.**
Use these pronouns to take the place of nouns that name **things:**

it   they   them

1. Use a **pronoun** to take the place of the words in brackets.

   a) Andrew was reading _it_. (the book)

   b) _they_ are bending in the wind. (The trees)

   c) I found _them_ behind the chair. (my mittens)

   d) _it_ is very tall. (The building)

   e) _____ have pictures of animals. (The stickers)

   f) Where did you get _them_? (the green marbles)

   g) She asked if _they_ are new. (my shoes)

2. Rewrite the sentence to use pronouns for **people** and **things.** Change each underlined word or words to a **pronoun**.

   a) <u>The sweater</u> was too big for <u>Brandon</u>.

   it was too big for him

   b) We made <u>the muffins</u> for <u>Mr. Chang</u>.

   We made them for him

   c) <u>The girls</u> gave <u>the toys</u> to <u>Sunil and me</u>.

   they gave them to us

   d) <u>The boxes</u> are too big for <u>Alan and Rosa</u> to carry.

   _____

   e) <u>Dave and I</u> sent <u>a birthday card</u> to <u>our grandfather</u>.

   _____

   f) Will <u>Amit and Brittany</u> sing for <u>the visitors</u>?

   will they sing for them

Some Adverbs Describe How

An **adverb** can describe **how, when**, **where,** or **how often** an action happens. An adverb describes a verb.

On this page, you will work with adverbs that describe **how** an action happens.

Example: Tara quickly tied her shoes.

The adverb *quickly* describes **how** Tara tied her shoes.

1. Underline the **adverb** that tells **how** an action happens.

   a) Fred slowly walked home.

   b) She quietly left the room.

   c) Carmella loudly shouted the answer.

   d) The boys carefully washed the glasses.

   e) The students correctly answered all of the questions.

   f) The father gently held his baby daughter.

In the sentences above, the adverb comes **before** the verb it describes. Sometimes an adverb comes **after** the verb it describes.

Examples: The woman spoke softly.   Eric ran up the steps quickly.

2. Underline the **adverb** that tells **how** an action happens.

   a) The ballerina danced gracefully across the stage.

   b) The painters hummed happily as they worked.

   c) The dog ate its food from the bowl hungrily.

   d) The grandmother smiled sweetly at her grandson.

   e) The knight killed the dragon boldly.

   f) The thief tiptoed silently from the room.

Some Adverbs Describe When

An **adverb** can describe **how, when**, **where**, or **how often** an action happens.
An adverb describes a verb.

On this page, you will work with **adverbs** that describe **when** an action happens.

Example: Evan washes his hands before eating.

The adverb *before* describes **when** Evan washes his hands.

1. Underline the adverb that tells **when** an action happens.

   a) The children fell asleep during the movie.

   b) Maggie will read her story next.

   c) Tomorrow, Alfredo will make a special dinner.

   d) Please close the window now.

   e) The rain will stop soon.

   f) The girls play soccer after supper.

   g) Yesterday, the dentist checked my teeth.

   h) Next, I will show you an amazing magic trick.

   i) Fernando smiled after he saw his friend.

2. Read the sentence and underline the **adverb.** Then complete the next sentence.

   a) Later, we will sing a song.

   The adverb _Later_ tells **when** the action _Sing_ happens.

   b) Walt will swim next.

   The adverb _next_ tells **when** the action _swim_ happens.

   c) Cathy will visit us tomorrow.

   The adverb _tomorrow_ tells **when** the action _visit_ happens.

Some Adverbs Describe Where

An **adverb** can describe **how, when**, **where**, or **how often** an action happens. An adverb describes a verb.

On this page, you will work with **adverbs** that describe **where** an action happens.

Example: Eddie and Tyler look <u>outside</u>.

The adverb *outside* describes **where** Eddie and Tyler look.

1. Read the sentence and underline the adverb. Then complete the next sentence.

   a) I hang the picture here.

   The adverb __here__ tells **where** the action __hang__ happens.

   b) Penny plays inside on rainy days.

   The adverb __plays__ tells **where** the action __inside__ happens.

   c) My brother ran downstairs.

   The adverb __ran__ tells **where** the action __downstairs__ happens.

   d) They put the flowers there.

   The adverb __there__ tells **where** the action __put__ happens.

Some **adverbs** describe **where** something happens, but they do not describe one exact place.

Example: Abdul hid his book <u>somewhere</u>.

The adverb *somewhere* describes **where** Abdul hid his book.

2. Underline the adverb that tells **where** an action happens.

   a) I searched <u>everywhere</u> for my umbrella.

   b) The frightened bird flew <u>away</u>.

   c) A lion roared <u>nearby</u>.

   d) You can put your coats <u>anywhere</u>.

   e) We went <u>nowhere</u> today.

Some Adverbs Describe How Often

An **adverb** can describe **how, when**, **where,** or **how often** an action happens. An adverb describes a verb.

On this page, you will work with **adverbs** that describe **how often** an action happens.

Example: They <u>sometimes</u> *go camping in August.*

The adverb *sometimes* describes **how often** they go camping in August.

1. Underline the adverb that tells **how often** an action happens.

   a) My neighbour <u>always</u> waves at me.

   b) Molly rang the doorbell <u>twice</u>.

   c) Mr. Cortez <u>often</u> hums his favourite song.

   d) My baby sister <u>never</u> cries.

   e) I flew on an airplane <u>once</u>.

Learn these **adverbs** that describe **how often** an action happens.

constantly (all the time)   **occasionally** (once in a while)
frequently (very often)   **seldom** (not very often)
usually (most of the time)   **rarely** (almost never)

2. In the **second** sentence, write one of the **adverbs** above. Choose an adverb that means the same as the underlined words.

   a) Sam eats yogurt <u>very often</u>.   Sam __frequently__ eats yogurt.

   b) The baby cries <u>all the time</u>.   The baby cries __constantly__.

   c) I <u>almost never</u> catch a cold.   I __rarely__ catch a cold.

   d) It rains <u>most of the time</u>.   It __usually__ rains.

   e) He dreams <u>not very often</u>.   He __seldom__ dreams.

   f) You sneeze <u>once in a while</u>.   You sneeze __occasionally__.

Using Adjectives to Compare More Than Two Things

You can use adjectives to compare **more than two things**.

Example: Anna is the <u>tallest</u> student in the class.

This sentence **compares** all the students in the class. Anna is the tallest.

For most adjectives that have one syllable, add **est** to make an adjective that compares **more than two things**. *Example: short   shortest*

1. Use the **adjective** in brackets to complete the first sentence in the pair. Use the correct form of the adjective to compare **more than two things**. Then, complete the second sentence to tell about what is being compared.

   a) Lily was the ___fastest___ runner in the race. (fast)

   This sentence compares all the ___runners___.

   b) Today is the ___coldest___ day of the year. (cold)

   This sentence compares all the ___days___.

   c) This is the ___warmest___ coat in my closet. (warm)

   This sentence compares ___coats___ in my closet.

   d) My bed is the ___softest___ bed in the house. (soft)

   This sentence compares ___beds___ in the house.

2. Use the **adjective** in brackets to compare **more than two things**. Remember to write *the* before an adjective that ends with *est.*

   a) The red truck is ___the cleanest___ truck in the garage. (clean)

   b) This lightbulb is ___the brightest___ lightbulb we have. (bright)

   c) The dictionary is ___the thickest___ book on the shelf. (thick)

   d) I took ___the smallest___ muffin on the plate. (small)

   e) Grandma was ___the oldest___ person at the party. (old)

   f) This crayon is ___the shortest___ one in the box. (short)

© Chalkboard Publishing

Spelling Adjectives That Compare

Watch out for these tricky adjectives that compare!

Adjective	To Compare Two Things	To Compare More Than Two Things
good	better	best
bad	worse	worst
far	farther	farthest
many	more	most

1. Use the **adjective** in brackets to complete the first sentence in the pair. Then circle the correct answer in the second sentence. Write *the* before an adjective that compares **more than two things.**

   a) The story about dragons was _better_ than the story about dinosaurs. (good)

   This sentence compares (two things   more than two things).

   b) Do you think a sore throat is _worse_ than a cough? (bad)

   This sentence compares (two things   more than two things).

   c) Hockey and baseball are good, but I think soccer is _best_ sport. (good)

   This sentence compares (two things   more than two things).

   d) Your house is _farther_ from school than my house. (far)

   This sentence compares (two things   more than two things).

   e) Of all the classes in our school, Mr. Rico's class has _most_ students. (many)

   This sentence compares (two things   more than two things).

   f) There were some bad storms last year, but this storm is _worst_. (bad)

   This sentence compares (two things   more than two things).

Adjectives That Use *More* and *Most* to Compare

For most adjectives that have **two or more syllables**, use *more* to compare **two things**. Use *the most* to compare **more than two things**.

Compare Two Things	Compare More Than Two Things
Karen is <u>more</u> helpful than Bill.	*Johnny is <u>the most helpful</u> of all the children in the class.*

1. Read the sentence and think about how many things are compared. Complete the sentence by writing *more* or *the most*.

a) Liz was frightened, but Larry was _____more_____ frightened.

b) We saw elephants and giraffes, but I thought the monkeys were
_____the most_____ interesting animals at the zoo.

c) Bob thinks apples are _____more_____ delicious than bananas.

d) Of all the women at the ball, Prince Charming thought Cinderella was
_____the most_____ beautiful.

e) The first question on the test was _____most_____ difficult than the
second question.

f) To wrap Jan's present, we chose _____most_____ colourful wrapping
paper in the store.

g) Skating on a lake is _____more_____ dangerous than skating at a rink.

h) Everyone was excited about the class trip, but Anthony was
_____most_____ excited.

Watch out for adjectives that have **two** syllables and **end with y**. For these adjectives, you can use the endings *er* and *est* when you want to compare.

*Examples: shiny   shinier   shiniest   easy   easier   easiest
hungry   hungrier   hungriest   healthy   healthier   healthiest*

Reading Comprehension Tips

Reading comprehension is the cornerstone of a child's academic success. By completing the activities in this book, children will develop and reinforce essential reading comprehension skills. Children will benefit from a wide variety of opportunities to practise engaging with text as active readers who can self-monitor their understanding of what they have read.

Children will focus on the following:

Identifying the Purpose of the Text

- The reader understands, and can tell you, why they read the text.

Understanding the Text

- What is the main idea of the text?
- What are the supporting details?
- Which parts are facts and which parts are opinions?

Analyzing the Text

- How does the reader's background knowledge enhance the text clues to help the reader answer questions about the text or draw conclusions?
- What inferences can be made by using information from the text with what the reader already knows?
- How does the information from the text help the reader make predictions?
- What is the cause and effect between events?

Making Connections

How does the topic or information being read remind the reader about what they already know?

- Text-to-self connections: How does this text relate to your own life?
- Text-to-text connections: Have I read something like this before? How is this text similar to something I have read before? How is this text different from something I have read before?
- Text-to-world connections: What does this text remind you of in the real world?

Using Text Features

- How do different text features help the reader?

Text Features

Text features help the reader to understand the text better. Here is a list of text features with a brief explanation of how they help the reader.

Contents	Here the reader will find the title of each section, what page each text starts on within sections, and where to find specific information.
Chapter Title	The chapter title gives the reader an idea of what the text will be about. The chapter title is often followed by subheadings within the text.
Title and Subheading	The title or topic is found at the top of the page. The subheading is right above a paragraph. There may be more than one subheading in a text.
Map	Maps help the reader understand where something is happening. It is a visual representation of a location.
Diagram and Illustration	Diagrams and illustrations give the reader additional visual information about the text.
Label	A label tells the reader the title of a map, diagram, or illustration. Labels also draw attention to specific elements within a visual.
Caption	Captions are words that are placed underneath the visuals. Captions give the reader more information about the map, diagram, or illustration.
Fact Box	A fact box tells the reader extra information about the topic.
Table	A table presents text information in columns and rows in a concise and often comparative way.
Bold and Italic text	**Bold** and *italic* text are used to emphasize a word or words, and signify that this is important vocabulary.

School Trip

My name is Sienna. Yesterday, my class went on a school trip to Niagara Falls, Ontario. I had never visited the falls, so I was very excited. It was a perfect spring day to visit the falls. The sun was shining and it was warm, but not too hot.

I sat near my best friend, Lisa, on the bus. Lisa and I decided to take turns sitting near the window. We flipped a coin and I sat near the window for the first half of the trip. Lisa and I switched spots after the bus stopped for twenty minutes halfway to Niagara Falls.

Forty-five minutes later, we saw the falls! Wow! They are much bigger and louder than I imagined. The bus parked and we followed our teacher to get a closer look. We stood at the fence overlooking the falls. Water from the falls sprayed up into our faces.

The best part of the day was taking a boat with lots of other people. The boat comes close to the falls and you get really wet. Luckily, the boat company gives you a raincoat for the trip.

Niagara Falls is an amazing place!

"School Trip"—Think About It!

1. How did the girls decide who would get the window seat?

eight _____

_____

2. What other ways can you think of to decide who goes first?

_____

_____

3. How long did the trip to Niagara Falls take?

_____

_____

4. Why do you think there is a fence near the falls?

_____

_____

5. What was the best part of this trip for the writer? Explain.

_____

_____

The Magic Wand

It is my birthday today. We had a party this afternoon and eight of my friends came. Aunt Ella, Uncle Ted, and my eleven-year-old cousin, Leo, came, too.

We had cake and ice cream, and everyone brought presents. I liked all my presents. I got six books, two T-shirts, a board game, a set of paints, and a racing car. My favourite present was from Cousin Leo. It was a magic wand!

I could not believe it! "Is it really magic?" I asked.

"It is," said Leo, "You have to follow three rules for it to work."

"What are the rules?" I asked.

"You cannot hurt anyone with it. You have to use it for something you really want. You can only use it once, then you have to pass it on to someone else."

"OK," I agreed.

Now I have a magic wand, but what should I use it for? There are so many things I want, such as a dog and a trip to California. And who should I pass it on to? Should I give it to my friend Jim, Sophie, or Daniel?

This is going to be a hard decision!

"The Magic Wand"—Think About It!

1. How many people came to the birthday party?

eight

2. Who gave the magic wand?

leo

3. What were the three magic wand rules?

you can not hurt one of them you

4. What would you wish for if you had a magic wand?

I will get a cets two

5. Who would you pass your magic wand on to and why?

I will pass it onto brothers why they want to have alot of computers and phone

Whale Watching

Today, we are going whale watching! We are visiting Aunt Bev and Uncle Fred in Vancouver, British Columbia. They have booked our whale-watching trip. A tour company takes people out on a special boat to see the whales. It is May, which is the perfect time of the year to see whales in British Columbia. Vancouver is near the Pacific Ocean and whales swim around here at this time of year.

I look out the window of Aunt Bev's and Uncle Fred's house. It looks as though it is going to rain. What if we cannot go?

"Do not worry," says Aunt Bev. "The boat will take us out even if it rains. We just need to wear the right clothes."

We grab raincoats and put on sturdy shoes so we do not slip on the wet deck of the boat. Uncle Fred pulls out a pair of binoculars to help us see whales and birds. Aunt Bev says she saw eagles when she took the whale trip last year.

We drive to the boat and hurry on board with about twenty other people. We are off!

For a while, all we see are waves. Then someone shouts, "Whales!" I cannot believe it! There is a humpback whale right near our boat!

Draw a picture to go with the text.

Write a caption for your picture.

_____

"Whale Watching"—Think About It!

1. Where will the family go to whale watch?

West

2. In what month does the trip take place?

may

3. Why is it a good time to see whales during that month?

tem puter

4. What kind of whale did they see?

5. Why is important to bring the right clothes to wear for a rainy day on the boat?

Sensational Similes

A **simile** is a phrase that contains the word "like" or "as" to make a comparison between two different things.

Examples: Caroline runs <u>like</u> a cheetah!   As happy <u>as</u> a clam.

1. Write some similes.

a) as hungry as ___as hungry as a bear___

b) runs like a ___a boy runs lik a cheata___

c) as blind as a ___he is bind as me___

d) swims like a ___W___

e) as fresh as a ___W___

f) smells like a ___W___

g) as cold as a ___W___

h) dancing like a ___W___

i) as hot as ___W___

j) soft, like a ___pillow___

k) as loud as a ___tunder___

2. Write your own simile. ___smells lik nice smell___

___borfum___

Alliteration

Alliteration is repeating the same letters or sounds at the start of two or more words in a sentence.

Example: Alfred alligator always acts angry.

1. Create your own examples of alliteration.

a) _____

b) _____

c) _____

d) _____

e) _____

f). _____

g) _____

h) _____

i) _____

j) _____

k) _____

l) _____

Acrostic Poem

In an **acrostic** poem, the first letter of each line forms a word or phrase vertically. An acrostic poem can describe the subject or even tell a brief story about it.

Create your own acrostic poem.

.... _____

.... _____

.... _____

.... _____

.... _____

.... _____

.... _____

.... _____

.... _____

.... _____

Cinquain Poem

A **cinquain** is a poem that has five lines.

Use the lines below to write cinquain poems about different subjects.

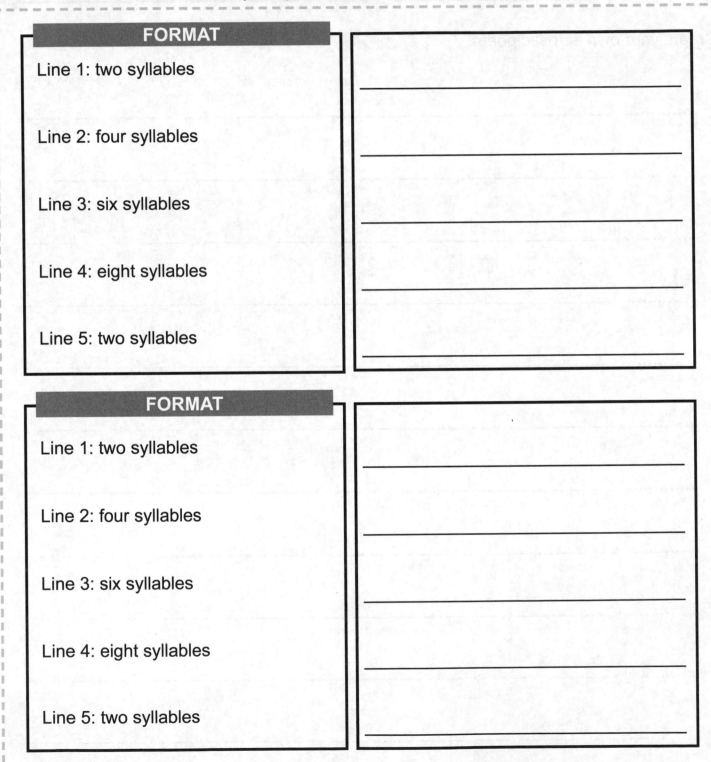

FORMAT

Line 1: two syllables

Line 2: four syllables

Line 3: six syllables

Line 4: eight syllables

Line 5: two syllables

FORMAT

Line 1: two syllables

Line 2: four syllables

Line 3: six syllables

Line 4: eight syllables

Line 5: two syllables

246

© Chalkboard Publishing

Brilliant Brochure Checklist

A brochure is a folded booklet that gives descriptive information.

Use the checklist to plan your brochure.

Topic: _____

Step 1: Plan Your Brochure

❏ Take a piece of paper and fold the paper the same way your brochure will be folded.

❏ Print the heading for each section. Leave room underneath the heading to write some information and to place pictures.

✔

Step 2: Rough Copy

❏ I checked the facts for each section of my brochure.

❏ I read my work to make sure it has all of the information.

❏ I added, deleted, or changed words to make my writing better.

✔

Step 3: Final Editing Checklist

❏ I checked for spelling.

❏ My brochure is neat and easy to read.

❏ I checked for punctuation.

❏ My pictures go with the information.

❏ I checked for clear sentences.

❏ My brochure is attractive.

✔

Friendly Letter

Write a letter to someone special.

_____
(date)

_____ , (greeting)

(body)

_____

_____

_____

_____

_____

_____

_____

_____

_____

_____

(closing) _____ ,

(signature) _____

Retell a Story

Read a story. Retell what happened in the story in your own words.

Story Title: the kid and the cat

BEGINNING

onec apon a time there was
a kid wus valking be nom and
tad are poor

Retell a Story (continued)

MIDDLE

_____

_____

_____

_____

_____

_____

Retell a Story (continued)

END

_____

_____

_____

_____

_____

_____

Retell a Story (continued)

Story Planner

Write ideas for your story in this story planner.

Story Title: _____

Setting Where will the story take place?	**Characters** Who will be in the story?

Problem in the Story

What is the problem in the story?

Events in the Story

What happens in the story?

How the Problem Is Solved

How does the story end?

© Chalkboard Publishing

Adjectives for Writing

Category	Adjectives
Size	big, small, short, tall, fat, skinny, large, medium, slim, thin, slender, tiny, lean, scrawny, huge, gigantic, jumbo, plump, wee, wide, narrow
Shape	round, square, pointed, jagged, oval, chunky, curly, straight, curved, flat, twisted, heart-shaped, spiky, wavy, bent, tangled, messy
Colour	red, orange, yellow, green, blue, purple, pink, grey, white, black, brown, silver, gold
Age	young, old, new, baby, newborn
Sound	loud, quiet, long, short, musical, surprising, soft, noisy, muffled, whispering, growling, grumbling
Light and Brightness	dull, bright, dark, light, clear, flashy, flashing, dim, faint, glowing, flickering, twinkly, twinkling, shiny, shining
Smell	good, bad, strong, sweet, salty, spicy, stinky, sour, delicious, yummy, fresh, rotten, rotting
Feel and Texture	soft, hard, smooth, rough, silky, fluffy, fuzzy, furry, wet, dry, bumpy, lumpy, scratchy, sweaty, slippery, slimy, gritty, dirty, sticky, gummy, jiggly, wiggly, squishy, watery, liquid, solid, rock hard, damp, stiff, firm
Taste	delicious, bitter, sweet, salty, tasty, spicy, yummy, bland, sour, strong
Speed and Movement	quick, quickly, fast, slow, slowly, rapid, rapidly, brisk, briskly, swift, swiftly, instant, instantly, late
Temperature	hot, cold, icy, frosty, chilly, burning, boiling, steamy, sizzling, cool, warm, freezing, frozen, damp, humid, melting

Write a Story

Story Title: _____

Beginning	☐	**I wrote an attention-grabbing first sentence.**
	☐	**I introduced the main character.**
	☐	**I wrote about where the story takes place.**

_____

_____

_____

_____

_____

_____

_____

_____

_____

☐ **I checked the spelling and punctuation.**   ☐ **I added adjectives.**

Write a Story (continued)

Middle   ☐   **I explained the problem in the story.**

_____

_____

_____

_____

_____

_____

_____

_____

_____

_____

_____

☐ **I checked the spelling and punctuation.**   ☐ **I added adjectives.**

Write a Story (continued)

| Events | ☐ I wrote about events that happen in the story before the problem is solved. |

Event 1: _____

_____

_____

_____

_____

Event 2: _____

_____

_____

_____

_____

☐ **I checked the spelling and punctuation.** ☐ **I added adjectives.**

Write a Story (continued)

| Ending | ☐ I explained how the problem was solved. |

_____

_____

_____

_____

_____

_____

_____

_____

_____

_____

_____

☐ I checked the spelling and punctuation. ☐ I added adjectives.

Write a Story (continued)

Picture Book Report

Title: _____

Author: _____

Illustrator: _____

Who is the main character in the story? This is who the story is mostly about.

_____

Draw a picture of the main character from the story.

Describe the main character.

_____

_____

_____

What is the story about? What was the problem in the story?

_____

_____

_____

Picture Book Report (continued)

Where does the story take place? This is called the setting of the story. Draw a picture that shows the setting.

Write about your picture.

_____

_____

_____

How did the story end? How was the problem solved?

_____

_____

_____

Do you think other people would enjoy this story? Explain your thinking.

_____

_____

_____

Picture Book Report (continued)

My Favourite Part

Draw a picture of your favourite part of the story.

Write about why that was your favourite part of the story.

_____

_____

_____

What do you think happened after the story ended?

_____

_____

_____

Trace Your Roots

Most Canadians have ancestors who decided to make Canada their home. Some Canadians have ancestors from early pioneer times. Some Canadians have grandparents or parents who moved to Canada. Some Canadians are newly arrived to Canada.

Think About It!

1. Using clues from the text, what is an ancestor?

_____

_____

2. What do you know about your ancestors?

_____

_____

3. In what ways are your family members alike?

_____

_____

_____

4. In what ways are your family members different?

_____

_____

_____

5. Draw a family tree to show the ancestry of your family members and what countries they came from.

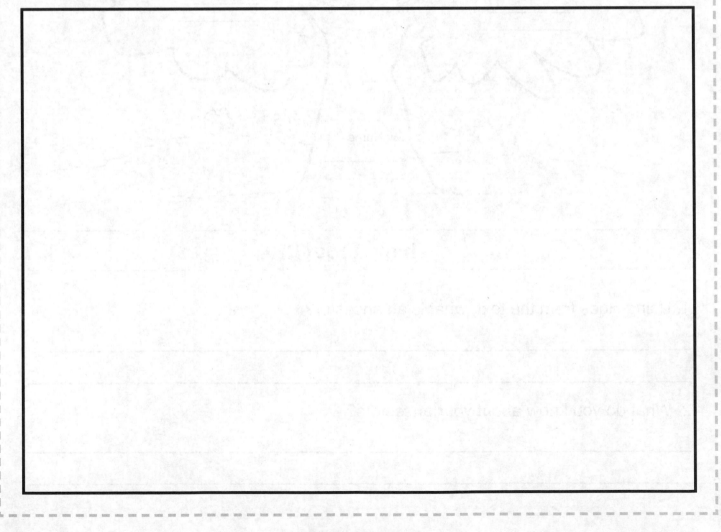

How Pioneers Cleared the Land

When pioneers first came to Canada, most of the land was covered with trees. But the pioneers wanted to grow food, so they had to clear the land.

First Things First

The first thing the pioneers did was to take out all the brush and cut down the small trees. These were then piled together. Now there was room for the men to swing their axes. This made it easier for them to chop down the larger trees.

Timber!

Many families often helped each other chop the trees and clear the field. This was called a "logging bee." Pioneers brought their oxen and tools, and worked together to finish the job more quickly.

First, the trees were cut down in such a way that they fell into huge piles. Next, the men worked to create several large piles and brought in a cart pulled by the oxen. Then, the logs were loaded onto the cart and taken away. Finally, the long pieces were kept for building barns and houses.

Roots, Rocks, and Stumps

The trees were gone, but there were still lots of roots and stumps on the land. The roots were usually taken out with a type of axe called a *mattock*. The mattock broke up the soil around the roots so the farmer could dig them out.

Tree stumps were much harder to take out. Sometimes farmers used oxen to pull them out of the soil. Other stumps were exploded to break them up. If a stump was too hard to take out or was not in the way, the farmer sometimes left it to rot.

The land was then cleared of large rocks. The soil was made ready for planting with the help of a plough and a horse or two to pull it. The plough broke up the soil so that seeds could be planted. Finally, the land was ready!

"How Pioneers Cleared the Land"—Think About It!

1. Why did pioneers have to clear the land?

_____

_____

_____

2. Write the steps for clearing the trees.

First, _____

Next, _____

Then, _____

Finally, _____

3. What was a "logging bee"?

_____

_____

4. Why do you think it was important for families to help each other out?

_____

_____

_____

5. What type of axe was used to take out roots?

_____

6. List two ways in which tree stumps were removed.

_____

_____

7. How was soil made ready for planting?

_____

_____

Pioneers Needed Water

The pioneers who settled Canada made their homes close to rivers or lakes. Water was very important to these people.

It Is Hot Out!

Pioneers drank a lot of water to stay healthy. They did a lot of hard work in the hot sun. There was no air conditioning in pioneer times. That meant even indoor work was hot in the summer.

Water Has Many Uses

Pioneers used water to wash themselves, their clothes, and their dishes, and to give to their animals. But they could not just turn on a tap to get water. They had to get their water from rivers or lakes. Some dug wells to get water.

Pioneers also needed water to help their plants grow. Often when they were finished washing, they threw the dirty water onto their gardens.

Taking a Bath

In summer, pioneers took baths in a nearby stream, river, or lake. But in cold weather, they needed warm water for their baths. They carried water into the house and heated it in a large pot over a fire.

The hot water was poured into a big tub. Pioneer houses had no bathrooms. Blankets were hung on ropes around the tub. That gave the bather some privacy. One by one, everyone in the family took a quick bath. They all used the same water.

River Travel

Rivers made it easy for the pioneers to get to town or move supplies. There were no cars at that time, and the land was covered with trees. So walking or riding a horse was difficult and took a long time. Pioneers found it easy to float down rivers on rafts. Indigenous people showed the pioneers how to build birchbark canoes. Pioneers also hollowed out logs to make dugout canoes.

"Pioneers Needed Water"—Think About It!

1. Why do you think pioneers built their homes close to rivers and lakes?

_____

_____

2. Using information from the reading, describe how water was important to pioneers.

_____

_____

_____

3. How did pioneers heat water for their baths?

_____

4. River travel was important to pioneers. Use details from the text to explain.

_____

_____

_____

5. How is getting water different in modern times?

_____

_____

_____

6. How did Indigenous people help the pioneers?

_____

_____

Pioneer Life: Building a House

Choosing a Spot for a House

One of the first jobs of a pioneer family was to build a log house. They carefully chose the spot for their new home. They wanted to be near lots of trees they could use for wood. They also wanted to be near a river or stream, so it would be easy to get water. If their land was not near water, they had to dig a well.

A log house took a lot of time to build. The family needed somewhere to live right away. Some families lived in a tent. Other families built a small home called a lean-to. The lean-to had three walls and was open on one side. Mosquitoes made it hard to sleep at night.

Building a Log House

The next job was to cut down trees to build a log house. Then the branches and bark were cut off the trees to make smooth logs. Once the logs were ready, it was time to start building. Other pioneers in the area came to help build the log house.

Inside a Log House

A family's first log house was usually small and had just one room. A bigger house would take longer to build. The family wanted the house to be finished before winter came.

The most important part of the log house was the fireplace. The fire warmed the house and was used for cooking. Many log houses did not have many windows, so fire also provided light. Pioneer children had the job of keeping the fire going. They chopped wood so that the family's wood box was always full.

"Pioneer Life: Building a House"—Think About It!

1. Every pioneer family made sure they brought an axe with them to their new land. What are two reasons why they needed an axe?

_____

_____

_____

2. Why did pioneers live in a tent or a lean-to?

_____

_____

_____

3. Give an example of how pioneer families worked together.

_____

_____

4. Why do you think it was important to finish the log house before winter came?

_____

_____

_____

5. Tell three ways that pioneer families used fire in their homes.

_____

_____

_____

6. What are two jobs that pioneer children did?

_____

_____

Pioneer Farms: Spring and Summer

Spring

Pioneer farmers looked forward to spring after a long, cold winter. One of the first jobs in spring was to make maple syrup and maple sugar. These were made from the sap inside sugar maple trees.

Farmers waited for all the snow on their fields to melt. When the soil was dry, it was time to get ready to plant. Farmers used horses to pull the heavy plough over the fields. The plough broke up the hard soil. Then, farmers planted seeds.

Spring was also time to clip the wool off the sheep. This was called shearing the sheep. The wool was used to make warm clothes.

Summer

Farmers watched their crops grow in the fields. All summer long, they pulled up the weeds so their crops would grow better.

Most farmers grew hay in some fields. They needed hay to feed to their horses, cows, and sheep during the winter. Farmers waited for hot, dry weather to harvest the hay. They wanted the hay to dry out in the sun before they stored it in the barn for the winter.

Summer was also the time to pick fruits and vegetables. Some fruits and vegetables were kept to eat during the winter. To keep fruits from spoiling, people dried them. Fruits were also stewed, or cooked in water and a little sugar, then stored in jars. Vegetables were put in jars that contained salt and vinegar. That way, they would last through the winter. Jars of fruits and vegetables were stored in a hole in the ground called a root cellar. The root cellar kept the food from freezing in winter, and kept the food cool during the warmer months.

"Pioneer Farms: Spring and Summer"—Think About It!

1. Why were sugar maple trees important to pioneer farmers?

_____

_____

_____

2. Soil can get hard when it dries out in spring. Plants do not grow well in hard soil. How did farmers get the soil ready for planting seeds?

_____

_____

_____

3. What kind of weather was best for harvesting hay? Tell why.

_____

_____

_____

4. A barn kept animals warm in winter. What was another reason a farmer needed a barn?

_____

_____

_____

5. How did pioneers keep fruits and vegetables from spoiling during the winter?

_____

_____

_____

6. What was the purpose of a root cellar?

_____

_____

Pioneer Farms: Fall and Winter

Fall

In fall, farmers harvested their crops. It was important to harvest the crops before winter came. Frost could ruin the crops.

Many farmers grew wheat. Wheat is used to make flour, and flour is used to make bread. Bread was an important food for pioneers.

Farmers harvested wheat using a tool with a long blade. They cut the stalks of wheat and tied it into bundles. Then they took the wheat to the barn. Farmers hit the wheat with a flail to make the seeds come off. This is called threshing. Only the seeds are used to make flour.

Pioneer farmer uses a flail to knock the wheat seeds off the stems.

The seeds are called grain. They are covered with a shell called chaff. During threshing, the chaff comes off the grain. Chaff cannot be used to make flour, so farmers had to get rid of the chaff. On a windy day, they put the grain and the chaff on a bed sheet. One person held each end of the sheet, and they tossed the grain and chaff into the air. The chaff is very light, so the wind blew it away. The grain fell back onto the sheet. Getting rid of the chaff is called winnowing.

Then farmers took the grain to a mill. At the mill, the grain was crushed to make flour.

Winter

Winter was a time for farmers to fix their tools and repair buildings and fences. Farmers also had more time to visit friends and relatives.

"Pioneer Farms: Fall and Winter"—Think About It!

1. In fall, farmers tried to harvest their crops as quickly as possible. Tell why.

_____

_____

2. Why did many pioneer farmers grow wheat?

_____

_____

_____

3. What was the purpose of threshing wheat?

_____

_____

_____

4. Tell why farmers did the winnowing on a windy day.

_____

_____

_____

_____

5. How was flour made?

_____

_____

_____

6. What work did farmers do in winter?

_____

_____

_____

Comparing Family Chores: Pioneer Days and Modern Days

Think about kinds of chores that different family members might do in modern days. Complete the chart.

Family Member	Pioneer Days	Modern Days
Men and Older Boys	• Clearing the land • Cutting trees for lumber • Building a home • Removing big rocks from fields • Ploughing fields • Planting crops • Harvesting crops • Hunting and fishing • Shearing sheep • Building fences • Making furniture • Digging wells	
Women and Older Girls	• Taking care of the children • Taking care of livestock • Making clothes and blankets • Preparing meals • Preserving and storing food • Planting crops • Making candles • Helping with the harvest	
Young Girls	• Helping take care of younger siblings • Feeding livestock • Picking vegetables	
Young Boys	• Gathering firewood • Feeding and tending livestock • Helping with the harvest	

Pioneer Occupations

In pioneer times, some people worked at trades, or jobs with special skills. They had special tools to do their jobs, too. Men who worked at trades often taught young boys to do the same job. It usually took between four and seven years for a boy to learn a trade. Here are some of the trades people worked at in pioneer times:

blacksmith

Blacksmith

A blacksmith's job was to fit oxen and horses with iron shoes. Iron shoes kept the hooves of these working animals from wearing down. The blacksmith also made iron tools such as hoes, rakes, spades, and sharp tools to cut grain.

Wainwright

Wainwrights built the top part of carriages, wagons, sleighs, and coaches. They used hard woods such as oak and elm. Wainwrights then hired other people with special trades to complete the rest of the carriage.

Wheelwrights

Wheelwrights made many sizes of wheels for carriages, wagons, carts, and wheelbarrows. Wheels were made with wooden hubs, spokes, and rims. Then, an iron ring was put around the outer part of the wheel to make it sturdy.

Cooper

The cooper was the person who made wooden barrels, washtubs, buckets, and butter churns. Barrels were used to store all kinds of liquids and dry items.

Harness Maker

Did you know harness makers were also saddle makers? A harness maker used special tools to carefully shape and sew leather harnesses and saddles for large animals, such as cows and horses.

"Pioneer Occupations"—Think About It!

1. What is a trade?

_____

2. Which of the people you learned about worked with animals?

_____

3. If you lived in pioneer times, what occupation would you want to do? Explain your thinking.

_____

_____

_____

4. Match each trade with the correct description.

Blacksmith	someone who made wooden barrels, washtubs, buckets, and butter churns
Wainwright	someone who fit oxen and horses with iron shoes
Wheelwright	someone who crafted many sizes of wheels for carriages, wagons, carts, and wheelbarrows
Cooper	someone who crafted leather harnesses and saddles for large animals
Harness Maker	someone who built the top part of carriages, wagons, sleighs, and coaches

Health Care in Pioneer Times

During pioneer times, there were few doctors and hospitals. When settlers got sick or injured, they were usually cared for at home.

Pioneers did not know the importance of washing their hands. Many pioneers believed that bathing too much washed away body oils that kept them from getting diseases.

Honey was used by pioneers to soothe sore throats and coughs. Honey was mixed with hot water and lemon. Honey was also used for healing cuts and scrapes.

When pioneers had a toothache, they visited a blacksmith. A blacksmith pulled the tooth out with a pair of tongs. Pulling out a tooth was very painful because there was no freezing or painkillers for the person.

Think About It!

1. What surprised you about health care during pioneer times?

_____

_____

2. List three ways that show how taking care of our health in the modern days has changed from pioneer times.

_____

_____

_____

_____

_____

_____

_____

Cariboo Gold Rush

A gold rush was a time when thousands of people moved to places that reported gold deposits. In the 1860s, people rushed to the Cariboo coastal area of British Columbia after they heard rumours that gold had been discovered.

People thought they could make quick money by panning for gold. They dipped a pan into streams and looked for gold in the wet soil they scooped up. People from far and wide came to get a mining certificate, then bought supplies and tools to try their luck.

New Towns

With so many people rushing to find gold, towns sprang up almost overnight. Houses and hotels were built along the rivers. Stores opened up. However, many people deserted the towns when they did not find gold. The rumours of gold did not come true.

As a result, many hotels and stores closed. Many of these towns became ghost towns. If you drive past them today, you can see what is left of these once-busy places.

Starting a New Life

Although people did not stay in these towns, many settled in British Columbia after the Cariboo Gold Rush. Others stayed in Yukon. Instead of making money by panning for gold, these new settlers began to work in forestry, ranching, or farming.

"Cariboo Gold Rush"—Think About It!

1. What was a gold rush?

_____

_____

2. In what province is the Cariboo coastal area?

_____

3. How did people look for gold?

_____

_____

4. What happened to new towns after the gold rushes were over?

_____

_____

_____

_____

5. Using information from the text and your own ideas, what is a ghost town?

_____

_____

_____

_____

6. What did the settlers who stayed in British Columbia and in Yukon do after the gold rush?

_____

_____

How Do We Use Land?

Every country, city, town, or village has to decide how to use its land in the best way. Every decision we make about how to use land affects everyone in a community. As the population increases, new decisions have to be made about land use.

Ways to Use Land

Some of the ways we have used land in the past are for farming, forestry, mining, outdoor and indoor recreation, shopping, parks, and living space for people.

Land Use in Cities

As cities become bigger, more land is being used to build new houses, apartment buildings, shops, roads, schools, and recreational areas. Many farms have been sold so that new housing and businesses could be built. Some people worry that we are losing too much farmland.

Losing Forests

As the population grows and people want more products and more homes, forests are cut down. In some places, new trees are planted to replace the trees that are cut down. Despite that, we are still losing forests. With fewer forests, animals have more trouble finding homes and food.

Every decision we make about how to use land affects our lives and the lives of animals that live near us.

"How Do We Use Land?"—Think About It!

1. What are some ways people have used land?

_____

_____

_____

_____

2. As cities grow, how is land used?

_____

_____

_____

_____

3. What has happened to many farms?

_____

_____

4. What happens when we lose forests?

_____

_____

_____

_____

5. Why are forests cut down?

_____

_____

_____

_____

Urban and Rural Communities

A community is a place where people live, work, and share the same interests. When people live in a village, reserve, or hamlet, it is called a rural community. When people live in a town, city, or suburb, their community is called an urban community. Some communities are smaller, such as the town of Fox Creek, Alberta. Some communities are very large, such as the city of Toronto, Ontario.

Rural Communities

Rural communities are usually small and have less traffic than towns or cities. People usually live spread out from each other and there is a lot of open space. Some people in rural communities work in jobs related to farming, forestry, mining, or fishing.

Urban Communities

Urban communities usually have lots of people, buildings, stores, and traffic. People usually live near each other in houses, duplexes, or apartment buildings.

Think About It!

Using information from the text and your own ideas, explain the kind of community you live in.

_____

_____

_____

_____

_____

_____

_____

Urban and Rural Living

Using information from the text on previous pages and your own ideas, fill out the tables.

Reasons for Living in an Urban Area

Reasons for Living in a Rural Area

Comparing Features of a Community

Pick a community and reseach its features.

Name of the community	
Location of the community	
What kind of community is it?	
What natural resources or physical features are there?	
How are the land and natural resources used?	
What kinds of structures are in this community?	
What kind of transportation is available in this community?	

The Great Lakes

What makes these five large bodies of water "great"?

Lake Superior

Lake Michigan

Lake Huron

Lake Ontario

Lake Erie

Importance

The Great Lakes are important for transporting people and goods by ships. They also have the most fresh water in the world.

People have lived around the Great Lakes for centuries. The land around the Great Lakes is good for farming. Today, many people still live near the Great Lakes.

Location and Size

Four of the Great Lakes are in both Canada and the United States. All of Lake Michigan is in the United States.

Lake Superior is the largest Great Lake. Lake Ontario is the smallest. Lake Erie is the shallowest. Lake Huron has the most shoreline around it.

Problems

Today, the Great Lakes are also becoming polluted. Chemicals from farms have run into the water. Sea creatures such as zebra mussels, sea lampreys, and a fish called a Eurasian ruffe have invaded the Great Lakes and are making it difficult for ships and people. There are fewer fish in the Great Lakes that people can safely eat.

We need to do all we can to keep the Great Lakes clean and safe for the future.

"The Great Lakes"—Think About It!

1. How many bodies of water make up the Great Lakes?

_____

2. How many of the Great Lakes are shared by Canada and the United States?

_____

_____

3. Which of the Great Lakes is the largest?

_____

4. The land around the Great lakes is bad for farming.
   Circle the answer.   **True**   **False**

Explain your thinking

_____

_____

_____

_____

5. What is causing the Great Lakes to become polluted?

_____

_____

6. What other problems do the Great Lakes have?

_____

_____

_____

_____

Fishing Communities

People have fished for hundreds of years. Fishers and their families lived in villages and towns near the sea, rivers, or lakes. Some of these communities were far from big cities and towns, and were hard to get to. People in small fishing communities helped each other through tough times.

Today, some fishing communities have large ports where ships and trains work together, large plants that pack fish, shipyards, and people who study fish.

Fisheries and Oceans Canada decides how many fish can be caught. This is to prevent overfishing. When fishers catch too many fish, nature cannot replace the fish quickly enough and the number of fish goes down.

In Atlantic Canada, there used to be a lot of cod. Because there was so much fishing over the years, there were fewer cod. In recent years, the government has told fishers they could catch only a certain number of cod. Today more people in Atlantic Canada fish for shellfish such as shrimp, scallops, and lobster, instead of cod.

"Fishing Communities"—Think About It!

1. List three facts you learned about fishing communities.

_____

_____

_____

2. Why are there fewer fish today than in the past?

_____

_____

3. What is the job of Fisheries and Oceans Canada?

_____

_____

4. What happened to the cod in Atlantic Canada?

_____

_____

_____

5. Complete the table using information from the text and your ideas.

Cause	Effect
Overfishing	
Fewer Cod in Atlantic Canada	

The **cause** is the reason something happens.
The **effect** is what happened.

Forestry Communities

Some Canadians live in forestry communities. Forestry means the cutting down and replanting of trees. Trees are a natural resource that is used to make wood products, such as paper or lumber for building. A natural resource is something people use that is found in nature. Usually, people in a forestry community have jobs that are centred on forestry. One of the important jobs in a forestry community is the replanting of trees so that this natural resource does not run out.

Think About It!

1. What does forestry mean?

_____

_____

2. Explain why you think it is important to replant trees.

_____

_____

_____

3. How do you think forestry communities affect your daily life?

_____

_____

4. What is another example of a natural resource? Explain your thinking.

_____

_____

_____

Manufacturing Communities

Many Canadians live in manufacturing communities. The word *manufacture* means to use raw materials to make a completed product.

Some examples of manufactured goods are: cars, televisions, furniture, food products, toys, and bubble gum. Usually, people in a manufacturing community work at a factory or plant. Not all people at the plant work to build something. Some people work at a plant or factory to supply services to other workers. These could be medical-, social-, security-, or food-related services.

Think About It!

1. What does manufacture mean?

_____

2. Why do you think there are so many different workers in a manufacturing community? Explain your thinking.

_____

_____

_____

_____

_____

3. How do you think manufacturing communities affect the lives of people in other communities? Explain your thinking.

_____

_____

_____

_____

_____

What Do Plants Need?

Here are things that plants need to stay alive:

Air: Plants need air just as you need air. You take in air through your nose and mouth. The leaves and roots of a plant can take in air.

Water: All types of plants need water. Plants that grow outdoors get water from rain. Indoor plants need to be watered. Outdoor gardens need to be watered when there is not enough rain.

Light: Plants use sunlight for energy. Some plants need more sunlight than others. Some plants can grow in shady places. Other plants need a lot of bright sunlight.

Warmth: All plants need warmth. Plants in a garden do not grow in winter because it is too cold. Some plants grow well in very hot places, such as deserts. Other plants grow well in places that are warm, but not too hot.

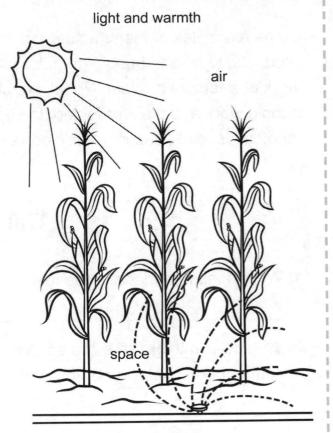

light and warmth

air

space

water

Space: A plant needs enough space to grow in. A plant's roots need space to spread out in the soil. If too many plants are growing close together, they may not get enough sunlight or water or nutrients.

On many farms, fields are planted in rows. The space between each row gives each plant enough space for its roots to spread out. The plants are not too close together, so each plant can get enough light.

"What Do Plants Need?"—Think About It!

1. Some of the things plants need are things that people need, too. In the chart below, write an "X" to show things that plants need and things that people need. The first one is done for you.

	Plants	People
Water	X	X
Time to sleep		
Air		
Soil		
Warmth		

2. Why do many indoor plants grow well near a window?

_____

_____

_____

3. A large plant will not grow well in a small pot. Explain why.

_____

_____

_____

4. Name a type of plant that you like. Tell why you like it.

_____

_____

_____

Parts of a Plant

Read the chart to find out about the different parts of a plant.

Part of a Plant	What Does This Part Do?
Roots	The roots grow in soil and soak up nutrients and water for the plant. Roots also hold the plant in place, so the wind does not blow it away.
Stem	The stem carries nutrients and water from the roots to the rest of the plant. The stem also holds up the plant.
Leaf	Leaves make food for the plant. Sunlight gives the leaves energy to make food.
Flower	Flowers grow fruit and seeds so that new plants can grow. Seeds are usually inside the fruit. On strawberries, you can see tiny seeds on the outside of the fruit.

Think About It!

1. Label the parts of the plant.

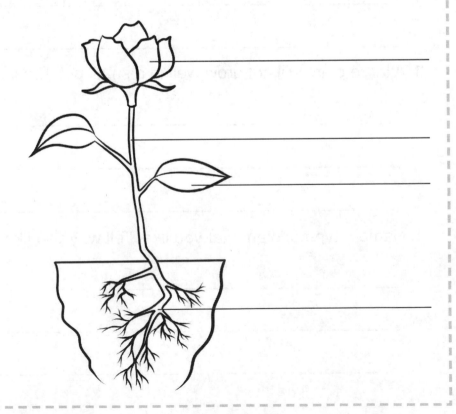

Answer the plant riddles.

2. Food and water move through me from the roots to the rest of the plant.

What part of a plant am I? _____

3. You cannot see me because I grow underground.

What part of a plant am I? _____

4. Because of me, a plant grows seeds.

What part of a plant am I? _____

5. We are two parts of a plant. Without us, plants would not have food.

What parts of a plant are we? _____ and _____

6. I am the part of a plant that grows fruit.

What part of a plant am I? _____

7. On a tree, I am very tall. On a dandelion, I am short.

What part of a plant am I? _____

8. I am the most colourful part of many plants.

What part of a plant am I? _____

Life Cycle of a Plant

Read about the life cycle of a plant that makes fruit with seeds inside.

1. A seed gets water. A tiny plant pushes out of the seed.

2. A root begins to grow down into the soil. The stem grows up out of the soil. Now the plant is called a sprout.

3. The sprout's stem grows taller and leaves appear. Now the plant is called a seedling.

4. Over time, the plant grows larger. More leaves grow. The plant becomes an adult plant. Now it can grow flowers.

5. Each flower turns into a fruit that has seeds inside. The fruit falls on the ground and rots away. The seeds do not rot. The seeds get buried in the soil.

Seed Facts

A seed always grows into the same type of plant that made it. A seed from an orange only grows into an orange tree.

One plant can make many seeds. Why do plants make so many seeds? Some of the seeds might not grow into adult plants. Here are two reasons why:

• The seed may fall on rocky ground where it cannot grow.
• The seed may fall in a dry place. It may not have enough water to grow.

"Life Cycle of a Plant"—Think About It!

1. Label the life cycle diagram. Use the words below.

adult plant   **seedling**   **seed**   **sprout**   **plant with fruit**

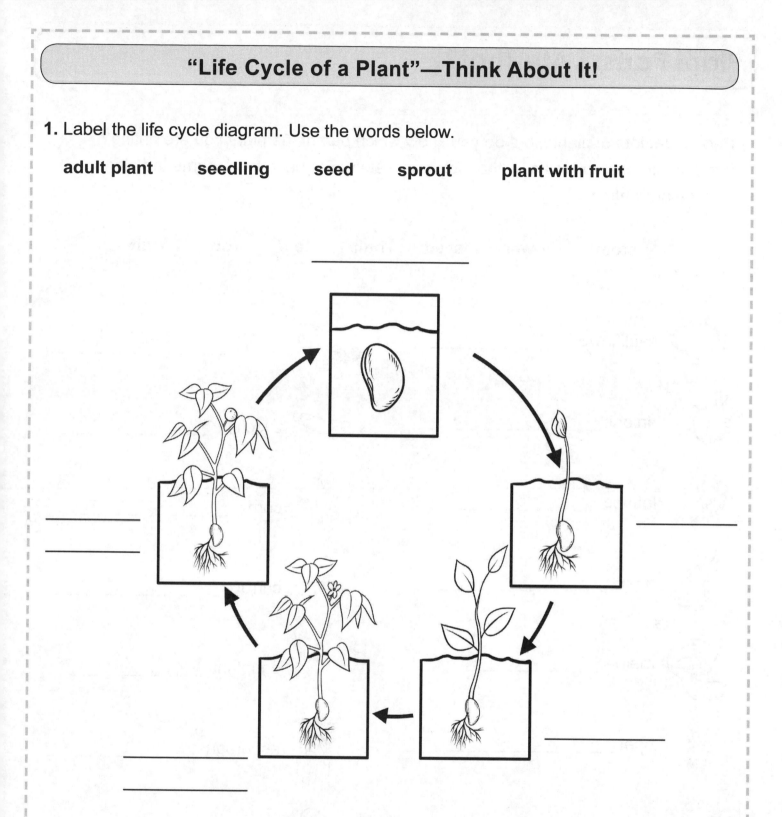

2. Tell a partner about the life cycle of a plant. Explain how it makes fruit with seeds inside. Use the diagram to help you.

Plant Parts: I Ate That?

People eat lots of plants, but do you know which *part* of the plant you are eating? It might surprise you to know that celery is a stem. For each food, name the plant *part* we are eating.

stem   flower   seed   bulb   leaf   root   fruit

cauliflower _____

onions _____

lettuce _____

pear _____

melon _____

beet _____

peas _____

lemon _____

zucchini _____

corn _____

carrot _____

eggplant _____

asparagus _____

apple _____

What plants do you like to eat? _____

_____

Poison Ivy! Watch Out!

Poison ivy is a plant that is covered in a special sap. The sap can cause an ugly, burning, itching rash on the skin of a person or animal who has touched it. Poison sumac and poison oak can cause an itching rash, too. How can you stay away from these nasty plants?

Here are a few ideas:

1. Learn what poison ivy, poison oak, and poison sumac look like. Have you ever heard, "Leaves of three, let it be"? That is a good start. Look at pictures of these plants, too. They look different at different times of the year.

2. Stay away from any place you have heard that these plants grow. Stay on the path when you walk in the woods.

3. Wear long pants and long-sleeved tops when you are in a place where these plants might be.

4. See your doctor if you break out in a rash, especially if you have a fever, too. If you do come in contact with any of these poison plants, wash your skin right away. Take a shower and use soap. Do not take a bath. In a bath, the sap will spread the rash to other parts of your body. If your dog has been in an area that has poison plants, give him or her a shower, too.

"Poison Ivy! Watch Out!"—Think About It!

1. Why would someone yell, "Watch out!" when seeing poison ivy?

   _____

   _____

   _____

2. What two other plants can give you a rash the way poison ivy does?

   _____

   _____

3. How many leaves does a poison ivy plant have?

   _____

4. Why is it a good idea to wear long-sleeved tops and long pants when walking in an area where there might be poison ivy?

   _____

   _____

   _____

5. What are two things you should do if you have come in contact with poison ivy?

   _____

   _____

Big Trees in British Columbia

Have you ever seen an 800-year-old tree? If you visit Cathedral Grove on British Columbia's Vancouver Island, you will see trees that old. Cathedral Grove is in MacMillan Provincial Park. The oldest trees there are Douglas fir trees and there are very few left. Many of the oldest trees burned down 350 years ago. Some were even cut down. The trees that are left are very precious.

Cathedral Grove is not far from the road. You can park your car and walk right over. As you walk on a trail, you will see trees towering above you. The trees are beautiful, and many people take pictures of them. You will also see red cedar trees. They are quite old, too, and they overlook Cameron Lake. If you look around, you might also see woodpeckers, owls, deer, and elk.

In 1997, a strong wind storm knocked down many of the trees in Cathedral Grove. It also destroyed some of the trails. Park workers are still trying to fix the trails. That is one reason they ask visitors to stay on the marked trails.

.

"Big Trees in British Columbia"—Think About It!

1. Where can you see 800-year-old trees?

_____

_____

2. What park is Cathedral Grove in?

_____

3. What happened to many of the trees in Cathedral Grove about 350 years ago?

_____

_____

4. Name two kinds of big trees in Cathedral Grove.

_____

_____

5. Why should visitors stay on marked trails in Cathedral Grove?

_____

_____

_____

© Chalkboard Publishing

What Can Forces Do?

Forces Make Things Move

A soccer ball sits on a field. The ball will not move by itself. Can you make the ball move? You could kick it.

You want to get socks from a drawer. How do you open the drawer? Pull the handle.

Objects need a force to make them move. You kick a soccer ball with your foot. You pull a drawer with your hand. Pushing and pulling are forces. Forces make things move.

You use *muscular force* to push and pull.

Forces Make Things Stop

Forces can also make objects stop. A shopping cart will roll down a hill. You can stop it by grabbing the handle. Or you could push against it. Pushing and pulling are forces. Pushing and pulling can make objects stop moving.

What Else Can Forces Do?

Change speed: Forces can change the speed of an object. You push a toy car to make it start moving. To make the car go faster, you can push it harder. You can use force to change the speed of a moving object. The second push makes the car go faster.

Change direction: Forces can make an object change direction. To change the direction of a baseball, you hit it with a bat. The pitcher throws the baseball to you. When you hit the baseball, you push it with the bat. The baseball changes direction and moves away from you.

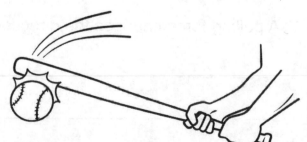

"What Can Forces Do?"—Think About It!

Which type of force do you use for each action below? Write **push** or **pull** beside each action.

1. Pick an apple from a tree. _____

2. Ring a doorbell. _____

3. Throw a ball. _____

4. Undo a zipper. _____

Read this story:

Tanya put her dog Sparky on a leash and took him for a walk. Sparky started to run down the sidewalk. This made Tanya run. Tanya got tired of running. She used the leash to make Sparky slow down. Then Sparky saw a squirrel and he wanted to chase it. Sparky pulled Tanya right through Mr. Lee's flower garden!

5. What are the pulling forces in this story? Give two examples.

_____

_____

6. Force can change the speed of something. Give two examples from the story.

_____

_____

7. A pulling force changes the direction of a moving thing. Give an example from the story.

_____

_____

The Force of Gravity

Gravity is the force that makes things fall. Gravity is a pulling force. It pulls things to the ground. Gravity stops objects from floating up. It holds things down.

Remember four things that forces can do:

1. Make an object start moving

2. Make an object stop moving

3. Change the speed of an object

4. Change the direction of a moving object

The force of gravity can do the same things.

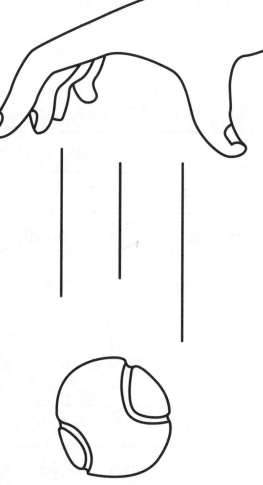

Gravity Makes an Object Start Moving: If you let go of a ball, it drops to the ground. You do not need to push the ball to make it fall. Gravity makes the ball start moving.

Gravity Makes an Object Stop Moving: If you toss a ball up, it will soon start to fall. Before the ball starts to fall, it will stop in the air. The ball stops for a very short time. You do not see it stop. The force of gravity makes the ball stop going up.

Gravity Changes the Speed of a Moving Object: When an object falls, it moves faster and faster as it gets closer to the ground. Gravity makes things move faster as they get closer to Earth.

Gravity Changes the Direction of a Moving Object: If you throw a ball to a friend far away, it starts to fall. The direction of the ball changes. It starts to fall down. Gravity changes the direction of the ball.

"The Force of Gravity"—Think About It!

1. Why does gravity make you go down a slide?

_____

_____

2. When you go down a slide, do you move faster near the top of the slide or near the bottom? Tell how you know.

_____

_____

_____

_____

3. In space, there is little gravity. What happens if you pour juice into a glass in space?

_____

_____

_____

_____

4. Think about riding a bicycle. How does gravity help you move?

_____

_____

_____

_____

The Force of Friction

What Is Friction?

Friction is a force. It is created when things rub against each other. What does friction do? Friction slows down objects.

Imagine you push a box across a smooth floor. It moves, then stops. The box and the floor rub against each other. There is friction between the floor and the box. Friction works against movement. It makes moving objects slow down.

smooth surface

Smooth and Rough Surfaces

When objects rub against each other, their surfaces touch. Rough surfaces create more friction than smooth surfaces.

Imagine pushing a toy car across a hard floor. Now imagine pushing it on carpet. The car slows down on both floors, then stops. On which floor will the car go further? Why? The carpet has a rougher surface than a hard floor. The carpet creates more friction. When there is more friction, an object slows down more quickly.

rough surface

Surfaces Rubbing Together

What happens when different surfaces rub against each other? Does the amount of friction change?

What Rubs Together?	How Much Friction?
A rough surface rubs on a rough surface	A lot of friction
A rough surface rubs on a smooth surface	Medium friction
A smooth surface rubs on a smooth surface	Very little friction

"The Force of Friction"—Think About It!

Use the examples below to answer questions 1 and 2.
- You roll a marble on a towel.
- You roll a marble on a glass table.

1. In which example is more friction created?

_____

_____

_____

2. Tell why you think your answer to question 1 is correct.

_____

_____

_____

3. Imagine you rub together two pieces of regular paper. Then you rub two pieces of sandpaper. When is there more friction? Tell how you know.

_____

_____

_____

4. Cars go faster on a paved road than on a gravel road. How can friction explain this?

_____

_____

_____

How Friction Helps Us

How does friction help us in daily life? Friction stops us from slipping.

Slippery Ice

There can be lots of ice on sidewalks in winter. Ice is very smooth, so it is easy to slip on. If you slip on ice, you might fall and hurt yourself. Winter boots usually have rough soles. Why?

winter boots

- A rough surface rubbing against a smooth surface creates medium friction.
- A smooth surface rubbing against a smooth surface creates very little friction.

Rough soles on ice create friction. Friction slows or stops movement. Rough soles stop us from slipping on ice.

Sometimes people put sand on ice. Sand makes the ice surface rough. It is harder to slip on sandy ice. The sand creates friction between the ice and your boots.

Slippery Stairs

wooden stairs

Slipping on stairs is very dangerous. You could really hurt yourself if you fall down the stairs.

Stairs are often made of smooth wood. When shoes rub against smooth wood, there might not be enough friction. The shoes might slip off the step.

Carpet can add friction to stairs. Rough strips of material work too. The added friction stops people from slipping.

"How Friction Helps Us"—Think About It!

1. Think about going downstairs in sock feet. Now think about going down stairs wearing shoes. Which example is more dangerous? Tell why.

_____

_____

_____

_____

2. In winter, some cars have snow tires. Snow tires help people drive in snow. Snow tires also help cars stop faster.

   In summer, cars have regular tires. Which tires have a rougher surface: snow tires, or regular tires? Why do you think so?

_____

_____

_____

_____

3. People do not leave snow tires on cars all year. When spring comes, people put regular tires back on.

   Why do people not leave snow tires on all year?
   (Hint: Think about friction and what it does.)

_____

_____

_____

_____

Contact and Non-contact Forces

What Is Contact?

When two things touch each other, we say they are in *contact* with each other. When your hand touches a book, it contacts the book.

Contact Forces

Some forces work through contact. You use muscular force to push and pull objects. To push a toy car across a table, you need to contact the toy car. Muscular force is a *contact force*. To push or pull an object with your muscles, you need to have contact with the object.

Friction is another contact force. Friction happens when two objects rub together. The two objects must be in contact with each other. If there is no contact between the objects, there is no friction.

Non-contact Forces

Some forces can work without contact. If you hold a magnet near a pin, the pin will move toward the magnet. Magnetic force makes the pin move, but the magnet is not touching the pin. There is no contact. Magnetic force can work when there is no contact between objects.

Forces that can work without contact are called *non-contact forces*. These forces can work when there is distance between the objects.

Gravity is another non-contact force. Gravity comes from Earth. Snowflakes fall to the ground because gravity pulls them down. Gravity pulls snowflakes when they are not touching Earth.

"Contact and Non-contact Forces"—Think About It!

1. Write the forces below in the correct column of the chart.

friction   magnetic force   muscular force   gravity

Contact Forces	Non-contact Forces

Use the pictures to help you answer question 2.

Magnetic force makes a nail stay in contact with a magnet.

The force of gravity keeps a rock from floating in the air.

2. Do non-contact forces work *only* when there is no contact between objects? Give reasons for your answer.

_____

_____

_____

_____

_____

_____

Experiment: The Force of Static Electricity

Have you ever felt a shock after walking across carpet? That shock comes from static electricity. Try this experiment to see what static electricity can do.

What You Need

- A sink
- A plastic comb
- Medium or long hair

What You Do

1. Turn on a thin stream of water.

2. Comb the hair at least ten times.

3. Slowly bring the comb close to the stream of water. (Do not let the comb touch the water.) Watch what happens to the water.

4. Finish the pictures below to show what you saw. Draw the stream of water.

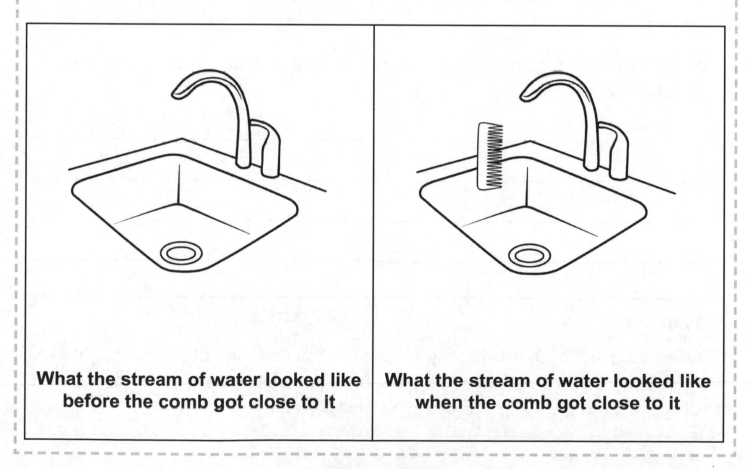

What the stream of water looked like before the comb got close to it

What the stream of water looked like when the comb got close to it

"Experiment: The Force of Static Electricity"—Think About It!

1. In this experiment, does static electricity create a pulling force or a pushing force? Tell how you know.

_____

_____

_____

_____

2. Is static electricity a contact force or a non-contact force? Tell how you know.

_____

_____

_____

_____

3. Would the same thing happen to the water if you used a magnet instead of a comb? Tell why or why not.

_____

_____

_____

_____

Try It!

Cut a small piece of tin foil into very tiny pieces. (You need only about six or eight tiny pieces.) Comb your hair at least ten times. Bring the comb close to the tin foil pieces, but do not touch them with the comb. See what happens.

Lightning Strikes

What kind of static electricity moves between two clouds or a cloud and the ground? Lightning!

Lightning is the flash of electricity you might see in the sky during a thunderstorm. The electricity from lightning cannot be used as a source of energy. Why? Because lightning is too powerful, happens too quickly, and does not last long.

Bolts of lightning can be very dangerous. Lightning is five times hotter than the surface of the Sun. When lightning strikes the ground, fires can start, trees can be destroyed, and people can be seriously hurt or killed.

Lightning Safety

Here are some tips to avoid lightning if a thunderstorm is close by:

• Stay away from water. Do not stand under an umbrella, and do not keep swimming.

• Go indoors or into a car, if possible.

• Stay away from telephone poles and trees.

• Stay on low ground, and avoid being the tallest object in the area.

• If you are in a field, crouch low.

• Stay away from anything metal, such as a bicycle or fence.

"Lightning Strikes"—Think About It!

1. What kind of static electricity moves between two clouds or a cloud and the ground?

   _____

2. Why can we not use lightning as a source of energy?

   _____

3. Why are bolts of lightning dangerous?

   _____

4. Design a safety poster that lists at least two ways to avoid lightning during a thunderstorm.

What Is a Structure?

A *structure* is something that holds or supports a load. A truck can hold a heavy load of boxes. A *load* is something that has weight.

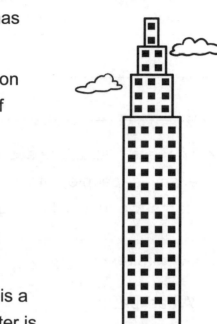

skyscraper

Your bed is a structure that supports a load. When you lie on your bed, you are the load. The bed supports the weight of your body.

A Structure Has Size

Structures come in many different sizes. A skyscraper is a huge structure. A skyscraper supports the weight of all the people, furniture, and equipment inside it.

A paper cup is smaller than a skyscraper, but a paper cup is a structure too. When you fill a paper cup with water, the water is the load. The cup has to support the weight of the water.

A Structure Has Shape

A structure can be almost any shape. A bookcase is a structure shaped like a rectangle. Buildings are structures. Think of all the different shapes that buildings can be. An airplane and a helicopter are both structures that can fly. They each have a different shape.

airplane   **helicopter**

A Structure Has a Purpose

A structure is built to do something. A bed gives you a soft place to lie down and sleep. A bookcase stores books. A truck carries large, heavy loads from place to place.

"What Is a Structure?"—Think About It!

1. What do all structures do?

_____

_____

_____

2. The load a structure supports can be made up of more than one thing. For example, people, furniture, and equipment are all part of the load in a skyscraper. Name two things that might be part of the load in each structure below.

An airplane: _____ _____

A backpack: _____ _____

A shopping cart: _____ _____

3. What load is a skateboard made to hold? What is the purpose of a skateboard?

Load:_____

Purpose: _____

_____

4. Is a fence a structure? Explain your thinking using the information from the reading and your own ideas.

_____

_____

_____

_____

Natural Structures

You can find many structures in nature.
Look at the two examples below.

Tree

A tree is a structure. It holds a load, has size and shape, and has a purpose.

It is easy to see that every tree has a size and shape. What load does a tree hold? A tree has to hold up the weight of its trunk, branches, and leaves. If a tree cannot hold up this load, it will fall over.

What is the purpose of a tree? A tree makes seeds so other trees just like it can grow.

tree

Beehive

Bees make a home called a beehive. Thousands of bees can live in one beehive. Bees make honey, and they store the honey inside the beehive.

A beehive is a structure. It has size and shape. The load that a beehive holds includes the bees and the honey. The purpose of a beehive is to give the bees a home, a place to store food, and a place to keep their eggs safe.

Beehives often hang from tree branches.

Brain Stretch

Make a list of other structures found in nature. _____

_____

_____

_____

"Natural Structures"—Think About It!

1. Many birds build homes called nests. Name two different things that can be part of the load in a bird's nest.

   _____   _____

2. What is the shape of a bird's nest?

   _____

3. What are some materials a bird uses to build a nest?

   _____

   _____

4. Spiders build structures called webs. What is one purpose of a spider web?

   _____

   _____

5. What are two things that can be part of the load on a spider web?

   _____

   _____

6. Beekeepers raise bees and sell the honey the bees make. A beekeeper builds special beehives where the bees live. Is this special type of beehive a natural structure? Tell why or why not.

   _____

   _____

   _____

   _____

Structures Word Search

A structure holds a load, has size and shape, and has a purpose. Some structures are found in nature. Some structures are made by people.

Use the list below. Circle the names of the structures.

E	S	P	I	D	E	R	W	E	B	B
G	T	I	C	E	B	E	R	G	S	E
G	O	N	T	Q	W	B	A	I	N	E
S	W	T	R	E	E	R	N	G	O	H
H	E	G	N	M	G	I	T	L	W	I
E	R	N	E	S	T	D	H	O	F	V
L	C	G	E	R	P	G	I	O	L	E
L	H	H	O	U	S	E	L	T	A	K
W	A	G	E	Z	I	S	L	E	K	B
O	I	Q	C	A	V	E	E	N	E	I
G	R	P	A	B	O	A	T	T	D	K
W	C	O	R	A	L	R	E	E	F	E
F	E	A	T	H	E	R	Q	H	U	T

In the word list, highlight the natural structures yellow. Highlight in orange the structures made by people.

anthill	beehive	bike	boat
bridge	cave	chair	coral reef
eggshell	feather	house	hut
iceberg	igloo	nest	snowflake
spider web	tent	tower	tree

Structures Collage

Cut and paste magazine pictures to create a collage of structures.

On one half of the page, paste only structures from nature.

On the other half of the page, paste only structures people make.

Structures from Nature

Structures People Make

What Is Soil Made Of?

Soil is made of many items. We can put these items in two groups: *living things* and *non-living things*.

Living Things in Soil

Did you know that soil is full of living things? If you dig in garden soil, you will probably see worms. If you look very closely, you might see tiny insects too. There are many more living things in soil. Many are too small to see.

Bacteria are tiny creatures that live in soil. Bacteria are so tiny that you need to use a microscope to see them. In one handful of soil, there might be thousands and thousands of tiny bacteria.

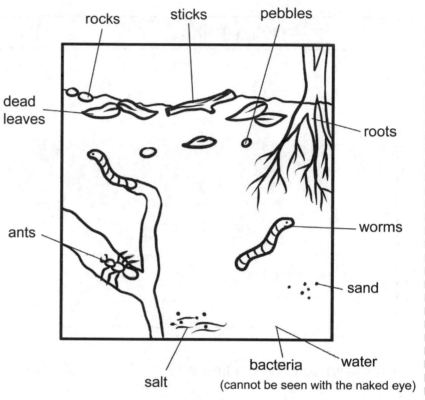

Non-living Things in Soil

Non-living things were never alive.

Water and air are two non-living things in soil. You probably will not see water in soil. When soil feels moist, there is water in it. You can not see air, but there is air in soil. Air fills the tiny spaces in soil.

Rock is another non-living part of soil. You may find large rocks or small pebbles in soil. Soil also contains tiny pieces of rock, such as sand.

Sometimes people put non-living things into soil. They add fertilizer to soil to help plants grow. They spray plants to kill harmful insects. Some of that spray goes into the soil. They put salt on roads and sidewalks to melt the winter ice. That salt ends up in the soil.

"What Is Soil Made Of?"—Think About It!

1. Each thing in the list is found in soil. Write each thing in the correct column of the chart.

dead leaves   ants   air   water   roots   pebbles

bacteria   sand   rock   worms   sticks   salt

Living Things	Non-living Things

2. Where in soil do you find air?

_____

_____

_____

3. Write two facts you have learned from the reading.

_____

_____

_____

Dirt and Soil

Many people call soil "dirt" but soil and dirt are two very different things.

What Is the Difference?

Soil is a good mixture of minerals, natural material, and the decayed remains of living things. Soil helps plants grow. Soil is important for life on Earth.

Dirt is dust and grime that is not useful. We clean dirt off our cars, windowsills, furniture, and floors. Dirt can get under our fingernails, or on our clothing. We wash dirt away. It does not improve life, or help anything grow. But soil does..

Useful Soil

Here are some other useful things that soil does:

1. Soil is a good home for animals, such as mice and groundhogs, that live in the ground.
2. Soil holds water and releases water. Soil also helps clean our water.
3. Soil is used in building dams, roads, and buildings.

Kinds of Soil

There are different kinds of soil. The best soil for growing plants is soil that has organic material in it. Organic material can include dead leaves, and leftover scraps of vegetables and fruits.

Protecting Soil

If you want to keep your soil from drying out in the summer heat, you can add mulch. Mulch can be twigs, leaves, and bark. Mulch helps protect soil and keeps out weeds, too.

"Dirt and Soil"—Think About It!

1. Which is more useful, soil or dirt? Why?

_____

_____

_____

2. What is soil?

_____

_____

3. What is dirt?

_____

_____

4. What is the best soil for growing plants?

_____

_____

5. What can you add to keep soil from drying out in the summer heat?

_____

_____

Erosion

Erosion is what happens when parts of the land wear away. Erosion is caused mostly by water. Rainfall, rivers, waves, and floods all change the land and wear it away.

Wind and Ice

Wind and ice also cause the land to erode. In dry areas, wind is a big cause of erosion. The wind picks up dust and dirt, and throws them against objects such as land and rocks. That gradually wears the land and rocks away. Wind erosion can also cause giant dust storms.

The ice in glaciers also wears away the land. A glacier is a giant river of ice that moves very slowly. As the glacier moves, it scrapes everything under it.

People and Erosion

People have made erosion worse in many places. They did this by cutting down trees to make room for farming and building. Without trees, the soil blows away in the wind and gets washed away by rain. Trees help stop erosion by keeping the soil in place. People can plant new trees to replace the trees that were cut down and help stop some of the erosion.

"Erosion"—Think About It!

1. What does erosion mean?

_____

_____

2. Name four things that change the land and wear it away.

_____

_____

_____

3. How have people made erosion worse in some places?

_____

_____

_____

4. What happens when there are no trees to hold the soil?

_____

_____

5. How can people help stop erosion?

_____

_____

_____

© Chalkboard Publishing

Air and Water for Plant Roots

Watering Plants

When you water an indoor plant, the water goes on top of the soil, then moves down into the soil. If you add lots of water, some of the water will come out of a hole in the bottom of the pot. The soil will feel damp for a few days, so we know that some of water stays in the soil. We say that the soil holds the water.

When it rains, or when you water a garden, the water moves into the soil. The soil at the top of the garden stays damp for a while, so we know that this soil is holding some of the water. The rest of the water sinks deeper and deeper into the soil.

How Does Water Move Through Soil?

Water moves through the spaces in soil. The spaces are between the particles. Water can move quickly through soil when there are large spaces between the particles. Water moves more slowly through smaller spaces.

How Do Plants Get Air and Water from Soil?

Plant roots grow down into soil. The roots need both air and water from the soil. Air and water are in the spaces between soil particles. If the spaces fill with water, how do the roots get air?

Remember that water moves down through soil. Water moves through the spaces between the particles. Water gets stuck in some spaces, so the soil stays damp. The rest of the water moves deeper into the soil, leaving empty spaces higher up. Some spaces hold water and others are filled with air. The plant roots get both air and water.

1. Some indoor plants will die if you water them every day. Think of the spaces in the soil. What is stopped from happening when the soil contains too much water?

_____

_____

Use this story to answer questions 2 and 3.

Abdul and Tina have two paper cups. They make four holes in the bottom of each cup. Abdul fills his cup halfway with small stones. Tina fills her cup halfway with sand. They pour the same amount of water into each cup. Then they watch to see which cup the water flows through faster.

2. Are the spaces between the particles larger in the cup of small stones? Or are the spaces larger in the cup of sand?

_____

3. Which cup will water flow through faster? Why?

_____

_____

_____

4. Imagine Abdul's cup had silt in it and Tina's cup had clay. Which cup would the water flow through faster? Explain why.

_____

_____

_____

_____

Glaciers

Glaciers are giant rivers of ice that move very slowly. As a glacier moves, it takes soil and rocks with it. Glaciers can change the shape of mountains and valleys over hundreds or thousands of years!

There are three main types of glaciers. **Alpine glaciers** are found near mountains. **Ice cap** or **ice field glaciers** sit on top of mountains. **Ice sheet glaciers** are found at the North Pole and the South Pole. About 99% of glacier ice is found near the North Pole and South Pole.

Scientists study glaciers to learn what is happening on Earth. The planet is getting warmer and there have been many changes to glaciers. Many glaciers are becoming smaller.

Glaciers are very important. They store about 75% of Earth's fresh water.

"Glaciers"—Think About It!

1. What are glaciers?

_____

2. Where is 99% of glacier ice found?

_____

_____

3. Name three main types of glaciers and where are they found?

_____

_____

_____

4. What happens to glaciers as the planet gets warmer?

_____

_____

5. Why are glaciers very important?

_____

_____

6. Would you want to visit a glacier? Tell why or why not?

_____

_____

_____

_____

Technology Collage

Look through magazines and newspapers to find examples of technology. Cut and paste the examples into a collage below. On a separate piece of paper, write about how technology is used in people's lives. Include how you use technology in your daily life.

Crazy Colouring Ideas

Have children practise their fine motor skills using different media to colour colouring pages or simple geometric shapes.

Colour a colouring page or large geometric shapes:

- on different surfaces, such as sandpaper, to create interesting textures

- alternating heavy and light strokes

- using only primary colours

- using only secondary colours

- using different shades of the same colour

- with different colours of chalk and setting it with hairspray

- using pastels

- using watercolours

- using vertical lines

- using horizontal lines

Fill in sections of a colouring page or geometric shape using:

- different colours of modelling clay

- tiny bits of torn construction paper

- mixed media

- different colours of thick yarn

- different patterns

- cotton swab dots

How to Draw a Polar Bear

Follow these steps to draw. Write an adventure story about the polar bear.

Use an eraser to remove overlapping lines.

Certificate of Merit—Grade 3

Fantastic Work!

Be Proud of Your Success!

READY FOR ANYTHING!

Name

Answers

Mathematics

Counting by 3s

Count by 3s.

1. Start at 12, _15_, **18**, **21**, **24**, **27**, **30**
2. Start at 45, **48**, **51**, **54**, **57**, **60**, **63**
3. Start at 57, **60**, **63**, **66**, **69**, **72**, **75**
4. Start at 87, **90**, **93**, **96**, **99**, **102**, **105**
5. Start at 33, **36**, **39**, **42**, **45**, **48**, **51**

Count back by 3s.

6. Start at 39, _36_, **33**, **30**, **27**, **24**, **21**
7. Start at 96, **93**, **90**, **87**, **84**, **81**, **78**
8. Start at 51, **48**, **45**, **42**, **39**, **36**, **33**
9. Start at 27, **24**, **21**, **18**, **15**, **12**, **9**
10. Start at 72, **69**, **66**, **63**, **60**, **57**, **54**

5

Counting by 4s

Count by 4s.

1. Start at 16, _20_, **24**, **28**, **32**, **36**, **40**
2. Start at 24, **28**, **32**, **36**, **40**, **44**, **48**
3. Start at 44, **48**, **52**, **56**, **60**, **64**, **68**
4. Start at 80, **84**, **88**, **92**, **96**, **100**, **104**
5. Start at 52, **56**, **60**, **64**, **68**, **72**, **76**

Count back by 4s.

6. Start at 72, _68_, **64**, **60**, **56**, **52**, **48**
7. Start at 68, **64**, **60**, **56**, **52**, **48**, **44**
8. Start at 60, **56**, **52**, **48**, **44**, **40**, **36**
9. Start at 36, **32**, **28**, **24**, **20**, **16**, **12**
10. Start at 92, **88**, **84**, **80**, **76**, **72**, **68**

6

Counting by 5s and 25s

Count by 5s.

1. Start at 310, _315_, **320**, **325**, **330**, **335**, **340**
2. Start at 545, **550**, **555**, **560**, **565**, **570**, **575**
3. Start at 780, **785**, **790**, **795**, **800**, **805**, **810**

Count back by 5s.

4. Start at 495, _490_, **485**, **480**, **475**, **470**, **465**
5. Start at 675, **670**, **665**, **660**, **655**, **650**, **645**
6. Start at 160, **155**, **150**, **145**, **140**, **135**, **130**

Count by 25s.

7. Start at 675, _700_, **725**, **750**, **775**, **800**, **825**
8. Start at 225, **250**, **275**, **300**, **325**, **350**, **375**

Count back by 25s.

9. Start at 700, _675_, **650**, **625**, **600**, **575**, **550**
10. Start at 425, **400**, **375**, **350**, **325**, **300**, **275**

7

Counting by 10s

Count by 10s.

1. Start at 170, _180_, **190**, **200**, **210**, **220**, **230**
2. Start at 233, **243**, **253**, **263**, **273**, **283**, **293**
3. Start at 800, **810**, **820**, **830**, **840**, **850**, **860**
4. Start at 655, **665**, **675**, **685**, **695**, **705**, **715**
5. Start at 400, **410**, **420**, **430**, **440**, **450**, **460**

Count back by 10s.

6. Start at 200, _190_, **180**, **170**, **160**, **150**, **140**
7. Start at 90, **80**, **70**, **60**, **50**, **40**, **30**
8. Start at 383, **373**, **363**, **353**, **343**, **333**, **323**

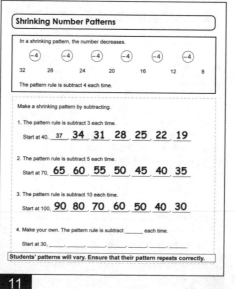

BRAIN STRETCH

A box has 10 snack bars. Write how many snack bars are in

a) 2 boxes **20** b) 3 boxes **30** c) 5 boxes **50** d) 7 boxes **70**

8

Counting by 100s

Count by 100s.

1. Start at 100, _200_, **300**, **400**, **500**, **600**, **700**
2. Start at 209, **309**, **409**, **509**, **609**, **709**, **809**
3. Start at 198, **298**, **398**, **498**, **598**, **698**, **798**
4. Start at 345, **445**, **545**, **645**, **745**, **845**, **945**
5. Start at 174, **274**, **374**, **474**, **574**, **674**, **774**

Count back by 100s.

6. Start at 986, _886_, **786**, **686**, **586**, **486**, **386**
7. Start at 621, **521**, **421**, **321**, **221**, **121**, **21**
8. Start at 863, **763**, **663**, **563**, **463**, **363**, **263**

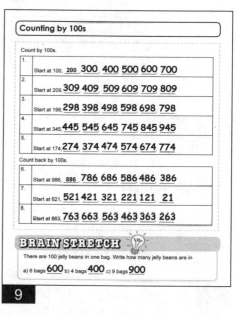

BRAIN STRETCH

There are 100 jelly beans in one bag. Write how many jelly beans are in

a) 6 bags **600** b) 4 bags **400** c) 9 bags **900**

9

Growing Number Patterns

In a growing pattern, the number increases.

(+3) (+3) (+3) (+3) (+3) (+3)

3   6   9   12   15   18   21

The pattern rule is add 3 each time.

Make a growing pattern by adding.

1. The pattern rule is add 7 each time.

Start at 7, _14_, **21**, **28**, **35**, **42**, **49**, **56**

2. The pattern rule is add 10 each time.

Start at 20, **30**, **40**, **50**, **60**, **70**, **80**, **90**

3. The pattern rule is add 5 each time.

Start at 5, **10**, **15**, **20**, **25**, **30**, **35**, **40**

4. Make your own. The pattern rule is add _____ each time.

Start at 7, ___ ___ ___ ___ ___ ___ ___

Students' patterns will vary. Ensure that their pattern repeats correctly.

10

Shrinking Number Patterns

In a shrinking pattern, the number decreases.

(−4) (−4) (−4) (−4) (−4) (−4)

32   28   24   20   16   12   8

The pattern rule is subtract 4 each time.

Make a shrinking pattern by subtracting.

1. The pattern rule is subtract 3 each time.

Start at 40, _37_, **34**, **31**, **28**, **25**, **22**, **19**

2. The pattern rule is subtract 5 each time.

Start at 70, **65**, **60**, **55**, **50**, **45**, **40**, **35**

3. The pattern rule is subtract 10 each time.

Start at 100, **90**, **80**, **70**, **60**, **50**, **40**, **30**

4. Make your own. The pattern rule is subtract _____ each time.

Start at 30, ___ ___ ___ ___ ___ ___ ___

Students' patterns will vary. Ensure that their pattern repeats correctly.

11

Odd and Even Numbers

Look at the ones digits to see if a number is odd or even.
Odd numbers end in 1, 3, 5, 7, or 9.
Even numbers end in 0, 2, 4, 6, or 8.

Colour the even numbers orange. Colour the odd numbers green. Write your own odd and even numbers and colour the balloons.

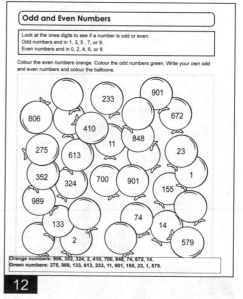

Orange numbers: 806, 382, 324, 2, 410, 700, 848, 74, 672, 14.
Green numbers: 275, 989, 133, 613, 233, 11, 901, 155, 23, 1, 579.

12

Comparing and Ordering Numbers

1. Count by 10s. Fill in the missing numbers.

Just before: **33**, 43, 53	Just before: **51**, 61, 71
Just after: 9, 19, **29**	Just before and after: **64**, 74, **84**
Between: 58, **68**, 78	Just after: 46, 56, **66**

2. Circle the larger number in each pair.

a) (342) or 324   b) (987) or 798   c) (301) or 103   d) (672) or 627

e) (120) or 102   f) 440 or (484)   g) 715 or (751)   h) (800) or 790

3. Order each group of numbers from smallest to largest.

164, 439, 181, 219, 170, 322   **164 170 181 219 322 439**

440, 463, 459, 330, 500, 143   **143 330 440 459 463 500**

4. Order each group of numbers from largest to smallest.

95, 84, 123   **123 95 84**   245, 212, 289   **289 245 212**

13

Hundreds, Tens, and Ones

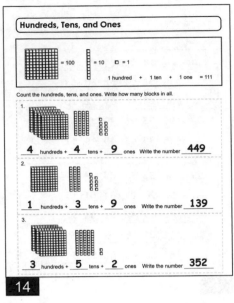

= 100   = 10   = 1

1 hundred + 1 ten + 1 one = 111

Count the hundreds, tens, and ones. Write how many blocks in all.

1. **4** hundreds + **4** tens + **9** ones   Write the number **449**

2. **1** hundreds + **3** tens + **9** ones   Write the number **139**

3. **3** hundreds + **5** tens + **2** ones   Write the number **352**

14

Hundreds, Tens, and Ones (continued)

Count the hundreds, tens, and ones. Write how many blocks in all.

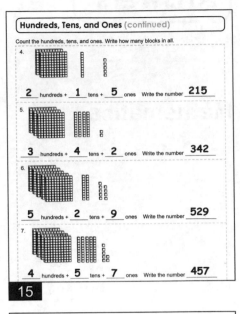

4. **2** hundreds + **1** tens + **5** ones   Write the number **215**

5. **3** hundreds + **4** tens + **2** ones   Write the number **342**

6. **5** hundreds + **2** tens + **9** ones   Write the number **529**

7. **4** hundreds + **5** tens + **7** ones   Write the number **457**

15

Hundreds, Tens, and Ones (continued)

Count the hundreds, tens, and ones. Write how many blocks in all.

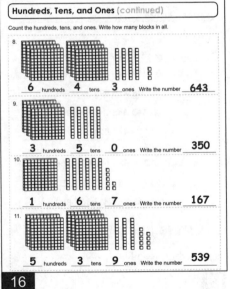

8. **6** hundreds **4** tens **3** ones   Write the number **643**

9. **3** hundreds **5** tens **0** ones   Write the number **350**

10. **1** hundreds **6** tens **7** ones   Write the number **167**

11. **5** hundreds **3** tens **9** ones   Write the number **539**

16

Place Value

Place value is the value of where the digit is in the number, such as ones, tens, hundreds, etc. For example, in the number 725,

7 stands for 700
2 stands for 20
5 stands for 5

725 in expanded form is **700 + 20 + 5**

Write the place value of the underlined digit.

1. 5<u>6</u>5 **500**	9. 90<u>8</u> **0**
2. 8<u>6</u>7 **60**	10. <u>6</u>72 **600**
3. <u>4</u>34 **400**	11. 39<u>6</u> **6**
4. 1<u>9</u>7 **90**	12. 4<u>1</u>0 **10**
5. <u>8</u>65 **800**	13. 50<u>9</u> **9**
6. 3<u>4</u>4 **40**	14. <u>8</u>21 **800**
7. <u>9</u>01 **900**	15. 2<u>3</u>6 **30**
8. 97<u>7</u> **7**	16. <u>9</u>98 **900**

Write each number in expanded form.

1. 895   **800 + 90 + 5**
2. 724   **700 + 20 + 4**
3. 659   **600 + 50 + 9**

17

What Is the Value?

Write the missing value.

1. 600 + 30 + **5** = 635
2. **9** hundreds + 4 tens + 7 ones = 947
3. 800 + 90 + **1** = 891
4. **3** hundreds + 0 tens + 8 ones = 308
5. 200 + **30** + 8 = 238
6. 4 hundreds + **4** tens + 0 ones = 440
7. 500 + **80** + 2 = 582
8. 9 hundreds + 2 tens + **4** ones = 924

BRAIN STRETCH

Compare and write >, <, or =.

a) 954 **>** 890   b) 376 **<** 420   c) 768 **=** 768

d) 534 **<** 558   e) 165 **<** 190   f) 832 **>** 650

18

Writing Numbers in Different Ways

Circle two correct ways to express each number.

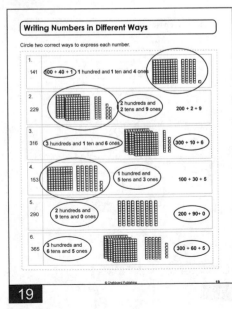

1. 141   (100 + 40 + 1)   (1 hundred and 1 ten and 4 ones)

2. 229   (2 hundreds and 2 tens and 9 ones)   200 + 2 + 9

3. 316   (3 hundreds and 1 ten and 6 ones)   (300 + 10 + 6)

4. 153   (1 hundred and 5 tens and 3 ones)   100 + 30 + 5

5. 290   (2 hundreds and 9 tens and 0 ones)   (200 + 90 + 0)

6. 365   (3 hundreds and 6 tens and 5 ones)   (300 + 60 + 5)

19

Writing Numbers in Standard Form

There are different ways to write a number.
  100 + 10 + 7
  1 hundred + 1 ten + 7 ones
  one hundred seventeen
  117
117 is written in standard form.

Write each number in standard form.

1. 600 + 50 + 8	**658**
2. 7 tens 5 ones	**75**
3. ninety-nine	**99**
4. 400 + 30 + 7	**437**
5. 8 hundreds 2 ones	**802**
6. seven hundred thirteen	**713**
7. 500 + 40 + 3	**543**
8. seventy	**70**
9. 3 hundreds 9 tens	**390**
10. sixty-three	**63**
11. 6 hundreds 2 tens 8 ones	**628**
12. 700 + 40 + 9	**749**

20

Writing Number Words

Number words for the teens:
eleven twelve thirteen fourteen fifteen sixteen seventeen eighteen nineteen

Number words for the tens:
twenty thirty forty fifty sixty seventy eighty ninety

The number word for 285 is **two hundred eighty-five**.

1. Write the number word.

a) 121   **one hundred twenty-one**

b) 572   **five hundred seventy-two**

c) 415   **four hundred fifteen**

d) 268   **two hundred sixty-eight**

e) 923   **nine hundred twenty-three**

2. Write the number word.

a) There are **twelve** (12) months in one year.

b) There are **fifty-two** (52) weeks in a year.

c) There are **three hundred sixty-five** (365) days in a year.

d) Some months of the year have **thirty** (30) days. Other months have **thirty-one** (31) days.

e) There are **twenty-four** (24) hours in a day.

f) There are **sixty** (60) minutes in one hour.

21

Number Roundup

To round to the nearest tens place, look at the ones digit.
If the ones digit has a 0, 1, 2, 3, or 4, round **down**.
If the ones digit has a 5, 6, 7, 8, or 9, round **up**.

To round to the nearest hundreds place, look at the tens digit.
If the tens digit has a 0, 1, 2, 3, or 4, round **down**.
If the tens digit has a 5, 6, 7, 8, or 9, round **up**.

Round each number.

	Number	Round to nearest 10	Round to nearest 100
1.	553	550	600
2.	201	200	200
3.	845	850	800
4.	397	400	400
5.	172	170	200
6.	664	660	700
7.	489	490	500
8.	736	740	700
9.	953	950	1,000
10.	888	890	900

22

Ordinal Numbers

An **ordinal number** describes the numerical position of an object in a rank or sequential order.

1. Write the ordinals. Hint: Use the **bold** part to help you.

first **1st** second **2nd** third **3rd**

fourth **4th** fifth **5th** sixth **6th** seventh **7th**

eighth **8th** ninth **9th** tenth **10th**

2. What is a) the first letter in the alphabet? **a**
   b) the 6th letter in the word "snowboard"? **o**
   c) the second letter in the word "ballet"? **a**
   d) the 10th letter in the alphabet? **j**
   e) the fourth letter in the word "Canada"? **a**

3. Some students had a contest to find out whose paper airplane flew the farthest.
   a) Helen came in seventh. Who came in first? **Chris**
   b) Who came in fifth? **Jason**
   c) In which position was Lisa? **third**
   d) In which position was Paul? **sixth**
   e) Jess came in **second**
   f) Who came in 4th? **Mandy**

Chris   Jess   Lisa   Mandy   Jason   Paul   Helen

23

Adding or Subtracting

You can find the sum of two numbers by counting on.
14 + 5 = 19   Count: 14, 15, 16, 17, 18, 19

You can find the difference between two numbers by counting back.
29 – 4 = 25   Count: 29, 28, 27, 26, 25

Use the number line to help find the sum or difference.

0 1 2 3 4 5 6 7 8 9 10 11 12 13 14 15 16 17 18 19 20 21 22 23 24 25 26 27 28 29 30

19 + 3 = **22**	14 + 2 = **16**	30 – 5 = **25**
23 – 5 = **18**	20 + 9 = **29**	28 + 2 = **30**
18 – 3 = **15**	16 – 8 = **8**	22 + 6 = **28**
23 + 5 = **28**	28 – 5 = **23**	20 – 1 = **19**
11 + 7 = **18**	18 + 7 = **25**	18 – 4 = **14**
30 – 9 = **21**	4 + 26 = **29**	22 – 7 = **15**

24

Adding Tens

Think of an addition fact to add tens.

Find 40 + 20.

Think 4 + 2 = 6.
4 tens + 2 tens = 6 tens
40 + 20 = 60

1. Use an addition fact to help you add tens.

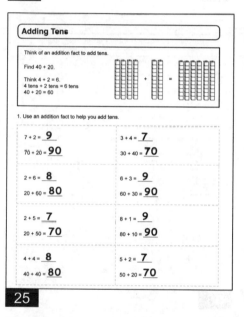

7 + 2 = **9**
70 + 20 = **90**

3 + 4 = **7**
30 + 40 = **70**

2 + 6 = **8**
20 + 60 = **80**

6 + 3 = **9**
60 + 30 = **90**

2 + 5 = **7**
20 + 50 = **70**

8 + 1 = **9**
80 + 10 = **90**

4 + 4 = **8**
40 + 40 = **80**

5 + 2 = **7**
50 + 20 = **70**

25

Three-Digit Addition Without Regrouping

Line up the ones, tens, and hundreds.	First add the ones.	Next add the tens.	Then add the hundreds.

hundreds	tens	ones
2	2	3
+ 3	4	5
		8

hundreds	tens	ones
2	2	3
+ 3	4	5
	6	8

hundreds	tens	ones
2	2	3
+ 3	4	5
5	6	8

1. Use a hundreds, tens, and ones chart to help you add. Shade the ones column yellow. Shade the tens column orange. Shade the hundreds column green.

```
  624      423      662      223      845
+ 231    + 515    + 327    + 762    + 134
  855      938      989      985      979

  146      346      459      284      723
+ 550    + 412    + 220    + 311    +  13
  696      758      679      595      736

  124      331      513      761      914
+ 733    + 426    + 314    + 137    +  34
  857      757      827      898      948

  492      612      356      130      153
+ 305    + 342    + 113    + 613    + 540
  797      954      469      743      693
```

26

Three-Digit Addition Without Regrouping (continued)

2. Use the hundreds, tens, and ones chart to add. Shade the ones column yellow. Shade the tens column orange. Shade the hundreds column green.

```
  455      735      166      246      570
+  14    + 132    + 502    + 323    + 325
  469      867      668      569      895

  314      543      377      432      317
+ 341    + 222    + 202    + 243    + 532
  655      765      579      675      849

  235      713      132      254      264
+ 113    + 222    + 713    + 444    + 313
  348      935      845      698      577

  342      111      581      623      350
+ 332    + 163    + 412    + 136    + 225
  674      274      993      759      575

  712      213      400      824      421
+ 246    + 534    + 215    + 133    + 116
  958      747      615      957      537
```

27

Three-Digit Addition with Regrouping

Line up the ones, tens, and hundreds.
Add the ones.
Then add the tens.

If there are more than 9 ones,
trade 10 tens for 1 hundred.
Regroup in the hundreds column.
Write the tens.
Add the hundreds.

hundreds	tens	ones
1	3	6
+ 2	9	3
6	2	9

Trade 10 tens from 120 for 1 hundred.
Regroup by writing 1 in the hundreds column.

1. Use a hundreds, tens, and ones chart to help you add. Shade the ones column yellow. Shade the tens column orange. Shade the hundreds column green.

```
  567      242      185      454      173
+ 352    + 497    + 571    + 290    + 183
  919      739      756      744      356

  222      366      574      439      696
+ 195    + 441    + 271    + 180    + 172
  417      807      845      619      868

  783      344      193      272      436
+ 185    + 582    + 193    + 352    + 392
  968      926      386      624      828
```

28

Three-Digit Addition with Regrouping (continued)

2. Use the hundreds, tens, and ones chart to add. Hint: If there are more than 9 ones, trade 10 ones for 1 ten. Regroup in the tens column.

```
  239      378      464      547      735
+ 412    + 219    + 418    + 117    + 225
  651      597      882      664      960

  524      236      342      519      513
+ 338    +  26    + 229    + 264    + 338
  862      262      571      783      851

  445      335      829      359      627
+ 419    + 148    +  19    + 431    + 226
  864      483      848      790      853
```

3. Add. Regroup in the tens column and the hundreds column.

```
  488      695      269      355      282
+  23    + 128    + 166    + 257    + 138
  511      823      435      612      420
```

29

Subtracting Tens

Think of a subtraction fact to subtract tens.

Find 40 – 20.
Think 4 – 2 = 2.
4 tens – 2 tens = 2 tens

40 – 20 = 20

4 tens
2 tens

1. Use a subtraction fact to help you subtract tens.

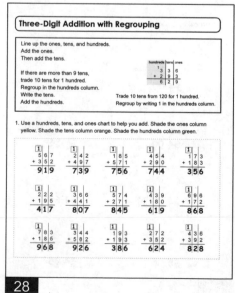

7 – 4 = **3**
70 – 40 = **30**

9 – 8 = **1**
90 – 80 = **10**

8 – 4 = **4**
80 – 40 = **40**

8 – 5 = **3**
80 – 50 = **30**

8 – 7 = **1**
80 – 70 = **10**

6 – 2 = **4**
60 – 20 = **40**

9 – 3 = **6**
90 – 30 = **60**

3 – 2 = **1**
30 – 20 = **10**

30

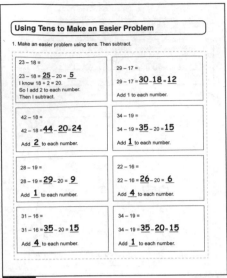

Using Tens to Make an Easier Problem

1. Make an easier problem using tens. Then subtract.

23 – 18 =
23 – 18 = **25** – 20 = **5**
I know 18 + 2 = 20.
So I add 2 to each number.
Then I subtract.

29 – 17 =
29 – 17 = **30** – **18** = **12**
Add 1 to each number.

42 – 18 =
42 – 18 = **44** – **20** = **24**
Add **2** to each number.

34 – 19 =
34 – 19 = **35** – **20** = **15**
Add **1** to each number.

28 – 19 =
28 – 19 = **29** – 20 = **9**
Add **1** to each number.

22 – 16 =
22 – 16 = **26** – 20 = **6**
Add **4** to each number.

31 – 16 =
31 – 16 = **35** – 20 = **15**
Add **4** to each number.

34 – 19 =
34 – 19 = **35** – **20** = **15**
Add **1** to each number.

`31`

Three-Digit Subtraction Without Regrouping

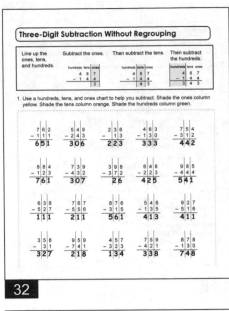

Line up the ones, tens, and hundreds.	Subtract the ones.	Then subtract the tens.	Then subtract the hundreds.

1. Use a hundreds, tens, and ones chart to help you subtract. Shade the ones column yellow. Shade the tens column orange. Shade the hundreds column green.

```
  762      549      236      463      754
- 111    - 243    -  13    - 130    - 312
  651      306      223      333      442

  884      739      398      648      985
- 123    - 432    - 372    - 223    - 444
  761      307       26      425      541

  638      767      876      548      927
- 527    - 556    - 315    - 135    - 516
  111      211      561      413      411

  358      959      457      759      878
- 031    - 741    - 323    - 421    - 130
  327      218      134      338      748
```

`32`

Three-Digit Subtraction Without Regrouping (continued)

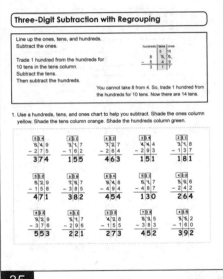

Line up the ones, tens, and hundreds.	Subtract the ones.	Then subtract the tens.	Then subtract the hundreds.

2. Use the hundreds, tens, and ones chart to subtract.

```
  579      662      747      244      864
- 236    - 120    - 134    - 114    - 431
  343      542      613      130      433

  276      474      337      195      993
-  40    - 232    - 320    -  60    -  73
  236      242       17      135      920

  555      783      618      648      574
- 110    - 341    - 312    - 623    - 450
  445      442      306       25      124

  888      266      457      948      238
- 234    - 125    - 343    - 225    - 122
  654      141      114      723      116
```

`33`

Taking Apart to Make Tens for Subtraction

31 – ⑥ = 31 + **4** – 6 + **4** = 35 – 10 = 25
6 + 4 = 10   So, add 4 to each number.

1. Make an easier problem using 10. Then subtract.

a) 15 – 9 = 15 + **1** – 9 + **1** = **16** – **10** = **6**   Add **1** to each number.

b) 19 – 7 = **19** + **1** – **7** + **1** = **20** – **8** = **12**   Add **1** to each number.

c) 16 – 8 = **16** + **2** – **8** + **2** = **18** – **10** = **8**   Add **2** to each number.

d) 27 – 9 = **27** + **1** – **9** + **1** = **28** – **10** = **18**   Add **1** to each number.

e) 54 – 6 = **54** + **4** – **6** + **4** = **58** – **10** = **48**   Add **4** to each number.

f) 61 – 5 = **61** + **5** – **5** + **5** = **66** – **10** = **56**   Add **5** to each number.

g) 42 – 7 = **42** + **3** – **7** + **3** = **45** – **10** = **35**   Add **3** to each number.

`34`

Three-Digit Subtraction with Regrouping

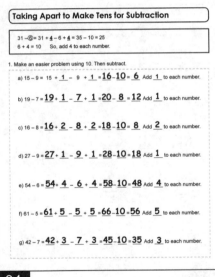

Line up the ones, tens, and hundreds.
Subtract the ones.

Trade 1 hundred from the hundreds for 10 tens in the tens column.
Subtract the tens.
Then subtract the hundreds.

You cannot take 8 from 4. So, trade 1 hundred from the hundreds for 10 tens. Now there are 14 tens.

1. Use a hundreds, tens, and ones chart to help you subtract. Shade the ones column yellow. Shade the tens column orange. Shade the hundreds column green.

```
  654      217      627      344      318
- 275    - 162    - 264    - 293    - 137
  374      155      463      151      181

  829      787      848      617      596
- 158    - 385    - 494    - 487    - 242
  471      382      454      130      264

  829      517      428      835      552
- 376    - 147    - 155    - 383    - 160
  553      221      273      452      392
```

`35`

Three-Digit Subtraction with Regrouping (continued)

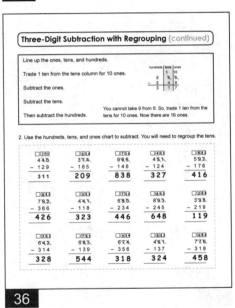

Line up the ones, tens, and hundreds.

Trade 1 ten from the tens column for 10 ones.

Subtract the ones.

Subtract the tens.

Then subtract the hundreds.

You cannot take 9 from 6. So, trade 1 ten from the tens for 10 ones. Now there are 16 ones.

2. Use the hundreds, tens, and ones chart to subtract. You will need to regroup the tens.

```
  440      374      986      451      592
- 129    - 165    - 148    - 124    - 176
  311      209      838      327      416

  792      441      680      893      338
- 366    - 118    - 234    - 245    - 219
  426      323      446      648      119

  642      683      674      461      776
- 314    - 139    - 356    - 137    - 318
  328      544      318      324      458
```

`36`

Word Problems

Decide if you need to add or subtract. Underline any words that help you decide. Circle Add or Subtract. Then solve the problem. Show your work.

1. Donisha had 234 stamps. She gave 29 to Dave. How many stamps does she have left?
   Add / **(Subtract)**
   There are **205** stamps left.

2. Ms. Stevens's class had 136 tulip bulbs to plant. The class planted 79 tulip bulbs. How many tulip bulbs still need to be planted?
   Add / **(Subtract)**
   There are **57** tulip bulbs to be planted.

3. Ethan scored 560 points on a computer game. Ben scored 298 points. How many points did they score altogether?
   (Add) / Subtract
   They scored **858** points altogether.

4. Jose collected 400 stamps. Jill collected 187 stamps. How many stamps did they collect altogether?
   (Add) / Subtract
   There are **587** stamps in all.

`37`

Counting with Coins

Find the value of the coins. Remember to use the $ sign.

1. **$4**

2. **$5.50**

3. **$3.75**

4. **$5.25**

5. **$4.50**

`38`

Estimating Coins

Estimates might vary. Sample answers:

1. Estimate $ **$4.00**   Count $ **$3.60**

2. Estimate $ **$4.00**   Count $ **$4.55**

3. Estimate $ **$3.00**   Count $ **$3.60**

4. Estimate $ **$5.00**   Count $ **$4.95**

`39`

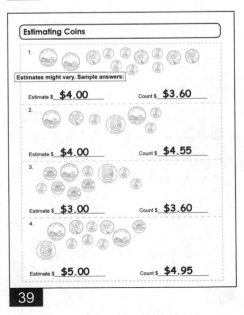

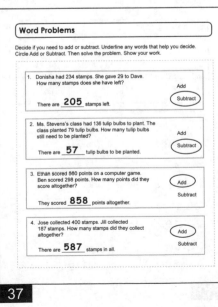

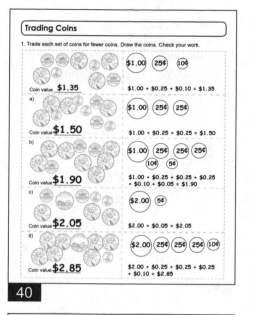

Trading Coins

1. Trade each set of coins for fewer coins. Draw the coins. Check your work.

Coin value **$1.35** → $1.00 25¢ 10¢
$1.00 + $0.25 + $0.10 = $1.35

a) Coin value **$1.50** → $1.00 25¢ 25¢
$1.00 + $0.25 + $0.25 = $1.50

b) Coin value **$1.90** → $1.00 25¢ 25¢ 25¢ 10¢ 5¢
$1.00 + $0.25 + $0.25 + $0.25 + $0.10 + $0.05 = $1.90

c) Coin value **$2.05** → $2.00 5¢
$2.00 + $0.05 = $2.05

d) Coin value **$2.85** → $2.00 25¢ 25¢ 25¢ 10¢
$2.00 + $0.25 + $0.25 + $0.25 + $0.10 = $2.85

40

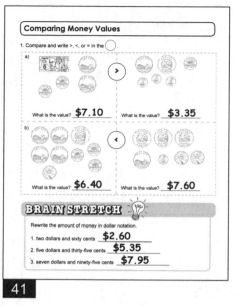

Comparing Money Values

1. Compare and write >, <, or = in the ◯.

a) (>)
What is the value? **$7.10**   What is the value? **$3.35**

b) (<)
What is the value? **$6.40**   What is the value? **$7.60**

BRAIN STRETCH

Rewrite the amount of money in dollar notation.

1. two dollars and sixty cents **$2.60**
2. five dollars and thirty-five cents **$5.35**
3. seven dollars and ninety-five cents **$7.95**

41

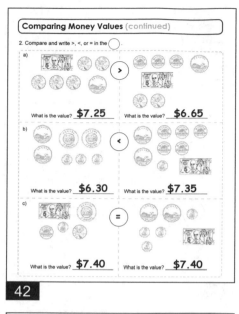

Comparing Money Values (continued)

2. Compare and write >, <, or = in the ◯.

a) (>)
What is the value? **$7.25**   What is the value? **$6.65**

b) (<)
What is the value? **$6.30**   What is the value? **$7.35**

c) (=)
What is the value? **$7.40**   What is the value? **$7.40**

42

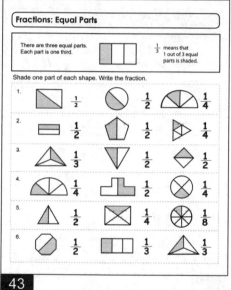

Fractions: Equal Parts

There are three equal parts.
Each part is one third.

$\frac{1}{3}$ means that 1 out of 3 equal parts is shaded.

Shade one part of each shape. Write the fraction.

1. $\frac{1}{2}$ $\frac{1}{2}$ $\frac{1}{4}$
2. $\frac{1}{2}$ $\frac{1}{2}$ $\frac{1}{4}$
3. $\frac{1}{3}$ $\frac{1}{2}$ $\frac{1}{2}$
4. $\frac{1}{4}$ $\frac{1}{2}$ $\frac{1}{4}$
5. $\frac{1}{2}$ $\frac{1}{4}$ $\frac{1}{8}$
6. $\frac{1}{2}$ $\frac{1}{3}$ $\frac{1}{3}$

43

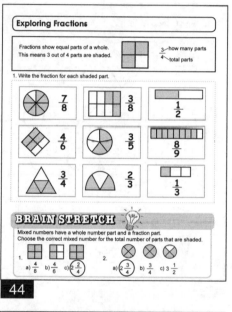

Exploring Fractions

Fractions show equal parts of a whole.
This means 3 out of 4 parts are shaded.

3 — how many parts
4 — total parts

1. Write the fraction for each shaded part.

$\frac{7}{8}$ $\frac{3}{8}$ $\frac{1}{2}$

$\frac{4}{6}$ $\frac{3}{5}$ $\frac{8}{9}$

$\frac{3}{4}$ $\frac{2}{3}$ $\frac{1}{3}$

BRAIN STRETCH

Mixed numbers have a whole number part and a fraction part.
Choose the correct mixed number for the total number of parts that are shaded.

1. a) $\frac{4}{8}$ b) $\frac{4}{6}$ c) $\left(2\frac{2}{4}\right)$
2. a) $\left(2\frac{3}{4}\right)$ b) $\frac{3}{4}$ c) $3\frac{1}{2}$

44

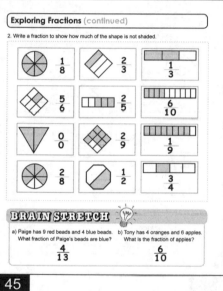

Exploring Fractions (continued)

2. Write a fraction to show how much of the shape is not shaded.

$\frac{1}{8}$ $\frac{2}{3}$ $\frac{1}{3}$

$\frac{5}{6}$ $\frac{2}{5}$ $\frac{6}{10}$

$\frac{0}{8}$ $\frac{2}{9}$ $\frac{1}{9}$

$\frac{2}{8}$ $\frac{1}{2}$ $\frac{3}{4}$

BRAIN STRETCH

a) Paige has 9 red beads and 4 blue beads. What fraction of Paige's beads are blue? $\frac{4}{13}$

b) Tony has 4 oranges and 6 apples. What is the fraction of apples? $\frac{6}{10}$

45

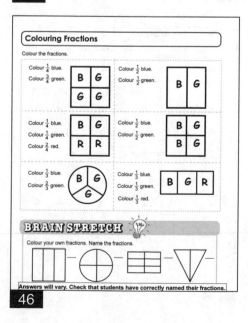

Colouring Fractions

Colour the fractions.

Colour $\frac{1}{4}$ blue.
Colour $\frac{3}{4}$ green.
| B | G |
| G | G |

Colour $\frac{1}{2}$ blue.
Colour $\frac{1}{2}$ green.
| B | G |

Colour $\frac{1}{4}$ blue.
Colour $\frac{1}{4}$ green.
Colour $\frac{2}{4}$ red.
| B | G |
| R | R |

Colour $\frac{1}{2}$ blue.
Colour $\frac{1}{2}$ green.
| B | G |

Colour $\frac{1}{3}$ blue.
Colour $\frac{2}{3}$ green.
(B G G circle)

Colour $\frac{1}{3}$ blue.
Colour $\frac{1}{3}$ green.
Colour $\frac{1}{3}$ red.
| B | G | R |

BRAIN STRETCH

Colour your own fractions. Name the fractions.

Answers will vary. Check that students have correctly named their fractions.

46

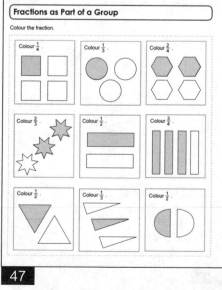

Fractions as Part of a Group

Colour the fraction.

Colour $\frac{1}{4}$.   Colour $\frac{1}{3}$.   Colour $\frac{2}{4}$.

Colour $\frac{2}{3}$.   Colour $\frac{1}{2}$.   Colour $\frac{3}{4}$.

Colour $\frac{1}{2}$.   Colour $\frac{1}{3}$.   Colour $\frac{1}{2}$.

47

Fraction Problems

Draw a picture and show the answer as a fraction.

1. Nathan cut a pizza into 4 equal slices. He ate 2 slices. What fraction of the pizza did he eat? $\frac{2}{4}$

2. Sue counts 8 mailboxes on her street. 3 are red. What fraction of the mailboxes are red? $\frac{3}{8}$

3. Mia has 3 books from the library. She read 1 of them. What fraction of the books did she read? $\frac{1}{3}$

4. Rachel has 8 crackers for a snack. She put cheese on 2 of them. What fraction of the crackers have cheese? $\frac{2}{8}$

5. Douglas has 2 cookies. He gave 1 cookie to his friend. What fraction of the cookies did he give away? $\frac{1}{2}$

48

Panel 49

Exploring Polygons

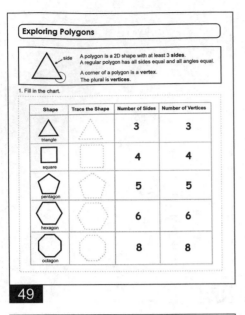

A polygon is a 2D shape with at least 3 **sides**.
A regular polygon has all sides equal and all angles equal.
A corner of a polygon is a **vertex**.
The plural is **vertices**.

1. Fill in the chart.

Shape	Trace the Shape	Number of Sides	Number of Vertices
triangle		3	3
square		4	4
pentagon		5	5
hexagon		6	6
octagon		8	8

Panel 50

Exploring Polygons (continued)

2. Fill in the chart.

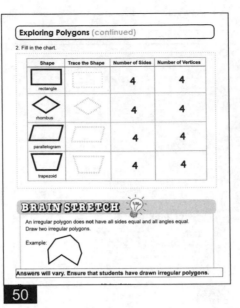

Shape	Trace the Shape	Number of Sides	Number of Vertices
rectangle		4	4
rhombus		4	4
parallelogram		4	4
trapezoid		4	4

BRAIN STRETCH

An irregular polygon does **not** have all sides equal and all angles equal.
Draw two irregular polygons.

Example:

Answers will vary. Ensure that students have drawn irregular polygons.

Panel 51

Exploring Polygons (continued)

3. Put an X if it is **not** a polygon. Colour the regular polygons blue.
Colour the irregular polygons red.

Irregular polygons are 2, 4, 9, 12, and 13. Regular polygons are 6, 7, and 15.

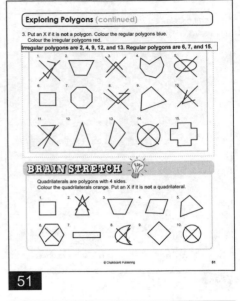

BRAIN STRETCH

Quadrilaterals are polygons with 4 sides.
Colour the quadrilaterals orange. Put an X if it is **not** a quadrilateral.

51

Panel 52

2D Shapes

Use the words below to write the correct name for each 2D shape.

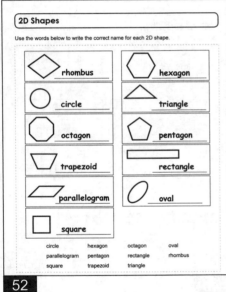

rhombus
circle
octagon
trapezoid
parallelogram
square

hexagon
triangle
pentagon
rectangle
oval

circle | hexagon | octagon | oval
parallelogram | pentagon | rectangle | rhombus
square | trapezoid | triangle

Panel 53

Sorting 2D Shapes

1. Read the rule. Colour the shapes that follow the rule.

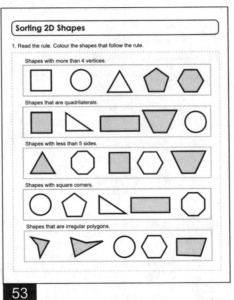

Shapes with more than 4 vertices.

Shapes that are quadrilaterals.

Shapes with less than 5 sides.

Shapes with square corners.

Shapes that are irregular polygons.

Panel 54

Sorting 2D Shapes (continued)

2. Sort the 2D shapes into groups.

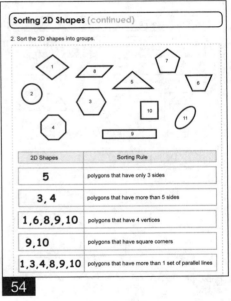

2D Shapes	Sorting Rule
5	polygons that have only 3 sides
3, 4	polygons that have more than 5 sides
1,6,8,9,10	polygons that have 4 vertices
9,10	polygons that have square corners
1,3,4,8,9,10	polygons that have more than 1 set of parallel lines

Panel 55

Identifying 3D Objects

1. Match the 3D object with its name.

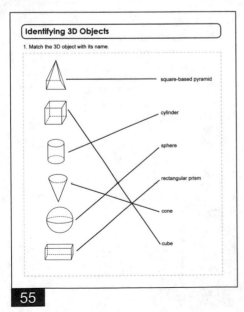

square-based pyramid
cylinder
sphere
rectangular prism
cone
cube

Panel 56

Identifying 3D Objects (continued)

2. Match the name of the 3D object with an item it looks like. Circle the answer.

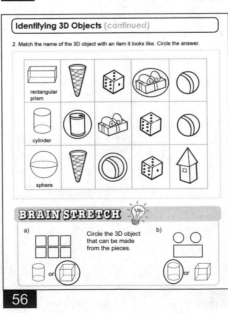

rectangular prism

cylinder

sphere

BRAIN STRETCH

a) Circle the 3D object that can be made from the pieces.

b)

Panel 57

Attributes of 3D Objects

1. Use the words below to complete the chart. A **face** is any **flat side** of a shape. An **edge** is where **any two flat faces** of a shape meet.

cone | cylinder | square-based pyramid | cube
triangular prism | sphere | rectangular prism

	3D Object	Name of 3D Object	Number of Faces	Number of Edges	Number of Vertices
A.		sphere	0	0	0
B.		cylinder	2	0	0
C.		rectangular prism	6	12	8
D.		cone	1	0	0
E.		triangular prism	5	9	6
F.		cube	6	12	8
G.		square-based pyramid	5	8	5

Attributes of 3D Objects (continued)

2. Circle the name of the 3D object that you can make from the pieces.

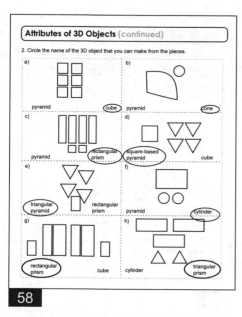

a) pyramid (cube)
b) pyramid (cone)
c) pyramid (rectangular prism)
d) (square-based pyramid) cube
e) (triangular pyramid) rectangular prism
f) pyramid (cylinder)
g) (rectangular prism) cube
h) cylinder (triangular prism)

58

Exploring Symmetry

A line of symmetry divides a figure into 2 parts that are the exact same size and shape. Some figures have more than 1 line of symmetry. Some figures have no lines of symmetry.

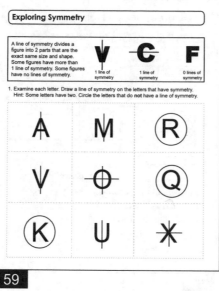

V — 1 line of symmetry
C — 1 line of symmetry
F — 0 lines of symmetry

1. Examine each letter. Draw a line of symmetry on the letters that have symmetry. Hint: Some letters have two. Circle the letters that do **not** have a line of symmetry.

A M (R)
V (Q)
K U *

59

Symmetry Fun

1. Each figure is half of a symmetrical shape. Complete each figure by using the dashed line of symmetry.

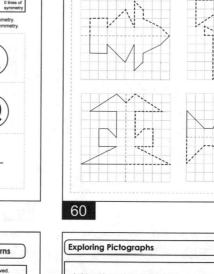

60

Congruent Figures

Congruent figures have the exact same shape and size.

1. Draw a line connecting the congruent shapes.

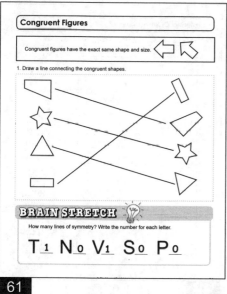

BRAIN STRETCH

How many lines of symmetry? Write the number for each letter.

T _1_ N _0_ V _1_ S _0_ P _0_

61

Exploring Transformations: Flips, Slides, and Turns

A transformation is a change in position. Look at how each figure has moved.

This is a flip.   This is a slide.   This is a turn.

1. How is the figure moved? Write slide, flip, or turn to tell about the move.

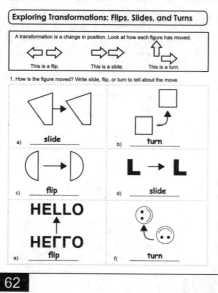

a) slide
b) turn
c) flip
d) slide
e) HELLO → HEΓΓO — flip
f) turn

62

Exploring Pictographs

A **pictograph** uses pictures to show data.
A key explains what quantity the picture represents.

Key ⬛ = 2

Here are the results of a survey about favourite drinks.
Use the pictograph to answer the questions about the results.

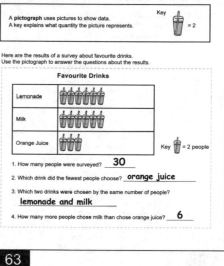

Favourite Drinks

Lemonade	🥤🥤🥤🥤🥤🥤
Milk	🥤🥤🥤🥤🥤🥤
Orange Juice	🥤🥤🥤

Key 🥤 = 2 people

1. How many people were surveyed? __30__
2. Which drink did the fewest people choose? __orange juice__
3. Which two drinks were chosen by the same number of people? __lemonade and milk__
4. How many more people chose milk than chose orange juice? __6__

63

Exploring Bar Graphs

A **bar graph** uses bars to show data. Each bar shows a quantity or number. The bars can go up or across the graph.

The two grade 3 classes made a bar graph about favourite activities at recess. Answer the questions.

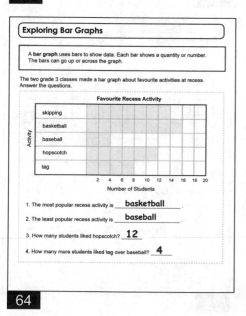

Favourite Recess Activity

(Activity: skipping, basketball, baseball, hopscotch, tag)
(Number of Students: 2 4 6 8 10 12 14 16 18 20)

1. The most popular recess activity is __basketball__.
2. The least popular recess activity is __baseball__.
3. How many students liked hopscotch? __12__
4. How many more students liked tag over baseball? __4__

64

Favourite Pizza Toppings Bar Graph

Ms. Gibson's grade 3 class did a survey about students' favourite pizza toppings.

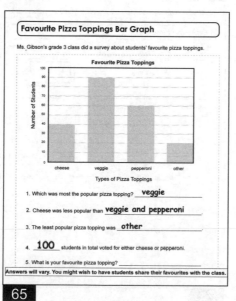

Favourite Pizza Toppings

(Number of Students vs Types of Pizza Toppings: cheese, veggie, pepperoni, other)

1. Which was most the popular pizza topping? __veggie__
2. Cheese was less popular than __veggie and pepperoni__
3. The least popular pizza topping was __other__
4. __100__ students in total voted for either cheese or pepperoni.
5. What is your favourite pizza topping?

Answers will vary. You might wish to have students share their favourites with the class.

65

Reading Tally Charts

A **tally** chart records counting in groups up to 5.
Each tally or mark represents 1. | = 1   ЖЖ = 5

Answer the questions using the information in the tally charts.

Tally Chart: Favourite Cookie

Cookie	Frequency
Chocolate Chip	ЖЖ III
Double Chocolate	ЖЖ ЖЖ III
Animal Crackers	II
Oatmeal Raisin	ЖЖ ЖЖ II
Vanilla Cream	ЖЖ IIII

1. Did more people choose chocolate chip or animal crackers? __chocolate chip__
2. How many people chose double chocolate? __13__
3. What is the least popular cookie? __animal crackers__
4. How many people voted? __44__

Tally Chart: Favourite Activity

Activity	Frequency
Playing Outside	ЖЖ ЖЖ III
Video Games	ЖЖ ЖЖ III
Reading	ЖЖ II
Watching TV	ЖЖ IIII
Computer	ЖЖ IIII
Listening to Music	ЖЖ ЖЖ III

1. How many people chose playing on the computer? __9__
2. How many people chose video games? __13__
3. How many people chose reading or watching TV? __16__

66

Favourite Snacks Bar Graph

Use the data from the tally chart to complete the bar graph. Answer the questions.

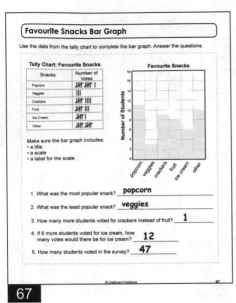

Tally Chart: Favourite Snacks

Snacks	Number of Votes
Popcorn	JHT JHT JHT I
Veggies	III
Crackers	JHT IIII
Fruit	JHT III
Ice Cream	JHT I
Other	JHT JHT

Make sure the bar graph includes:
• a title
• a scale
• a label for the scale

1. What was the most popular snack? **popcorn**
2. What was the least popular snack? **veggies**
3. How many more students voted for crackers instead of fruit? **1**
4. If 6 more students voted for ice cream, how many votes would there be for ice cream? **12**
5. How many students voted in the survey? **47**

67

Favourite Meal Survey Tally Chart

Iris surveyed her classmates about their favourite meal. Use the information from Iris's survey to complete the tally chart.

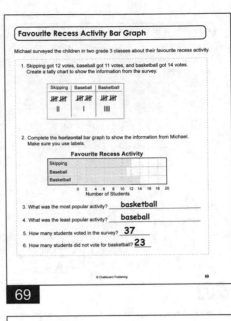

Favourite Meal Survey

Name	Meal
Roy	breakfast
Jody	dinner
Patrick	dinner
Timothy	dinner
Rachel	breakfast
Sam	dinner
Kara	lunch
Kendra	breakfast
Jeremy	breakfast
Lisa	lunch
Juan	dinner

Favourite Meal

Meal	Tally
breakfast	IIII
lunch	II
dinner	JHT

1. Which meal did the most students choose? **dinner**
2. Which meal did the fewest students choose? **lunch**
3. How many students did Iris survey? **11**
4. How many students chose breakfast? **4**
5. How many students chose lunch? **2**
6. How many students chose dinner? **5**

68

Favourite Recess Activity Bar Graph

Michael surveyed the children in two grade 3 classes about their favourite recess activity.

1. Skipping got 12 votes, baseball got 11 votes, and basketball got 14 votes. Create a tally chart to show the information from the survey.

Skipping	Baseball	Basketball
JHT JHT II	JHT JHT I	JHT JHT IIII

2. Complete the **horizontal** bar graph to show the information from Michael. Make sure you use labels.

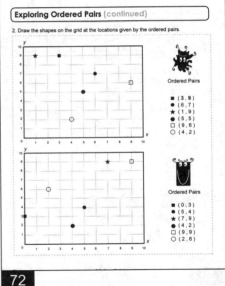

Favourite Recess Activity

3. What was the most popular activity? **basketball**
4. What was the least popular activity? **baseball**
5. How many students voted in the survey? **37**
6. How many students did not vote for basketball? **23**

69

Favourite Vegetable Bar Graph

Mr. Clark's class took a survey of favourite vegetables. Use the data from the frequency table to complete the bar graph.

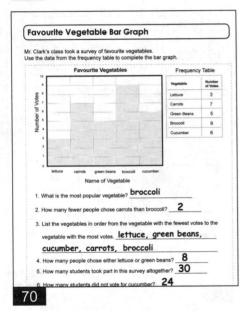

Favourite Vegetables

Frequency Table

Vegetable	Number of Votes
Lettuce	3
Carrots	7
Green Beans	5
Broccoli	9
Cucumber	6

1. What is the most popular vegetable? **broccoli**
2. How many fewer people chose carrots than broccoli? **2**
3. List the vegetables in order from the vegetable with the fewest votes to the vegetable with the most votes. **lettuce, green beans, cucumber, carrots, broccoli**
4. How many people chose either lettuce or green beans? **8**
5. How many students took part in this survey altogether? **30**
6. How many students did not vote for cucumber? **24**

70

Exploring Ordered Pairs

An ordered pair describes a point on a grid. It has 2 numbers in a certain order.
• The first number tells how many units to count to the right.
• The second number tells how many units to count up.
Hint: Always start counting at the bottom left corner, at 0.

Count 1 unit right. Go up 3 units. The ordered pair is (1, 3).

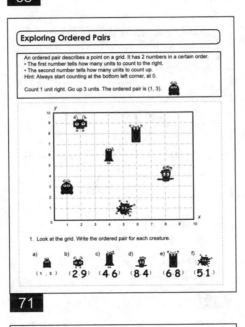

1. Look at the grid. Write the ordered pair for each creature.

a) **(1 , 3)** b) **(2 , 9)** c) **(4 , 6)** d) **(8 , 4)** e) **(6 , 8)** f) **(5 , 1)**

71

Exploring Ordered Pairs (continued)

2. Draw the shapes on the grid at the locations given by the ordered pairs.

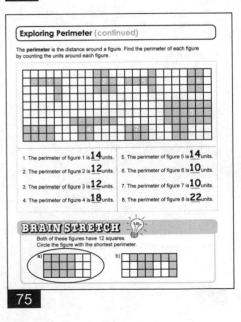

Ordered Pairs

■ (3 , 9)
● (6 , 7)
★ (1 , 9)
● (5 , 5)
□ (9 , 6)
○ (4 , 2)

Ordered Pairs

■ (0 , 3)
● (5 , 4)
★ (7 , 9)
● (4 , 2)
□ (9 , 9)
○ (2 , 6)

72

Exploring Measurement

1. What would be the best unit of measure for the following?

kilometres   metres   centimetres

The length of a classroom.	**metres**
The width of a stamp.	**centimetres**
The distance between two cities.	**kilometres**
The length of a book.	**centimetres**
The length of your arm.	**centimetres**
The length of a bus.	**metres**

2. Match the best measurement tool to measure each of the following:

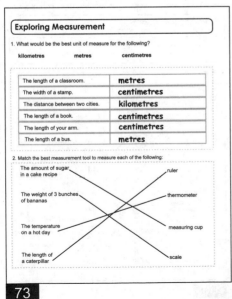

The amount of sugar in a cake recipe — ruler
The weight of 3 bunches of bananas — thermometer
The temperature on a hot day — measuring cup
The length of a caterpillar — scale

73

Exploring Perimeter

The perimeter is the distance around a figure. To find the distance around, add the sides.

5 m + 5 m + 3 m + 3 m = 16 m

The distance around is 16 metres.

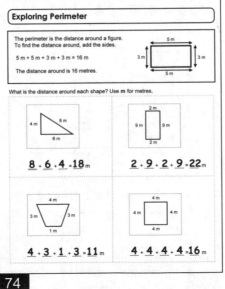

What is the distance around each shape? Use **m** for metres.

8 + **6** + **4** = **18** m

2 + **9** + **2** + **9** = **22** m

4 + **3** + **1** + **3** = **11** m

4 + **4** + **4** + **4** = **16** m

74

Exploring Perimeter (continued)

The **perimeter** is the distance around a figure. Find the perimeter of each figure by counting the units around each figure.

1. The perimeter of figure 1 is **14** units.
2. The perimeter of figure 2 is **12** units.
3. The perimeter of figure 3 is **12** units.
4. The perimeter of figure 4 is **18** units.
5. The perimeter of figure 5 is **14** units.
6. The perimeter of figure 6 is **10** units.
7. The perimeter of figure 7 is **10** units.
8. The perimeter of figure 8 is **22** units.

BRAIN STRETCH

Both of these figures have 12 squares. Circle the figure with the shortest perimeter.

a) (circled) b)

75

© Chalkboard Publishing

Exploring Area

Area is the number of units that covers a figure.

1 square ▢ = 1 unit.

Count the number of square units that cover the figure.
The area of the shaded shape is 7 square units.

1. Find the area of each shaded figure.

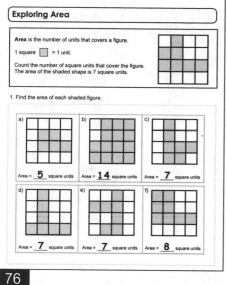

a) Area = **5** square units
b) Area = **14** square units
c) Area = **7** square units

d) Area = **7** square units
e) Area = **7** square units
f) Area = **8** square units

76

Exploring Area (continued)

2. Find the area of each figure.

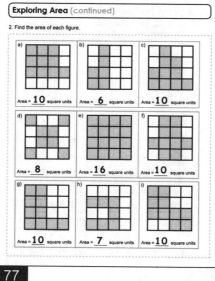

a) Area = **10** square units
b) Area = **6** square units
c) Area = **10** square units

d) Area = **8** square units
e) Area = **16** square units
f) Area = **10** square units

g) Area = **10** square units
h) Area = **7** square units
i) Area = **10** square units

77

Exploring Length

Write the length in centimetres. Write **cm** for centimetres.

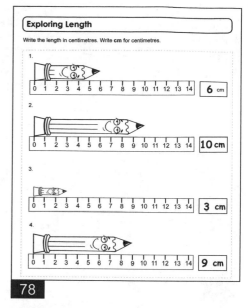

1. **6** cm

2. **10** cm

3. **3** cm

4. **9** cm

78

What Time Is It?

A clock shows time using numbers and hands.
The face of a clock shows the numbers 1 to 12.
It takes 5 minutes for the long minute hand to
move from one number to the next.

The time is 2:40.

Write the time.

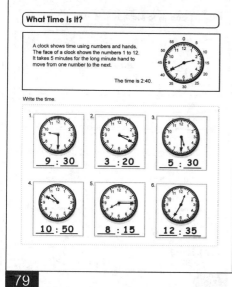

1. **9 : 30**
2. **3 : 20**
3. **5 : 30**

4. **10 : 50**
5. **8 : 15**
6. **12 : 35**

79

Drawing the Hands

Draw the two hands on the clock to show the time.
Highlight the hour hand blue. Highlight the minute hand red.

Remember, the short hand tells the hour.
The long hand tells the minutes.

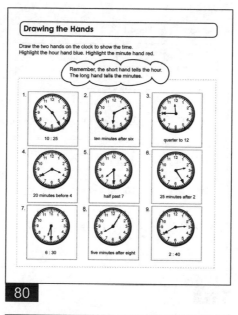

1. 10 : 25
2. ten minutes after six
3. quarter to 12

4. 20 minutes before 4
5. half past 7
6. 25 minutes after 2

7. 6 : 30
8. five minutes after eight
9. 2 : 40

80

Elapsed Time

Elapsed time is the amount of time that has
passed from the start of a time period to
the end of a time period.

25 minutes have elapsed.

Write the start time and the end time.

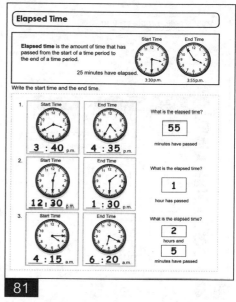

1. Start Time **3 : 40** p.m. End Time **4 : 35** p.m.
   What is the elapsed time?
   55 minutes have passed

2. Start Time **12 : 30** p.m. End Time **1 : 30** p.m.
   What is the elapsed time?
   1 hour has passed

3. Start Time **4 : 15** a.m. End Time **6 : 20** a.m.
   What is the elapsed time?
   2 hours and
   5 minutes have passed

81

Basketball Fun

1. Michael practises basketball for 25 minutes every
   night. Complete the chart to show his start and end time
   for each practice.

   a.m. refers to before noon
   p.m. refers to after noon

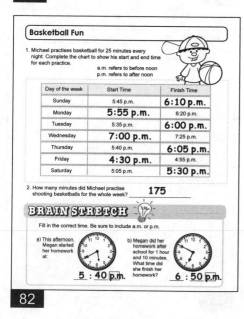

Day of the week	Start Time	Finish Time
Sunday	5:45 p.m.	**6:10 p.m.**
Monday	**5:55 p.m.**	6:20 p.m.
Tuesday	5:35 p.m.	**6:00 p.m.**
Wednesday	**7:00 p.m.**	7:25 p.m.
Thursday	5:40 p.m.	**6:05 p.m.**
Friday	**4:30 p.m.**	4:55 p.m.
Saturday	5:05 p.m.	**5:30 p.m.**

2. How many minutes did Michael practise
   shooting basketballs for the whole week? **175**

BRAIN STRETCH

Fill in the correct time. Be sure to include a.m. or p.m.

a) This afternoon,
Megan started
her homework
at:
5 : 40 p.m.

b) Megan did her
homework after
school for 1 hour
and 10 minutes.
What time did
she finish her
homework?
6 : 50 p.m.

82

Reading a Calendar

Use the calendar to answer the questions.

March						
S	M	T	W	T	F	S
			1	2	3	4	5
6	7	8	9	10	11	12
13	14	15	16	17	18	19
20	21	22	23	24	25	26
27	28	29	30	31		

June						
S	M	T	W	T	F	S
			1	2	3	4
5	6	7	8	9	10	11
12	13	14	15	16	17	18
19	20	21	22	23	24	25
26	27	28	29	30		

1. What day of the week is March 14?
   Monday

2. How many Wednesdays are there
   in March?
   5

3. What is the date 1 week and
   2 days after March 3?
   March 12

4. What is the date of the first Tuesday
   in March?
   1

5. On what day of the week will the
   next month begin?
   Friday

6. What is the date of the
   third Monday?
   21

1. Katherine will have a birthday
   party in 4 days. Today is June 6.
   What is the date of her birthday?
   June 10

2. Alexander's karate tournament is
   in two weeks. Today is June 11.
   What date is the karate
   tournament?
   June 25

3. Jane will go on a trip in 6 days.
   Today is June 10. On what date
   will Jane go on her trip?
   June 16

4. Carolyn leaves for New York
   in 9 days. Today is June 17.
   What date will she leave?
   June 26

83

Addition and Multiplication

1. Write the addition sentence and the multiplication sentence.

Look at the groups of 3.

Addition Sentence:
There are 3 equal groups.
3 + 3 + 3 = **9**
addends   sum

Multiplication Sentence:
There are 3 equal groups.
3 × 3 = **9**
factors   product

7 + 7 = **14**   2 × 7 = **14**

10 + 10 = **20**   2 × 10 = **20**

3 + 3 + 3 + 3 + 3 = **15**   5 × 3 = **15**

2 + 2 + 2 + 2 + 2 + 2 + 2 + 2 + 2 = **18**   9 × 2 = **18**

7 + 7 + 7 = **21**   3 × 7 = **21**

6 + 6 = **12**   2 × 6 = **12**

84

Multiplying by Skip Counting

When you multiply two numbers, the answer is called the **product**.
Skip count on the number line to multiply. Write the product.

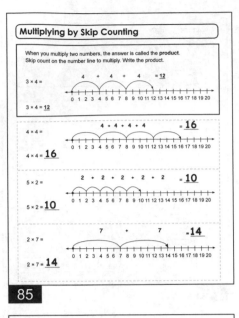

$3 \times 4 =$ _4 + 4 + 4_ = **12**

$3 \times 4 =$ **12**

$4 \times 4 =$ _4 + 4 + 4 + 4_ = **16**

$4 \times 4 =$ **16**

$5 \times 2 =$ _2 + 2 + 2 + 2 + 2_ = **10**

$5 \times 2 =$ **10**

$2 \times 7 =$ _7 + 7_ = **14**

$2 \times 7 =$ **14**

Using Arrays to Help You Multiply

In the **array**, there are 2 rows with 4 blocks in each row.
Skip count by 4s to count the blocks.
The multiplication statement is $2 \times 4 = 8$.

$2 \times 4 = 8$
factors → product

1. Write a multiplication statement for each array.

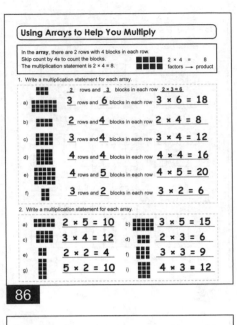

_2_ rows and _3_ blocks in each row   **2 × 3 = 6**

a) _3_ rows and _6_ blocks in each row   **3 × 6 = 18**

b) _2_ rows and _4_ blocks in each row   **2 × 4 = 8**

c) _3_ rows and _4_ blocks in each row   **3 × 4 = 12**

d) _4_ rows and _4_ blocks in each row   **4 × 4 = 16**

e) _4_ rows and _5_ blocks in each row   **4 × 5 = 20**

f) _3_ rows and _2_ blocks in each row   **3 × 2 = 6**

2. Write a multiplication statement for each array.

a) **2 × 5 = 10**   b) **3 × 5 = 15**
c) **3 × 4 = 12**   d) **2 × 3 = 6**
e) **2 × 2 = 4**   f) **3 × 3 = 9**
g) **5 × 2 = 10**   i) **4 × 3 = 12**

Using Arrays to Help You Multiply (continued)

3. Draw an array for each. Write the multiplication statement.

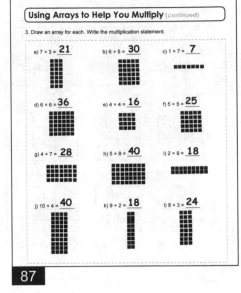

a) 7 × 3 = **21**   b) 6 × 5 = **30**   c) 1 × 7 = **7**

d) 6 × 6 = **36**   e) 4 × 4 = **16**   f) 5 × 5 = **25**

g) 4 × 7 = **28**   h) 5 × 8 = **40**   i) 2 × 9 = **18**

j) 10 × 4 = **40**   k) 9 × 2 = **18**   l) 8 × 3 = **24**

Multiplication Table for 0 to 10

The numbers on the dark borders are the **factors**.
The numbers inside the table are the **products**.
Try it! To find the product of 6 × 9, for example, find 6 in the left border and put your finger on it.
Then find 9 in the top border and put your finger on it.
Slide your finger on the 6 to the right across the row.
Slide your finger on the 9 down the column. Keep sliding your fingers until they meet.
The number in the square where the row and column meet is the product of the two numbers.
So 6 × 9 = 54.

×	0	1	2	3	4	5	6	7	8	9	10
0	0	0	0	0	0	0	0	0	0	0	0
1	0	1	2	3	4	5	6	7	8	9	10
2	0	2	4	6	8	10	12	14	16	18	20
3	0	3	6	9	12	15	18	21	24	27	30
4	0	4	8	12	16	20	24	28	32	36	40
5	0	5	10	15	20	25	30	35	40	45	50
6	0	6	12	18	24	30	36	42	48	54	60
7	0	7	14	21	28	35	42	49	56	63	70
8	0	8	16	24	32	40	48	56	64	72	80
9	0	9	18	27	36	45	54	63	72	81	90
10	0	10	20	30	40	50	60	70	80	90	100

Multiplying by 0 and 1

The product is always the same as the greater factor when any number is multiplied by 1.

For example, $10 \times 1 = 10$.

The product is always 0 when any factor is multiplied by 0.

For example, $0 \times 4 = 0$.

Multiply.

$0 \times 12 =$ **0** $11 \times 1 =$ **11** $8 \times 0 =$ **0** $1 \times 3 =$ **3**

$5 \times 1 =$ **5** $7 \times 1 =$ **7** $3 \times 0 =$ **0** $0 \times 6 =$ **0**

$6 \times 1 =$ **6** $10 \times 1 =$ **10** $1 \times 8 =$ **8** $1 \times 0 =$ **0**

$0 \times 7 =$ **0** $4 \times 1 =$ **4** $9 \times 1 =$ **9** $0 \times 10 =$ **0**

Using Doubles to Multiply

What is the double of 13?

$13 = 10 + 3$
The double of 10 is 20.
The double of 3 is 6.
$20 + 6 = 26$
The double of 13 is 26.

1. Draw a model. Then double the number.

What is the double of 14?

$14 = 10 + $ **4**
The double of 10 is **20**
The double of **4** is **8**
$20 + 8 = 28$
The double of 14 is **28**

What is the double of 11?

$11 = 10 + $ **1**
The double of 10 is **20**
The double of **1** is **2**
$20 + 2 = 22$
The double of 11 is **22**

What is the double of 19?

$19 = 10 + $ **9**
The double of 10 is **20**
The double of **9** is **18**
$20 + 18 = 38$
The double of 19 is **38**

What is the double of 23?

$23 = 20 + $ **3**
The double of 20 is **40**
The double of **3** is **6**
$40 + 6 = 46$
The double of 23 is **46**

Using Doubles to Multiply (continued)

If you know 2 times a number, you can double it to find 4 times the number.

For 4 × 6, you know:
$2 \times 6 = 12$
$2 \times 6 = 12$
Double the 2 to get 4. Double the product to get 24.
$4 \times 6 = 24$

So, $4 \times 6 = 24$.

2. Use doubles to multiply. Draw an array to help you multiply.

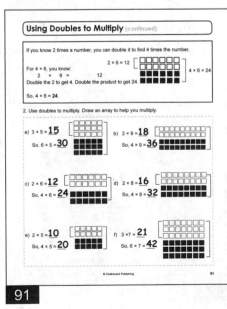

a) 3 × 5 = **15**   So, 6 × 5 = **30**

b) 2 × 9 = **18**   So, 4 × 9 = **36**

c) 2 × 6 = **12**   So, 4 × 6 = **24**

d) 2 × 8 = **16**   So, 4 × 8 = **32**

e) 2 × 5 = **10**   So, 4 × 5 = **20**

f) 3 × 7 = **21**   So, 6 × 7 = **42**

Matching Multiplication to Addition: Facts for 2

Complete the multiplication facts for 2. Use a multiplication table to help you. Then write the sums. Underline each matching sum and product. Use a different colour for each pair.

$1 \times 2 =$ **2** $2 + 2 + 2 + 2 + 2 + 2 + 2 + 2 =$ **16**

$2 \times 2 =$ **4** $2 + 0 =$ **2**

$3 \times 2 =$ **6** $2 + 2 + 2 + 2 + 2 + 2 + 2 + 2 + 2 =$ **18**

$4 \times 2 =$ **8** $2 + 2 + 2 + 2 + 2 + 2 + 2 =$ **14**

$5 \times 2 =$ **10** $2 + 2 + 2 =$ **6**

$6 \times 2 =$ **12** $2 + 2 + 2 + 2 + 2 =$ **10**

$7 \times 2 =$ **14** $2 + 2 + 2 + 2 =$ **8**

$8 \times 2 =$ **16** $2 + 2 + 2 + 2 + 2 + 2 =$ **12**

$9 \times 2 =$ **18** $2 + 2 + 2 + 2 + 2 + 2 + 2 + 2 + 2 + 2 =$ **20**

$10 \times 2 =$ **20** $2 + 2 =$ **4**

Two Times Table

1. Multiply. Colour the odd products yellow. Colour the even products pink.

10 ×2	8 ×2	1 ×2	3 ×2	7 ×2
20	**16**	**2**	**6**	**14**

6 ×2	5 ×2	2 ×2	4 ×2	9 ×2
12	**10**	**4**	**8**	**18**

2. Multiply.

$2 \times $ **8** $= 16$ $2 \times $ **1** $= 2$ $2 \times $ **2** $= 4$ $2 \times $ **10** $= 20$

$2 \times $ **4** $= 8$ $2 \times $ **7** $= 14$ $2 \times $ **6** $= 12$ $2 \times $ **9** $= 18$

$2 \times $ **3** $= 6$ $2 \times $ **5** $= 10$

Tip for Multiplying by 2
Double the number!
For example, 4 × 2.
Think: 4 + 4 = 8. So, 4 × 2 = 8.
Remember to practise skip counting by 2s!

Matching Multiplication to Addition: Facts for 3 (page 94)

Complete the multiplication facts for 3. Use a multiplication table to help you. Then write the sums. Underline each matching sum and product. Use a different colour for each pair.

1 × 3 = 3	3 + 3 + 3 + 3 + 3 + 3 + 3 + 3 + 3 = 27
2 × 3 = 6	3 + 3 = 6
3 × 3 = 9	3 + 3 + 3 + 3 = 12
4 × 3 = 12	3 + 3 + 3 + 3 + 3 = 15
5 × 3 = 15	3 + 0 = 3
6 × 3 = 18	3 + 3 + 3 + 3 + 3 + 3 = 18
7 × 3 = 21	3 + 3 + 3 + 3 + 3 + 3 + 3 + 3 = 24
8 × 3 = 24	3 + 3 + 3 + 3 + 3 + 3 + 3 + 3 + 3 + 3 = 30
9 × 3 = 27	3 + 3 + 3 = 9
10 × 3 = 30	3 + 3 + 3 + 3 + 3 + 3 + 3 = 21

94

Three Times Table (page 95)

1. Multiply. Colour the odd products yellow. Colour the even products pink.

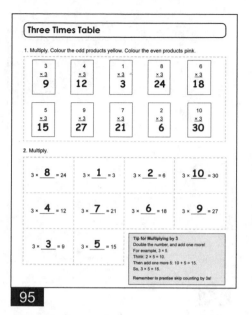

3 ×3 = 9	4 ×3 = 12	1 ×3 = 3	8 ×3 = 24	6 ×3 = 18
5 ×3 = 15	9 ×3 = 27	7 ×3 = 21	2 ×3 = 6	10 ×3 = 30

2. Multiply.

3 × 8 = 24	3 × 1 = 3	3 × 2 = 6	3 × 10 = 30
3 × 4 = 12	3 × 7 = 21	3 × 6 = 18	3 × 9 = 27
3 × 3 = 9	3 × 5 = 15		

Tip for Multiplying by 3
Double the number, and add one more!
For example, 3 × 5.
Think: 2 × 5 = 10.
Then add one more 5: 10 + 5 = 15.
So, 3 × 5 = 15.
Remember to practise skip counting by 3s!

95

Double, Plus One More Group (page 96)

3 × 4 =

2 × 4 = 8
3 × 4 = 12

The double of 4 is 8.
One group is 4.
8 + 4 = 12
So, 3 × 4 = 12.

1. Find the double. Then add one more group.

3 × 7 =

2 × 7 = 14
3 × 7 = 21

The double of 7 is 14.
One group is 7.
14 + 7 = 21
So, 3 × 7 = 21.

3 × 5 =

2 × 5 = 10
3 × 5 = 15

The double of 5 is 10.
One group is 5.
10 + 5 = 15
So, 3 × 5 = 15.

3 × 6 =

2 × 6 = 12
3 × 6 = 18

The double of 6 is 12.
One group is 6.
12 + 6 = 18
So, 3 × 6 = 18.

96

Matching Multiplication to Addition: Facts for 4 (page 97)

Complete the multiplication facts for 4. Use a multiplication table to help you. Then write the sums. Underline each matching sum and product. Use a different colour for each pair.

1 × 4 = 4	4 + 4 + 4 + 4 + 4 + 4 + 4 = 28
2 × 4 = 8	4 + 4 + 4 + 4 + 4 + 4 + 4 + 4 + 4 + 4 = 40
3 × 4 = 12	4 + 4 = 8
4 × 4 = 16	4 + 4 + 4 + 4 + 4 + 4 = 24
5 × 4 = 20	4 + 4 + 4 + 4 = 16
6 × 4 = 24	4 + 4 + 4 = 12
7 × 4 = 28	4 + 4 + 4 + 4 + 4 + 4 + 4 + 4 + 4 = 36
8 × 4 = 32	4 + 4 + 4 + 4 + 4 = 20
9 × 4 = 36	4 + 4 + 4 + 4 + 4 + 4 + 4 + 4 = 32
10 × 4 = 40	4 + 0 = 4

97

Four Times Table (page 98)

1. Multiply. Colour the odd products yellow. Colour the even products pink.

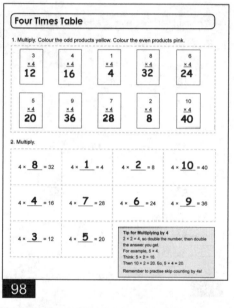

3 ×4 = 12	4 ×4 = 16	1 ×4 = 4	8 ×4 = 32	6 ×4 = 24
5 ×4 = 20	9 ×4 = 36	7 ×4 = 28	2 ×4 = 8	10 ×4 = 40

2. Multiply.

4 × 8 = 32	4 × 1 = 4	4 × 2 = 8	4 × 10 = 40
4 × 4 = 16	4 × 7 = 28	4 × 6 = 24	4 × 9 = 36
4 × 3 = 12	4 × 5 = 20		

Tip for Multiplying by 4
2 × 2 = 4, so double the number, then double the answer you get.
For example, 5 × 4.
Think: 5 × 2 = 10.
Then 10 × 2 = 20. So, 5 × 4 = 20.
Remember to practise skip counting by 4s!

98

Matching Multiplication to Addition: Facts for 5 (page 99)

Complete the multiplication facts for 5. Use a multiplication table to help you. Then write the sums. Underline each matching sum and product. Use a different colour for each pair.

1 × 5 = 5	5 + 5 + 5 + 5 = 20
2 × 5 = 10	5 + 5 = 10
3 × 5 = 15	5 + 5 + 5 + 5 + 5 + 5 = 30
4 × 5 = 20	5 + 5 + 5 = 15
5 × 5 = 25	5 + 5 + 5 + 5 + 5 + 5 + 5 + 5 + 5 = 45
6 × 5 = 30	5 + 5 + 5 + 5 + 5 = 25
7 × 5 = 35	5 + 5 + 5 + 5 + 5 + 5 + 5 + 5 + 5 + 5 = 50
8 × 5 = 40	5 + 5 + 5 + 5 + 5 + 5 + 5 + 5 = 40
9 × 5 = 45	5 + 0 = 5
10 × 5 = 50	5 + 5 + 5 + 5 + 5 + 5 + 5 = 35

99

Five Times Table (page 100)

1. Multiply. Colour the odd products yellow. Colour the even products pink.

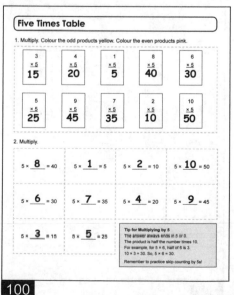

3 ×5 = 15	4 ×5 = 20	1 ×5 = 5	8 ×5 = 40	6 ×5 = 30
5 ×5 = 25	9 ×5 = 45	7 ×5 = 35	2 ×5 = 10	10 ×5 = 50

2. Multiply.

5 × 8 = 40	5 × 1 = 5	5 × 2 = 10	5 × 10 = 50
5 × 6 = 30	5 × 7 = 35	5 × 4 = 20	5 × 9 = 45
5 × 3 = 15	5 × 5 = 25		

Tip for Multiplying by 5
The answer always ends in 5 or 0.
The product is half the number times 10.
For example, for 5 × 6, half of 6 is 3.
10 × 3 = 30. So, 5 × 6 = 30.
Remember to practice skip counting by 5s!

100

Matching Multiplication to Addition: Facts for 6 (page 101)

Complete the multiplication facts for 6. Use a multiplication table to help you. Then write the sums. Underline each matching sum and product. Use a different colour for each pair.

1 × 6 = 6	6 + 6 = 12
2 × 6 = 12	6 + 0 = 6
3 × 6 = 18	6 + 6 + 6 + 6 + 6 + 6 + 6 + 6 = 48
4 × 6 = 24	6 + 6 + 6 = 18
5 × 6 = 30	6 + 6 + 6 + 6 + 6 + 6 + 6 = 42
6 × 6 = 36	6 + 6 + 6 + 6 + 6 + 6 = 36
7 × 6 = 42	6 + 6 + 6 + 6 + 6 + 6 + 6 + 6 + 6 + 6 = 60
8 × 6 = 48	6 + 6 + 6 + 6 + 6 + 6 + 6 + 6 + 6 = 54
9 × 6 = 54	6 + 6 + 6 + 6 + 6 = 30
10 × 6 = 60	6 + 6 + 6 + 6 = 24

101

Six Times Table (page 102)

1. Multiply. Colour the odd products yellow. Colour the even products pink.

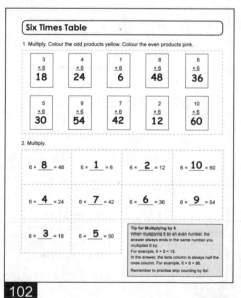

3 ×6 = 18	4 ×6 = 24	1 ×6 = 6	8 ×6 = 48	6 ×6 = 36
5 ×6 = 30	9 ×6 = 54	7 ×6 = 42	2 ×6 = 12	10 ×6 = 60

2. Multiply.

6 × 8 = 48	6 × 1 = 6	6 × 2 = 12	6 × 10 = 60
6 × 4 = 24	6 × 7 = 42	6 × 6 = 36	6 × 9 = 54
6 × 3 = 18	6 × 5 = 30		

Tip for Multiplying by 6
When multiplying 6 by an even number, the answer always ends in the same number you multiplied by 6.
For example, 6 × 2 = 12.
In the answer, the tens column is always half the ones column. For example, 6 × 6 = 36.
Remember to practise skip counting by 6s!

102

Matching Multiplication to Addition: Facts for 7

Complete the multiplication facts for 7. Use a multiplication table to help you. Then write the sums. Underline each matching sum and product. Use a different colour for each pair.

1 × 7 = **7**   7+7+7+7+7+7+7+7+7 = **63**

2 × 7 = **14**   7+7+7 = **21**

3 × 7 = **21**   7+7+7+7+7+7+7+7 = **56**

4 × 7 = **28**   7+7+7+7+7+7 = **42**

5 × 7 = **35**   7+7+7+7+7 = **35**

6 × 7 = **42**   7+0 = **7**

7 × 7 = **49**   7+7+7+7+7+7+7+7+7+7 = **70**

8 × 7 = **56**   7+7+7+7 = **28**

9 × 7 = **63**   7+7+7+7+7+7+7 = **49**

10 × 7 = **70**   7+7 = **14**

103

Seven Times Table

1. Multiply. Colour the odd products yellow. Colour the even products pink.

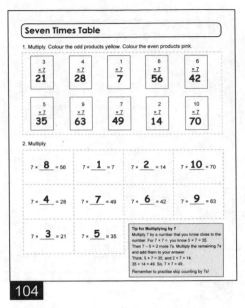

| 3 ×7 **21** | 4 ×7 **28** | 1 ×7 **7** | 8 ×7 **56** | 6 ×7 **42** |
| 5 ×7 **35** | 9 ×7 **63** | 7 ×7 **49** | 2 ×7 **14** | 10 ×7 **70** |

2. Multiply.

7 × **8** = 56   7 × **1** = 7   7 × **2** = 14   7 × **10** = 70

7 × **4** = 28   7 × **7** = 49   7 × **6** = 42   7 × **9** = 63

7 × **3** = 21   7 × **5** = 35

Tip for Multiplying by 7
Multiply 7 by a number that you know close to the number. For 7 × 7 =, you know 5 × 7 = 35.
Then 7 – 5 = 2 more 7s. Multiply the remaining 7s and add them to your answer.
Think: 5 × 7 = 35, and 2 × 7 = 14.
35 + 14 = 49. So, 7 × 7 = 49.

Remember to practise skip counting by 7s!

104

Matching Multiplication to Addition: Facts for 8

Complete the multiplication facts for 8. Use a multiplication table to help you. Then write the sums. Underline each matching sum and product. Use a different colour for each pair.

1 × 8 = **8**   8+8+8+8+8 = **40**

2 × 8 = **16**   8+8+8+8+8+8 = **48**

3 × 8 = **24**   8+8+8 = **24**

4 × 8 = **32**   8+8+8+8 = **32**

5 × 8 = **40**   8+8+8+8+8+8+8 = **56**

6 × 8 = **48**   8+8+8+8+8+8+8+8 = **64**

7 × 8 = **56**   8+8 = **16**

8 × 8 = **64**   8+8+8+8+8+8+8+8+8+8 = **80**

9 × 8 = **72**   8+8+8+8+8+8+8+8+8 = **72**

10 × 8 = **80**   8+0 = **8**

105

Eight Times Table

1. Multiply. Colour the odd products yellow. Colour the even products pink.

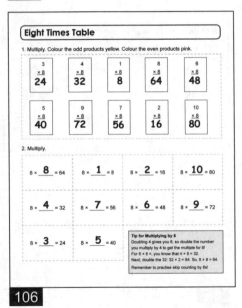

| 3 ×8 **24** | 4 ×8 **32** | 1 ×8 **8** | 8 ×8 **64** | 6 ×8 **48** |
| 5 ×8 **40** | 9 ×8 **72** | 7 ×8 **56** | 2 ×8 **16** | 10 ×8 **80** |

2. Multiply.

8 × **8** = 64   8 × **1** = 8   8 × **2** = 16   8 × **10** = 80

8 × **4** = 32   8 × **7** = 56   8 × **6** = 48   8 × **9** = 72

8 × **3** = 24   8 × **5** = 40

Tip for Multiplying by 8
Doubling 4 gives you 8, so double the number you multiply by 4 to get the multiple for 8!
For 8 × 8 =, you know that 4 × 8 = 32.
Next, double the 32: 32 × 2 = 64. So, 8 × 8 = 64.
Remember to practise skip counting by 8s!

106

Matching Multiplication to Addition: Facts for 9

Complete the multiplication facts for 9. Use a multiplication table to help you. Then write the sums. Underline each matching sum and product. Use a different colour for each pair.

1 × 9 = **9**   9+9+9+9+9 = **45**

2 × 9 = **18**   9+9 = **18**

3 × 9 = **27**   9+9+9+9+9+9+9 = **63**

4 × 9 = **36**   9+9+9+9+9+9+9+9+9+9 = **90**

5 × 9 = **45**   9+9+9+9 = **36**

6 × 9 = **54**   9+9+9+9+9+9 = **54**

7 × 9 = **63**   9+9+9+9+9+9+9+9+9 = **81**

8 × 9 = **72**   9+0 = **9**

9 × 9 = **81**   9+9+9 = **27**

10 × 9 = **90**   9+9+9+9+9+9+9+9 = **72**

107

Nine Times Table

1. Multiply. Colour the odd products yellow. Colour the even products pink.

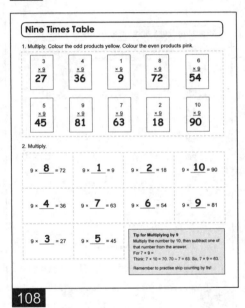

| 3 ×9 **27** | 4 ×9 **36** | 1 ×9 **9** | 8 ×9 **72** | 6 ×9 **54** |
| 5 ×9 **45** | 9 ×9 **81** | 7 ×9 **63** | 2 ×9 **18** | 10 ×9 **90** |

2. Multiply.

9 × **8** = 72   9 × **1** = 9   9 × **2** = 18   9 × **10** = 90

9 × **4** = 36   9 × **7** = 63   9 × **6** = 54   9 × **9** = 81

9 × **3** = 27   9 × **5** = 45

Tip for Multiplying by 9
Multiply the number by 10, then subtract one of that number from the answer.
For 7 × 9 =
Think: 7 × 10 = 70. 70 – 7 = 63. So, 7 × 9 = 63.
Remember to practise skip counting by 9s!

108

Using Patterns to Multiply by 9

| Use the ten facts to help you multiply by 9. 9 × 6 = | You know that 10 × 6 is one more group of sixes than 9 × 6. 10 × 6 = 60 Now take away one group of 6. 60 – 6 = 54 So, 9 × 6 = 54. |

1. Use the ten facts to help you multiply by 9. Show your work.

a) 9 × 7 =   10 × 7 = 70
             70 – 7 = 63
             So, 9 × 7 = 63.

b) 9 × 3 =   10 × 3 = 30
             30 – 3 = 27
             So, 9 × 3 = 27.

2. a) Use the pattern in the tens and ones digits to help you learn the nine facts.

1 × 9 = **9**
2 × 9 = **1 8**
3 × 9 = **2 7**
4 × 9 = **3 6**
5 × 9 = **4 5**
6 × 9 = **5 4**
7 × 9 = **6 3**
8 × 9 = **7 2**
9 × 9 = **8 1**
10 × 9 = **9 0**

b) What pattern do you notice about the nine facts?

The tens digit increases by one each time, while the ones digit decreases by one each time.

109

Matching Multiplication to Addition: Facts for 10

Complete the multiplication facts for 10. Use a multiplication table to help you. Then write the sums. Underline each matching sum and product. Use a different colour for each pair.

1 × 10 = **10**   10+10+10+10+10+10+10+10+10 = **90**

2 × 10 = **20**   10+10 = **20**

3 × 10 = **30**   10+10+10+10+10+10+10+10+10+10 = **100**

4 × 10 = **40**   10+10+10+10+10+10+10+10 = **80**

5 × 10 = **50**   10+10+10 = **30**

6 × 10 = **60**   10+10+10+10+10 = **50**

7 × 10 = **70**   10+10+10+10+10+10+10 = **70**

8 × 10 = **80**   10+10+10+10 = **40**

9 × 10 = **90**   10+10+10+10+10+10 = **60**

10 × 10 = **100**   10+0 = **10**

110

Ten Times Table

1. Multiply. Colour the odd products yellow. Colour the even products pink.

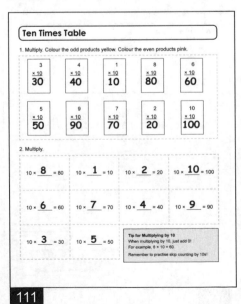

| 3 ×10 **30** | 4 ×10 **40** | 1 ×10 **10** | 8 ×10 **80** | 6 ×10 **60** |
| 5 ×10 **50** | 9 ×10 **90** | 7 ×10 **70** | 2 ×10 **20** | 10 ×10 **100** |

2. Multiply.

10 × **8** = 80   10 × **1** = 10   10 × **2** = 20   10 × **10** = 100

10 × **6** = 60   10 × **7** = 70   10 × **4** = 40   10 × **9** = 90

10 × **3** = 30   10 × **5** = 50

Tip for Multiplying by 10
When multiplying by 10, just add 0!
For example: 6 × 10 = 60.
Remember to practise skip counting by 10s!

111

346

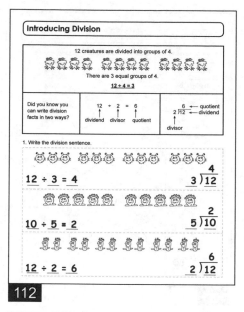

Introducing Division

12 creatures are divided into groups of 4.

There are 3 equal groups of 4.

$$12 \div 4 = 3$$

Did you know you can write division facts in two ways?

$$\underset{\text{dividend}}{12} \div \underset{\text{divisor}}{2} = \underset{\text{quotient}}{6}$$

$$2\overset{6 \;\leftarrow \text{quotient}}{\overline{)12}} \;\leftarrow \text{dividend}$$

divisor

1. Write the division sentence.

$$\underline{12} \div \underline{3} = \underline{4} \qquad 3\overline{)12}^{\,4}$$

$$\underline{10} \div \underline{5} = \underline{2} \qquad 5\overline{)10}^{\,2}$$

$$\underline{12} \div \underline{2} = \underline{6} \qquad 2\overline{)12}^{\,6}$$

112

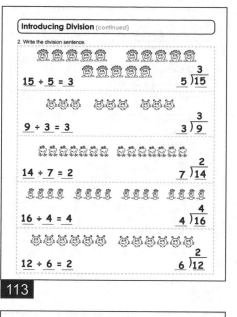

Introducing Division (continued)

2. Write the division sentence.

$$\underline{15} \div \underline{5} = \underline{3} \qquad 5\overline{)15}^{\,3}$$

$$\underline{9} \div \underline{3} = \underline{3} \qquad 3\overline{)9}^{\,3}$$

$$\underline{14} \div \underline{7} = \underline{2} \qquad 7\overline{)14}^{\,2}$$

$$\underline{16} \div \underline{4} = \underline{4} \qquad 4\overline{)16}^{\,4}$$

$$\underline{12} \div \underline{6} = \underline{2} \qquad 6\overline{)12}^{\,2}$$

113

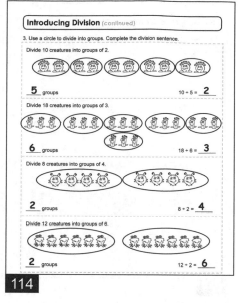

Introducing Division (continued)

3. Use a circle to divide into groups. Complete the division sentence.

Divide 10 creatures into groups of 2.

5 groups $\qquad 10 \div 5 = \mathbf{2}$

Divide 18 creatures into groups of 3.

6 groups $\qquad 18 \div 6 = \mathbf{3}$

Divide 8 creatures into groups of 4.

2 groups $\qquad 8 \div 2 = \mathbf{4}$

Divide 12 creatures into groups of 6.

2 groups $\qquad 12 \div 2 = \mathbf{6}$

114

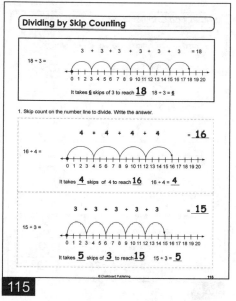

Dividing by Skip Counting

$$3 + 3 + 3 + 3 + 3 + 3 = 18$$

$$18 \div 3 =$$

0 1 2 3 4 5 6 7 8 9 10 11 12 13 14 15 16 17 18 19 20

It takes **6** skips of 3 to reach **18** $18 \div 3 = \mathbf{6}$

1. Skip count on the number line to divide. Write the answer.

$$4 + 4 + 4 + 4 = \mathbf{16}$$

$$16 \div 4 =$$

0 1 2 3 4 5 6 7 8 9 10 11 12 13 14 15 16 17 18 19 20

It takes **4** skips of 4 to reach **16** $16 \div 4 = \mathbf{4}$

$$3 + 3 + 3 + 3 + 3 = \mathbf{15}$$

$$15 \div 3 =$$

0 1 2 3 4 5 6 7 8 9 10 11 12 13 14 15 16 17 18 19 20

It takes **5** skips of **3** to reach **15** $15 \div 3 = \mathbf{5}$

© Chalkboard Publishing 115

115

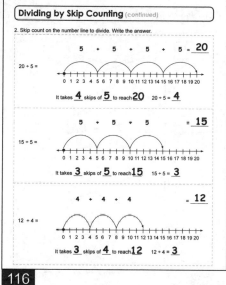

Dividing by Skip Counting (continued)

2. Skip count on the number line to divide. Write the answer.

$$5 + 5 + 5 + 5 = \mathbf{20}$$

$$20 \div 5 =$$

0 1 2 3 4 5 6 7 8 9 10 11 12 13 14 15 16 17 18 19 20

It takes **4** skips of **5** to reach **20** $20 \div 5 = \mathbf{4}$

$$5 + 5 + 5 = \mathbf{15}$$

$$15 \div 5 =$$

0 1 2 3 4 5 6 7 8 9 10 11 12 13 14 15 16 17 18 19 20

It takes **3** skips of **5** to reach **15** $15 \div 5 = \mathbf{3}$

$$4 + 4 + 4 = \mathbf{12}$$

$$12 \div 4 =$$

0 1 2 3 4 5 6 7 8 9 10 11 12 13 14 15 16 17 18 19 20

It takes **3** skips of **4** to reach **12** $12 \div 4 = \mathbf{3}$

116

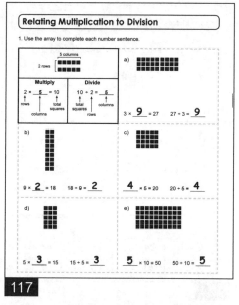

Relating Multiplication to Division

1. Use the array to complete each number sentence.

5 columns

2 rows

Multiply	Divide
$2 \times \mathbf{5} = 10$	$10 \div 2 = \mathbf{5}$
rows columns	total squares columns
total squares	rows

a)

$$3 \times \mathbf{9} = 27 \qquad 27 \div 3 = \mathbf{9}$$

b)

$$9 \times \mathbf{2} = 18 \qquad 18 \div 9 = \mathbf{2}$$

c)

$$4 \times 5 = 20 \qquad 20 \div 5 = \mathbf{4}$$

d)

$$5 \times \mathbf{3} = 15 \qquad 15 \div 5 = \mathbf{3}$$

e)

$$\mathbf{5} \times 10 = 50 \qquad 50 \div 10 = \mathbf{5}$$

117

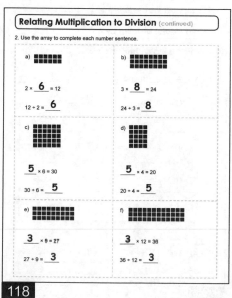

Relating Multiplication to Division (continued)

2. Use the array to complete each number sentence.

a)

$$2 \times \mathbf{6} = 12$$

$$12 \div 2 = \mathbf{6}$$

b)

$$3 \times \mathbf{8} = 24$$

$$24 \div 3 = \mathbf{8}$$

c)

$$\mathbf{5} \times 6 = 30$$

$$30 \div 6 = \mathbf{5}$$

d)

$$\mathbf{5} \times 4 = 20$$

$$20 \div 4 = \mathbf{5}$$

e)

$$\mathbf{3} \times 9 = 27$$

$$27 \div 9 = \mathbf{3}$$

f)

$$\mathbf{3} \times 12 = 36$$

$$36 \div 12 = \mathbf{3}$$

118

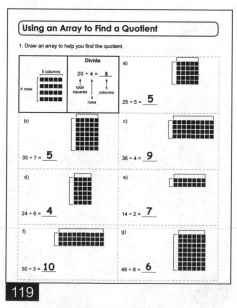

Using an Array to Find a Quotient

1. Draw an array to help you find the quotient.

Divide

5 columns

4 rows

$$20 \div 4 = \mathbf{5}$$

total squares 5 columns

4 rows

a)

$$25 \div 5 = \mathbf{5}$$

b)

$$35 \div 7 = \mathbf{5}$$

c)

$$36 \div 4 = \mathbf{9}$$

d)

$$24 \div 6 = \mathbf{4}$$

e)

$$14 \div 2 = \mathbf{7}$$

f)

$$30 \div 3 = \mathbf{10}$$

g)

$$48 \div 8 = \mathbf{6}$$

119

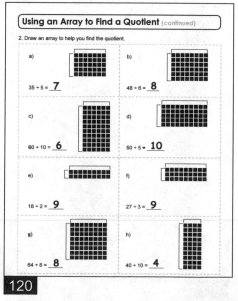

Using an Array to Find a Quotient (continued)

2. Draw an array to help you find the quotient.

a)

$$35 \div 5 = \mathbf{7}$$

b)

$$48 \div 6 = \mathbf{8}$$

c)

$$60 \div 10 = \mathbf{6}$$

d)

$$50 \div 5 = \mathbf{10}$$

e)

$$18 \div 2 = \mathbf{9}$$

f)

$$27 \div 3 = \mathbf{9}$$

g)

$$64 \div 8 = \mathbf{8}$$

h)

$$40 \div 10 = \mathbf{4}$$

120

Relating Multiplication to Division

1. Use the multiplication fact to find the quotient.

a) 10 × 2 = 20
20 ÷ 10 = **2**

b) 7 × 8 = 56
56 ÷ 8 = **7**

c) 4 × 6 = 24
24 ÷ 4 = **6**

d) 10 × 7 = 70
70 ÷ 7 = **10**

e) 3 × 9 = 27
27 ÷ 3 = **9**

f) 8 × 2 = 16
16 ÷ 2 = **8**

g) 9 × 9 = 81
81 ÷ 9 = **9**

h) 10 × 7 = 70
70 ÷ 7 = **10**

i) 8 × 9 = 72
72 ÷ 8 = **9**

j) 5 × 8 = 40
40 ÷ 8 = **5**

k) 9 × 6 = 54
54 ÷ 9 = **6**

l) 6 × 5 = 30
30 ÷ 5 = **6**

121

Using Related Multiplication Facts to Divide by 0 and 1

The quotient is always 1 when any number other than 0 is divided by itself. For example, 5 ÷ 5 = 1. Think of a related multiplication fact. 5 × 1 = 5, so 5 ÷ 5 = 1	The quotient is always the same as the dividend when any number is divided by 1. For example, 8 ÷ 1 = 8. Think of a related multiplication fact. 8 × 1 = 8, so 8 ÷ 1 = 8

The quotient is always 0 when 0 is divided by any number.

For example, 0 ÷ 3 = 0.

Think of a related multiplication fact.

3 × 0 = 0, so 0 ÷ 3 = 0

You cannot divide any number by 0.

Divide.

0 ÷ 2 = **0**	11 ÷ 1 = **11**	9 ÷ 1 = **9**	0 ÷ 1 = **0**
3 ÷ 3 = **1**	0 ÷ 9 = **0**	5 ÷ 1 = **5**	6 ÷ 1 = **6**
0 ÷ 6 = **0**	12 ÷ 12 = **1**	0 ÷ 7 = **0**	8 ÷ 8 = **1**
7 ÷ 7 = **1**	0 ÷ 4 = **0**	10 ÷ 1 = **10**	0 ÷ 8 = **0**

122

Dividing by 2

Match the division sentence with the correct quotient. Hint: Practise skip counting by 2s.

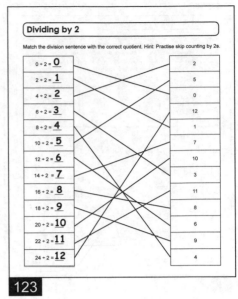

0 ÷ 2 = **0**
2 ÷ 2 = **1**
4 ÷ 2 = **2**
6 ÷ 2 = **3**
8 ÷ 2 = **4**
10 ÷ 2 = **5**
12 ÷ 2 = **6**
14 ÷ 2 = **7**
16 ÷ 2 = **8**
18 ÷ 2 = **9**
20 ÷ 2 = **10**
22 ÷ 2 = **11**
24 ÷ 2 = **12**

2, 5, 0, 12, 1, 7, 10, 3, 11, 8, 6, 9, 4

123

Math Riddle: Dividing by 2

What is a polar bear's favourite food?

I C E   B U R G E R S
4 8 11   1 2 7   0 11 7 6

Watch out! Some letters are not used in the riddle!

1. Find the quotient.

A 18 ÷ 2 = **9**	B 2 ÷ 2 = **1**	C 16 ÷ 2 = **8**
E 22 ÷ 2 = **11**	F 6 ÷ 2 = **3**	G 0 ÷ 2 = **0**
I 8 ÷ 2 = **4**	M 10 ÷ 2 = **5**	N 24 ÷ 2 = **12**
R 14 ÷ 2 = **7**	S 12 ÷ 2 = **6**	U 4 ÷ 2 = **2**

2. Find the missing dividend.

0 ÷ 2 = 0	**24** ÷ 2 = 12	**12** ÷ 2 = 6	**22** ÷ 2 = 11
2 ÷ 2 = 1	**20** ÷ 2 = 10	**16** ÷ 2 = 8	**4** ÷ 2 = 2

124

Dividing by 3

Match the division sentence with the correct quotient. Hint: Practise skip counting by 3s.

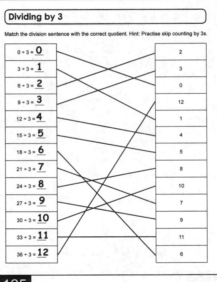

0 ÷ 3 = **0**
3 ÷ 3 = **1**
6 ÷ 3 = **2**
9 ÷ 3 = **3**
12 ÷ 3 = **4**
15 ÷ 3 = **5**
18 ÷ 3 = **6**
21 ÷ 3 = **7**
24 ÷ 3 = **8**
27 ÷ 3 = **9**
30 ÷ 3 = **10**
33 ÷ 3 = **11**
36 ÷ 3 = **12**

2, 3, 0, 12, 1, 4, 5, 8, 10, 7, 9, 11, 6

125

Math Riddle: Dividing by 3

What kind of hats do penguins wear?

I C E   C A P S
7 8 11   8 5 6 4

Watch out! Some letters are not used in the riddle!

1. Find the quotient.

A 15 ÷ 3 = **5**	B 3 ÷ 3 = **1**	C 24 ÷ 3 = **8**
E 33 ÷ 3 = **11**	H 6 ÷ 3 = **2**	I 21 ÷ 3 = **7**
M 27 ÷ 3 = **9**	N 36 ÷ 3 = **12**	O 30 ÷ 3 = **10**
P 18 ÷ 3 = **6**	S 12 ÷ 3 = **4**	T 9 ÷ 3 = **3**

2. Find the missing dividend.

9 ÷ 3 = 3	**36** ÷ 3 = 12	**27** ÷ 3 = 9	**21** ÷ 3 = 7
30 ÷ 3 = 10	**15** ÷ 3 = 5	**24** ÷ 3 = 8	**18** ÷ 3 = 6

126

Dividing by 1, 2, and 3

1. Use long division to find the quotient.

a) 1)4̄ → **4**
b) 2)4̄ → **2**
c) 2)16̄ → **8**
d) 1)6̄ → **6**

e) 3)27̄ → **9**
f) 2)12̄ → **6**
g) 1)8̄ → **8**
h) 3)24̄ → **8**

i) 3)3̄ → **1**
j) 2)8̄ → **4**
k) 3)21̄ → **7**
l) 2)14̄ → **7**

m) 2)10̄ → **5**
n) 3)30̄ → **10**
o) 1)5̄ → **5**
p) 2)18̄ → **9**

127

Dividing by 4

Match the division sentence with the correct quotient. Hint: Practise skip counting by 4s.

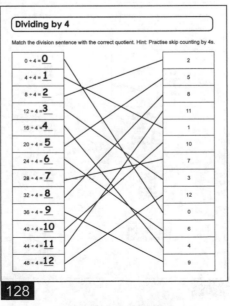

0 ÷ 4 = **0**
4 ÷ 4 = **1**
8 ÷ 4 = **2**
12 ÷ 4 = **3**
16 ÷ 4 = **4**
20 ÷ 4 = **5**
24 ÷ 4 = **6**
28 ÷ 4 = **7**
32 ÷ 4 = **8**
36 ÷ 4 = **9**
40 ÷ 4 = **10**
44 ÷ 4 = **11**
48 ÷ 4 = **12**

2, 5, 8, 11, 1, 10, 7, 3, 12, 0, 6, 4, 9

128

Math Riddle: Dividing by 4

Which building has the most storeys?

T H E   L I B R A R Y
11 1 5   10 4 12 7 2 7 8

Watch out! Some letters are not used in the riddle!

1. Find the quotient.

A 8 ÷ 4 = **2**	B 48 ÷ 4 = **12**	E 20 ÷ 4 = **5**
H 4 ÷ 4 = **1**	I 16 ÷ 4 = **4**	L 40 ÷ 4 = **10**
M 36 ÷ 4 = **9**	N 12 ÷ 4 = **3**	R 28 ÷ 4 = **7**
S 24 ÷ 4 = **6**	T 44 ÷ 4 = **11**	Y 32 ÷ 4 = **8**

2. Find the missing dividend.

20 ÷ 4 = 5	**4** ÷ 4 = 1	**28** ÷ 4 = 7	**40** ÷ 4 = 10
36 ÷ 4 = 9	**12** ÷ 4 = 3	**16** ÷ 4 = 4	**8** ÷ 4 = 2

129

Dividing by 5

Match the division sentence with the correct quotient. Hint: Practise skip counting by 5s.

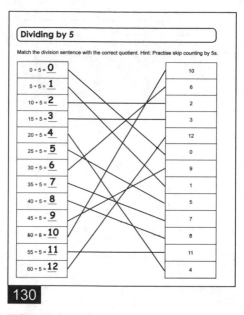

Division	Quotient
$0 \div 5 = 0$	10
$5 \div 5 = 1$	6
$10 \div 5 = 2$	2
$15 \div 5 = 3$	3
$20 \div 5 = 4$	12
$25 \div 5 = 5$	0
$30 \div 5 = 6$	9
$35 \div 5 = 7$	1
$40 \div 5 = 8$	5
$45 \div 5 = 9$	7
$50 \div 5 = 10$	8
$55 \div 5 = 11$	11
$60 \div 5 = 12$	4

Math Riddle: Dividing by 5

What belongs to you but is used more by other people?

Y O U R   N A M E
6 12 10 4   1 2 7 5

Watch out! Some letters are not used in the riddle!

1. Find the quotient.

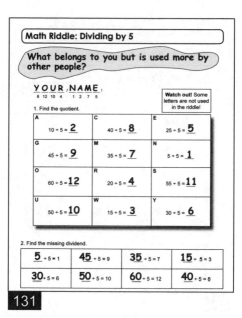

A $10 \div 5 = 2$	C $40 \div 5 = 8$	E $25 \div 5 = 5$
G $45 \div 5 = 9$	M $35 \div 5 = 7$	N $5 \div 5 = 1$
O $60 \div 5 = 12$	R $20 \div 5 = 4$	S $55 \div 5 = 11$
U $50 \div 5 = 10$	W $15 \div 5 = 3$	Y $30 \div 5 = 6$

2. Find the missing dividend.

$5 \div 5 = 1$	$45 \div 5 = 9$	$35 \div 5 = 7$	$15 \div 5 = 3$
$30 \div 5 = 6$	$50 \div 5 = 10$	$60 \div 5 = 12$	$40 \div 5 = 8$

131

Dividing by 6

Match the division sentence with the correct quotient. Hint: Practise skip counting by 6s.

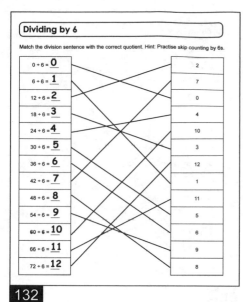

Division	Quotient
$0 \div 6 = 0$	2
$6 \div 6 = 1$	7
$12 \div 6 = 2$	0
$18 \div 6 = 3$	4
$24 \div 6 = 4$	10
$30 \div 6 = 5$	3
$36 \div 6 = 6$	12
$42 \div 6 = 7$	1
$48 \div 6 = 8$	11
$54 \div 6 = 9$	5
$60 \div 6 = 10$	6
$66 \div 6 = 11$	9
$72 \div 6 = 12$	8

132

Math Riddle: Dividing by 6

What did the tornado say to the sports car?

L E T S   G O   F O R   A   S P I N
7 8 10 11   6 9   12 9   4   3 11 5 2 1

Watch out! Some letters are not used in the riddle!

1. Find the quotient.

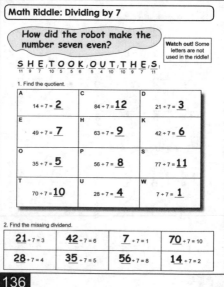

A $18 \div 6 = 3$	E $48 \div 6 = 8$	F $72 \div 6 = 12$
G $36 \div 6 = 6$	I $12 \div 6 = 2$	L $42 \div 6 = 7$
N $6 \div 6 = 1$	O $54 \div 6 = 9$	P $30 \div 6 = 5$
R $24 \div 6 = 4$	S $66 \div 6 = 11$	T $60 \div 6 = 10$

2. Find the missing dividend.

$18 \div 6 = 3$	$42 \div 6 = 7$	$36 \div 6 = 6$	$54 \div 6 = 9$
$24 \div 6 = 4$	$30 \div 6 = 5$	$60 \div 6 = 10$	$48 \div 6 = 8$

133

Dividing by 4, 5, and 6

1. Use long division to find the quotient.

a) $4\overline{)12} = 3$
b) $4\overline{)4} = 1$
c) $6\overline{)60} = 10$
d) $4\overline{)40} = 10$

e) $6\overline{)18} = 3$
f) $4\overline{)12} = 3$
g) $5\overline{)35} = 7$
h) $6\overline{)42} = 7$

i) $5\overline{)10} = 2$
j) $6\overline{)30} = 5$
k) $5\overline{)5} = 1$
l) $5\overline{)40} = 8$

m) $6\overline{)66} = 11$
n) $4\overline{)20} = 5$
o) $4\overline{)28} = 7$
p) $5\overline{)20} = 4$

134

Dividing by 7

Match the division sentence with the correct quotient. Hint: Practise skip counting by 7s.

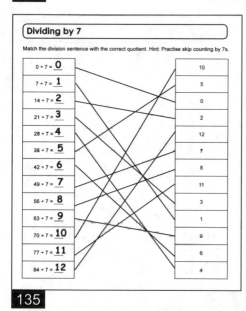

Division	Quotient
$0 \div 7 = 0$	10
$7 \div 7 = 1$	5
$14 \div 7 = 2$	0
$21 \div 7 = 3$	2
$28 \div 7 = 4$	12
$35 \div 7 = 5$	7
$42 \div 7 = 6$	8
$49 \div 7 = 7$	11
$56 \div 7 = 8$	3
$63 \div 7 = 9$	1
$70 \div 7 = 10$	9
$77 \div 7 = 11$	6
$84 \div 7 = 12$	4

135

Math Riddle: Dividing by 7

How did the robot make the number seven even?

S H E   T O O K   O U T   T H E   S
11 9 7   10 5 5 6   5 4 10   10 9 7   11

Watch out! Some letters are not used in the riddle!

1. Find the quotient.

A $14 \div 7 = 2$	C $84 \div 7 = 12$	D $21 \div 7 = 3$
E $49 \div 7 = 7$	H $63 \div 7 = 9$	K $42 \div 7 = 6$
O $35 \div 7 = 5$	P $56 \div 7 = 8$	S $77 \div 7 = 11$
T $70 \div 7 = 10$	U $28 \div 7 = 4$	W $7 \div 7 = 1$

2. Find the missing dividend.

$21 \div 7 = 3$	$42 \div 7 = 6$	$7 \div 7 = 1$	$70 \div 7 = 10$
$28 \div 7 = 4$	$35 \div 7 = 5$	$56 \div 7 = 8$	$14 \div 7 = 2$

136

Dividing by 8

Match the division sentence with the correct quotient. Hint: Practise skip counting by 8s.

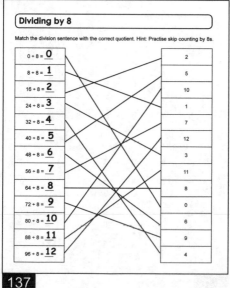

Division	Quotient
$0 \div 8 = 0$	2
$8 \div 8 = 1$	5
$16 \div 8 = 2$	10
$24 \div 8 = 3$	1
$32 \div 8 = 4$	7
$40 \div 8 = 5$	12
$48 \div 8 = 6$	3
$56 \div 8 = 7$	11
$64 \div 8 = 8$	8
$72 \div 8 = 9$	0
$80 \div 8 = 10$	6
$88 \div 8 = 11$	9
$96 \div 8 = 12$	4

Math Riddle: Dividing by 8

What has four legs but cannot walk?

A   C H A I R
3   9 2 3 5 8

Watch out! Some letters are not used in the riddle!

1. Find the quotient.

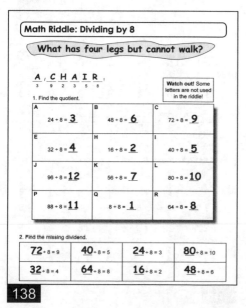

A $24 \div 8 = 3$	B $48 \div 8 = 6$	C $72 \div 8 = 9$
E $32 \div 8 = 4$	H $16 \div 8 = 2$	I $40 \div 8 = 5$
J $96 \div 8 = 12$	K $56 \div 8 = 7$	L $80 \div 8 = 10$
P $88 \div 8 = 11$	Q $8 \div 8 = 1$	R $64 \div 8 = 8$

2. Find the missing dividend.

$72 \div 8 = 9$	$40 \div 8 = 5$	$24 \div 8 = 3$	$80 \div 8 = 10$
$32 \div 8 = 4$	$64 \div 8 = 8$	$16 \div 8 = 2$	$48 \div 8 = 6$

139 — Dividing by 9

Match the division sentence with the correct quotient. Hint: Practise skip counting by 9s.

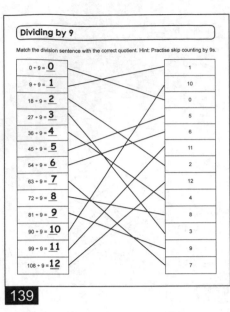

Division sentence	Quotient
0 ÷ 9 = 0	1
9 ÷ 9 = 1	10
18 ÷ 9 = 2	0
27 ÷ 9 = 3	5
36 ÷ 9 = 4	6
45 ÷ 9 = 5	11
54 ÷ 9 = 6	2
63 ÷ 9 = 7	12
72 ÷ 9 = 8	4
81 ÷ 9 = 9	8
90 ÷ 9 = 10	3
99 ÷ 9 = 11	9
108 ÷ 9 = 12	7

140 — Math Riddle: Dividing by 9

Where do fish like to sleep?

O N A S E A B E D
6 10 4 1 4 2 4 5 2 9

Watch out! Some letters are not used in the riddle!

1. Find the quotient.

A 36 ÷ 9 = 4	B 45 ÷ 9 = 5	C 72 ÷ 9 = 8
D 81 ÷ 9 = 9	E 18 ÷ 9 = 2	M 99 ÷ 9 = 11
N 90 ÷ 9 = 10	O 54 ÷ 9 = 6	P 27 ÷ 9 = 3
R 108 ÷ 9 = 12	S 9 ÷ 9 = 1	T 63 ÷ 9 = 7

2. Find the missing dividend.

27 ÷ 9 = 3	63 ÷ 9 = 7	18 ÷ 9 = 2	36 ÷ 9 = 4
45 ÷ 9 = 5	81 ÷ 9 = 9	72 ÷ 9 = 8	90 ÷ 9 = 10

141 — Dividing by 7, 8, and 9

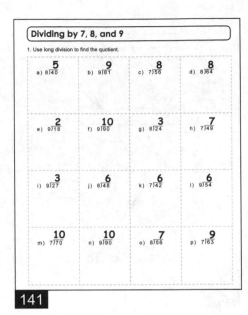

1. Use long division to find the quotient.

a) 8)40 = 5   b) 9)81 = 9   c) 7)56 = 8   d) 8)64 = 8

e) 9)18 = 2   f) 9)90 = 10   g) 8)24 = 3   h) 7)49 = 7

i) 9)27 = 3   j) 8)48 = 6   k) 7)42 = 6   l) 9)54 = 6

m) 7)70 = 10   n) 9)90 = 10   o) 8)56 = 7   p) 7)63 = 9

142 — Dividing by 10

Match the division sentence with the correct quotient. Hint: Practise skip counting by 10s.

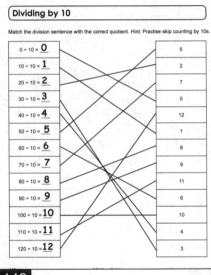

Division sentence	Quotient
0 ÷ 10 = 0	5
10 ÷ 10 = 1	2
20 ÷ 10 = 2	7
30 ÷ 10 = 3	0
40 ÷ 10 = 4	12
50 ÷ 10 = 5	1
60 ÷ 10 = 6	8
70 ÷ 10 = 7	9
80 ÷ 10 = 8	11
90 ÷ 10 = 9	6
100 ÷ 10 = 10	10
110 ÷ 10 = 11	4
120 ÷ 10 = 12	3

143 — Math Riddle: Dividing by 10

What do you call a famous fish?

A S T A R F I S H
8 7 5 8 3 9 6 7 2

Watch out! Some letters are not used in the riddle!

1. Find the quotient.

A 80 ÷ 10 = 8	B 40 ÷ 10 = 4	E 120 ÷ 10 = 12
F 90 ÷ 10 = 9	G 110 ÷ 10 = 11	H 20 ÷ 10 = 2
I 60 ÷ 10 = 6	J 100 ÷ 10 = 10	R 30 ÷ 10 = 3
S 70 ÷ 10 = 7	T 50 ÷ 10 = 5	Y 10 ÷ 10 = 1

2. Find the missing dividend.

60 ÷ 10 = 6	70 ÷ 10 = 7	40 ÷ 10 = 4	90 ÷ 10 = 9
100 ÷ 10 = 10	30 ÷ 10 = 3	80 ÷ 10 = 8	50 ÷ 10 = 5

144

Test 1—Multiplying by 1, 2, and 3

```
 5   4   6   8   4   2   1
×2  ×3  ×1  ×2  ×1  ×3  ×2
10  12   6  16   4   6   2

 3   5   2   4   8   7   9
×1  ×3  ×2  ×2  ×3  ×1  ×2
 3  15   4   8  24   7  18

 8   6   3   1   5   6
×1  ×3  ×2  ×1  ×1  ×2        Number Correct
 8  18   6   1   5  12          /20
```

Test 2—Multiplying by 1, 2, and 3

```
 2   5   3   4   5   7   4
×1  ×2  ×3  ×2  ×3  ×2  ×1
 2  10   9   8  15  14   4

 2   1   5   8   9   6   4
×3  ×1  ×1  ×3  ×2  ×1  ×3
 6   1   5  24  18   6  12

 1   7   3   3   6  10
×2  ×3  ×1  ×2  ×2  ×3        Number Correct
 2  21   3   6  12  30          /20
```

145

Test 3—Multiplying by 1, 2, and 3

```
 2   5   4   3   1   8   3
×2  ×3  ×1  ×1  ×2  ×3  ×2
 4  15   4   3   2  24   6

 4   8   2   4   3   9   6
×3  ×2  ×1  ×2  ×3  ×1  ×3
12  16   2   8   9   9  18

 7   1   5   9   8   6
×1  ×3  ×1  ×3  ×1  ×2        Number Correct
 7   3   5  27   8  12          /20
```

Test 4—Multiplying by 1, 2, and 3

```
 4   5   3   1   3   2   3
×1  ×3  ×2  ×1  ×3  ×2  ×1
 4  15   6   1   9   4   3

 9   2   5  10   8   2   9
×3  ×1  ×2  ×1  ×2  ×3  ×1
27   2  10  10  16   6   9

 4   7   6   1   9   8
×3  ×2  ×1  ×3  ×2  ×1        Number Correct
12  14   6   3  18   8          /20
```

146

Test 5—Multiplying by 1, 2, and 3

```
 5   3   4   2   1   9   6
×3  ×2  ×1  ×1  ×3  ×2  ×3
15   6   4   2   3  18  18

 7   3   6   4   9   1   5
×1  ×3  ×1  ×2  ×3  ×1  ×2
 7   9   6   8  27   1  10

 5   1   3   2   8   4
×1  ×2  ×1  ×3  ×1  ×3        Number Correct
 5   2   3   6   8  12          /20
```

Test 6—Multiplying by 1, 2, and 3

```
 4   5   2   5   4   1   3
×1  ×3  ×2  ×1  ×3  ×2  ×1
 4  15   4   5  12   2   3

 4   8   5   3   7   1   6
×2  ×1  ×2  ×3  ×2  ×1  ×3
 8   8  10   9  14   1  18

 9   3   9   8   6   2
×3  ×2  ×1  ×3  ×2  ×1        Number Correct
27   6   9  24  12   2          /20
```

147

Test 7—Multiplying by 1, 2, and 3

```
 4   3   5   3   2   4   1
×2  ×3  ×1  ×2  ×1  ×3  ×2
 8   9   5   6   2  12   2

 6   2   7   5   2   1   6
×1  ×2  ×3  ×2  ×3  ×1  ×2
 6   4  21  10   6   1  12

 7   5   9   1   8  10
×2  ×3  ×1  ×3  ×2  ×1        Number Correct
14  15   9   3  16  10          /20
```

Test 8—Multiplying by 1, 2, and 3

```
 4   5   3   1   5   2   3
×1  ×3  ×2  ×3  ×1  ×2  ×1
 4  15   6   3   5   4   3

 6   2   8   4   3   7   5
×3  ×1  ×2  ×2  ×3  ×1  ×2
18   2  16   8   9   7  10

 4   1   1   6   9   7
×3  ×1  ×2  ×1  ×3  ×2        Number Correct
12   1   2   6  27  14          /20
```

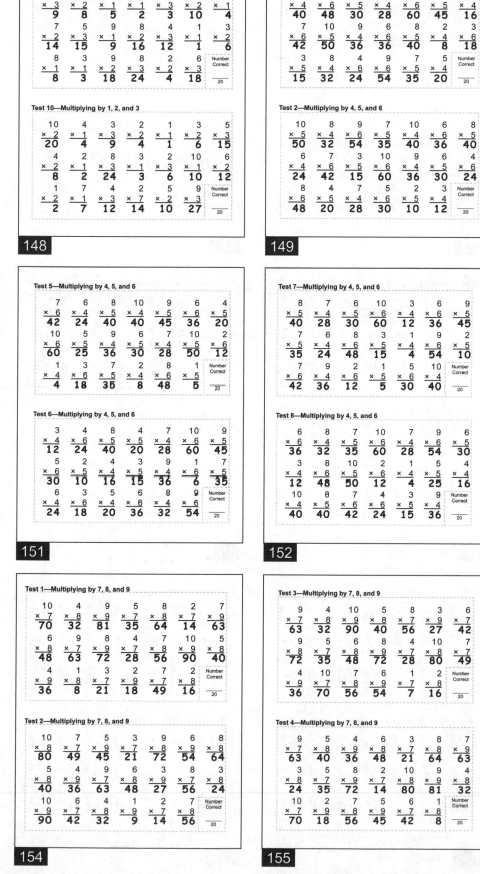

Answer Key

Page 148

Test 9—Multiplying by 1, 2, and 3

3×3=9	4×2=8	5×1=5	2×1=2	1×3=3	5×2=10	4×1=4
7×2=14	5×3=15	9×1=9	8×2=16	4×3=12	1×1=1	3×2=6
8×1=8	3×1=3	9×2=18	8×3=24	2×2=4	6×3=18	Number Correct /20

Test 10—Multiplying by 1, 2, and 3

10×2=20	4×1=4	3×3=9	2×2=4	1×1=1	3×2=6	5×3=15
4×2=8	2×1=2	8×3=24	3×1=3	3×1=3	10×1=10	6×2=12
1×2=2	7×1=7	4×3=12	2×7=14	5×2=10	9×3=27	Number Correct /20

Page 149

Test 1—Multiplying by 4, 5, and 6

10×4=40	8×6=48	6×5=30	7×4=28	10×6=60	9×5=45	4×4=16
7×6=42	10×5=50	9×4=36	6×6=36	8×5=40	2×4=8	3×6=18
3×5=15	8×4=32	4×6=24	9×6=54	7×5=35	5×4=20	Number Correct /20

Test 2—Multiplying by 4, 5, and 6

10×5=50	8×4=32	9×6=54	7×5=35	10×4=40	6×6=36	8×5=40
6×4=24	7×6=42	3×5=15	10×6=60	9×4=36	6×5=30	4×6=24
8×6=48	4×5=20	7×4=28	5×6=30	2×5=10	3×4=12	Number Correct /20

Page 150

Test 3—Multiplying by 4, 5, and 6

9×4=36	7×5=35	10×6=60	8×4=32	6×5=30	9×6=54	7×4=28
8×6=48	10×4=40	5×5=25	6×6=36	3×4=12	8×5=40	2×6=12
3×5=15	6×4=24	1×6=6	9×5=45	5×6=30	2×4=8	Number Correct /20

Test 4—Multiplying by 4, 5, and 6

1×4=4	10×6=60	7×4=28	6×5=30	8×4=32	3×6=18	9×5=45
1×5=5	5×4=20	7×6=42	4×5=20	6×4=24	2×6=12	10×5=50
9×4=36	5×5=25	1×6=6	2×5=10	8×6=48	4×4=16	Number Correct /20

Page 151

Test 5—Multiplying by 4, 5, and 6

7×6=42	6×4=24	8×5=40	10×4=40	9×5=45	6×6=36	4×5=20
10×6=60	5×5=25	9×4=36	6×5=30	7×4=28	10×5=50	2×6=12
1×4=4	3×6=18	7×5=35	2×4=8	8×6=48	1×5=5	Number Correct /20

Test 6—Multiplying by 4, 5, and 6

3×4=12	4×6=24	8×5=40	5×4=20	7×4=28	10×6=60	9×5=45
5×6=30	2×5=10	4×4=16	3×5=15	9×4=36	1×6=6	7×5=35
6×4=24	3×6=18	5×4=20	6×6=36	8×4=32	9×6=54	Number Correct /20

Page 152

Test 7—Multiplying by 4, 5, and 6

8×5=40	7×4=28	6×5=30	10×6=60	3×4=12	6×6=36	9×5=45
7×5=35	6×4=24	8×6=48	3×5=15	1×4=4	9×6=54	2×5=10
7×6=42	9×4=36	2×6=12	1×5=5	5×6=30	10×4=40	Number Correct /20

Test 8—Multiplying by 4, 5, and 6

6×6=36	8×4=32	7×5=35	10×6=60	7×4=28	9×6=54	6×5=30
3×4=12	8×6=48	10×5=50	2×6=12	1×4=4	5×5=25	4×4=16
10×4=40	8×5=40	7×6=42	4×6=24	3×5=15	9×4=36	Number Correct /20

Page 153

Test 9—Multiplying by 4, 5, and 6

10×4=40	7×6=42	9×5=45	8×4=32	6×5=30	10×6=60	2×4=8
4×5=20	3×6=18	6×4=24	1×6=6	5×4=20	2×5=10	4×4=16
8×6=48	3×5=15	7×4=28	4×6=24	1×4=4	10×5=50	Number Correct /20

Test 10—Multiplying by 4, 5, and 6

1×5=5	2×4=8	6×5=30	9×6=54	8×4=32	3×6=18	9×5=45
5×4=20	7×5=35	2×6=12	8×5=40	9×4=36	10×6=60	7×4=28
10×4=40	2×5=10	6×6=36	3×4=12	10×5=50	8×6=48	Number Correct /20

Page 154

Test 1—Multiplying by 7, 8, and 9

10×7=70	4×8=32	9×9=81	5×7=35	8×8=64	2×7=14	7×9=63
6×8=48	9×7=63	8×9=72	4×7=28	7×8=56	10×9=90	5×8=40
4×9=36	1×8=8	3×7=21	2×9=18	7×7=49	2×8=16	Number Correct /20

Test 2—Multiplying by 7, 8, and 9

10×8=80	7×7=49	5×9=45	3×7=21	9×8=72	6×9=54	8×8=64
5×8=40	4×9=36	9×7=63	6×8=48	3×9=27	8×7=56	3×8=24
10×9=90	6×7=42	4×8=32	1×9=9	2×7=14	7×8=56	Number Correct /20

Page 155

Test 3—Multiplying by 7, 8, and 9

9×7=63	4×8=32	10×9=90	5×8=40	8×7=56	3×9=27	6×7=42
9×8=72	5×7=35	6×8=48	8×9=72	4×7=28	10×8=80	7×7=49
4×9=36	10×7=70	7×8=56	6×9=54	1×7=7	2×8=16	Number Correct /20

Test 4—Multiplying by 7, 8, and 9

9×7=63	5×8=40	4×9=36	6×8=48	3×7=21	8×8=64	7×9=63
3×8=24	5×7=35	8×9=72	2×7=14	10×8=80	9×9=81	4×8=32
10×7=70	2×9=18	7×8=56	5×9=45	6×7=42	1×8=8	Number Correct /20

Page 156

Test 5—Multiplying by 7, 8, and 9

10×9=90	4×7=28	9×8=72	5×9=45	5×7=35	2×8=16	7×9=63
3×8=24	1×9=9	8×7=56	1×8=8	8×9=72	1×7=7	8×8=64
3×7=21	10×8=80	6×9=54	7×7=49	4×8=32	9×9=81	Number Correct /20

Test 6—Multiplying by 7, 8, and 9

2×8=16	7×9=63	5×7=35	3×9=27	9×7=63	6×8=48	8×9=72
3×7=21	4×8=32	9×9=81	8×7=56	10×8=80	5×9=45	2×7=14
10×9=90	1×7=7	8×8=64	3×8=24	2×9=18	6×7=42	Number Correct /20

Test 7—Multiplying by 7, 8, and 9

7 × 9 = 63	4 × 8 = 32	9 × 7 = 63	5 × 9 = 45	8 × 7 = 56	2 × 8 = 16	6 × 9 = 54
1 × 8 = 8	5 × 7 = 35	2 × 9 = 18	9 × 8 = 72	6 × 7 = 42	10 × 9 = 90	3 × 8 = 24
4 × 7 = 28	1 × 9 = 9	7 × 8 = 56	10 × 7 = 70	5 × 8 = 40	2 × 7 = 14	

Number Correct __/20

Test 8—Multiplying by 7, 8, and 9

9 × 8 = 72	8 × 7 = 56	4 × 9 = 36	5 × 7 = 35	3 × 8 = 24	7 × 9 = 63	6 × 7 = 42
6 × 9 = 54	5 × 8 = 40	7 × 7 = 49	3 × 9 = 27	1 × 7 = 7	2 × 8 = 16	4 × 8 = 32
10 × 7 = 70	2 × 9 = 18	8 × 8 = 64	1 × 8 = 8	9 × 9 = 81	4 × 7 = 28	

Number Correct __/20

157

Test 9—Multiplying by 7, 8, and 9

10 × 7 = 70	4 × 8 = 32	9 × 9 = 81	5 × 7 = 35	8 × 8 = 64	2 × 9 = 18	7 × 7 = 49
3 × 9 = 27	1 × 7 = 7	8 × 7 = 56	4 × 9 = 36	6 × 7 = 42	8 × 9 = 72	5 × 9 = 45
6 × 8 = 48	10 × 9 = 90	3 × 7 = 21	2 × 8 = 16	7 × 9 = 63	2 × 7 = 14	

Number Correct __/20

Test 10—Multiplying by 7, 8, and 9

1 × 9 = 9	7 × 7 = 49	4 × 8 = 32	6 × 9 = 54	9 × 7 = 63	3 × 8 = 24	8 × 9 = 72
5 × 8 = 40	4 × 9 = 36	2 × 7 = 14	10 × 8 = 80	5 × 9 = 45	3 × 7 = 21	6 × 8 = 48
10 × 7 = 70	8 × 8 = 64	3 × 9 = 27	4 × 7 = 28	8 × 7 = 56	9 × 9 = 81	

Number Correct __/20

158

Test 1—Dividing by 1, 2, and 3

10 ÷ 2 = 5	12 ÷ 3 = 4	6 ÷ 1 = 6	16 ÷ 2 = 8	4 ÷ 1 = 4	18 ÷ 3 = 6	2 ÷ 2 = 1
3 ÷ 1 = 3	15 ÷ 3 = 5	4 ÷ 2 = 2	8 ÷ 2 = 4	24 ÷ 3 = 8	7 ÷ 1 = 7	18 ÷ 2 = 9
8 ÷ 1 = 8	20 ÷ 2 = 10	6 ÷ 2 = 3	1 ÷ 1 = 1	5 ÷ 1 = 5	12 ÷ 2 = 6	

Number Correct __/20

Test 2—Dividing by 1, 2, and 3

2 ÷ 1 = 2	10 ÷ 2 = 5	9 ÷ 3 = 3	8 ÷ 2 = 4	15 ÷ 3 = 5	14 ÷ 2 = 7	4 ÷ 1 = 4
21 ÷ 3 = 7	6 ÷ 2 = 3	5 ÷ 1 = 5	24 ÷ 3 = 8	18 ÷ 2 = 9	6 ÷ 1 = 6	12 ÷ 3 = 4
2 ÷ 2 = 1	6 ÷ 3 = 2	3 ÷ 1 = 3	1 ÷ 1 = 1	12 ÷ 2 = 6	30 ÷ 3 = 10	

Number Correct __/20

161

Test 3—Dividing by 1, 2, and 3

4 ÷ 2 = 2	15 ÷ 3 = 5	4 ÷ 1 = 4	3 ÷ 1 = 3	2 ÷ 2 = 1	24 ÷ 3 = 8	6 ÷ 2 = 3
12 ÷ 3 = 4	16 ÷ 2 = 8	2 ÷ 1 = 2	8 ÷ 2 = 4	9 ÷ 3 = 3	9 ÷ 1 = 9	18 ÷ 3 = 6
7 ÷ 1 = 7	3 ÷ 3 = 1	20 ÷ 2 = 10	27 ÷ 3 = 9	8 ÷ 1 = 8	12 ÷ 2 = 6	

Number Correct __/20

Test 4—Dividing by 1, 2, and 3

4 ÷ 1 = 4	10 ÷ 1 = 10	6 ÷ 2 = 3	1 ÷ 1 = 1	9 ÷ 3 = 3	4 ÷ 2 = 2	30 ÷ 3 = 10
27 ÷ 3 = 9	2 ÷ 1 = 2	10 ÷ 2 = 5	15 ÷ 3 = 5	16 ÷ 2 = 8	6 ÷ 3 = 2	9 ÷ 1 = 9
12 ÷ 3 = 4	14 ÷ 2 = 7	6 ÷ 1 = 6	3 ÷ 3 = 1	18 ÷ 2 = 9	8 ÷ 1 = 8	

Number Correct __/20

162

Test 5—Dividing by 1, 2, and 3

15 ÷ 3 = 5	6 ÷ 2 = 3	4 ÷ 1 = 4	14 ÷ 2 = 7	3 ÷ 3 = 1	18 ÷ 2 = 9	6 ÷ 1 = 6
7 ÷ 1 = 7	6 ÷ 2 = 3	18 ÷ 3 = 6	8 ÷ 2 = 4	27 ÷ 3 = 9	1 ÷ 1 = 1	10 ÷ 2 = 5
5 ÷ 1 = 5	20 ÷ 2 = 10	3 ÷ 1 = 3	30 ÷ 3 = 10	8 ÷ 1 = 8	12 ÷ 3 = 4	

Number Correct __/20

Test 6—Dividing by 1, 2, and 3

4 ÷ 1 = 4	15 ÷ 3 = 5	4 ÷ 2 = 2	5 ÷ 1 = 5	12 ÷ 3 = 4	2 ÷ 2 = 1	3 ÷ 1 = 3
18 ÷ 2 = 9	8 ÷ 1 = 8	10 ÷ 2 = 5	9 ÷ 3 = 3	14 ÷ 2 = 7	1 ÷ 1 = 1	18 ÷ 3 = 6
27 ÷ 3 = 9	6 ÷ 2 = 3	9 ÷ 1 = 9	24 ÷ 3 = 8	12 ÷ 2 = 6	2 ÷ 1 = 2	

Number Correct __/20

163

Test 7—Dividing by 1, 2, and 3

8 ÷ 2 = 4	9 ÷ 3 = 3	5 ÷ 1 = 5	20 ÷ 2 = 10	2 ÷ 1 = 2	12 ÷ 3 = 4	2 ÷ 2 = 1
6 ÷ 1 = 6	4 ÷ 2 = 2	21 ÷ 3 = 7	10 ÷ 2 = 5	27 ÷ 3 = 9	1 ÷ 1 = 1	6 ÷ 2 = 3
14 ÷ 2 = 7	15 ÷ 3 = 5	9 ÷ 1 = 9	3 ÷ 3 = 1	16 ÷ 2 = 8	10 ÷ 1 = 10	

Number Correct __/20

Test 8—Dividing by 1, 2, and 3

4 ÷ 1 = 4	15 ÷ 3 = 5	6 ÷ 2 = 3	30 ÷ 3 = 10	5 ÷ 1 = 5	4 ÷ 2 = 2	3 ÷ 1 = 3
18 ÷ 3 = 6	2 ÷ 1 = 2	16 ÷ 2 = 8	9 ÷ 3 = 3	7 ÷ 1 = 7	12 ÷ 2 = 6	
12 ÷ 3 = 4	1 ÷ 1 = 1	20 ÷ 2 = 10	6 ÷ 1 = 6	21 ÷ 3 = 7	10 ÷ 2 = 5	

Number Correct __/20

164

Test 9—Dividing by 1, 2, and 3

9 ÷ 3 = 3	8 ÷ 2 = 4	5 ÷ 1 = 5	2 ÷ 1 = 2	21 ÷ 3 = 7	10 ÷ 2 = 5	4 ÷ 1 = 4
14 ÷ 2 = 7	15 ÷ 3 = 5	9 ÷ 1 = 9	16 ÷ 2 = 8	12 ÷ 3 = 4	1 ÷ 1 = 1	6 ÷ 2 = 3
8 ÷ 1 = 8	3 ÷ 1 = 3	18 ÷ 2 = 9	24 ÷ 3 = 8	4 ÷ 2 = 2	18 ÷ 3 = 6	

Number Correct __/20

Test 10—Dividing by 1, 2, and 3

20 ÷ 2 = 10	4 ÷ 1 = 4	9 ÷ 3 = 3	4 ÷ 2 = 2	1 ÷ 1 = 1	6 ÷ 2 = 3	15 ÷ 3 = 5
16 ÷ 2 = 8	2 ÷ 1 = 2	24 ÷ 3 = 8	3 ÷ 1 = 3	6 ÷ 3 = 2	10 ÷ 1 = 10	12 ÷ 2 = 6
2 ÷ 2 = 1	7 ÷ 1 = 7	12 ÷ 3 = 4	9 ÷ 1 = 9	10 ÷ 2 = 5	27 ÷ 3 = 9	

Number Correct __/20

165

Test 1—Dividing by 4, 5, and 6

40 ÷ 4 = 10	48 ÷ 6 = 8	30 ÷ 5 = 6	28 ÷ 4 = 7	60 ÷ 6 = 10	45 ÷ 5 = 9	16 ÷ 4 = 4
42 ÷ 6 = 7	50 ÷ 5 = 10	32 ÷ 4 = 8	36 ÷ 6 = 6	40 ÷ 5 = 8	8 ÷ 4 = 2	18 ÷ 6 = 3
15 ÷ 5 = 3	36 ÷ 4 = 9	24 ÷ 6 = 4	54 ÷ 6 = 9	35 ÷ 5 = 7	20 ÷ 4 = 5	

Number Correct __/20

Test 2—Dividing by 4, 5, and 6

50 ÷ 5 = 10	32 ÷ 4 = 8	54 ÷ 6 = 9	35 ÷ 5 = 7	40 ÷ 4 = 10	36 ÷ 6 = 6	40 ÷ 5 = 8
24 ÷ 4 = 6	42 ÷ 6 = 7	15 ÷ 5 = 3	60 ÷ 6 = 10	36 ÷ 4 = 9	30 ÷ 5 = 6	24 ÷ 6 = 4
48 ÷ 6 = 8	20 ÷ 5 = 4	28 ÷ 4 = 7	30 ÷ 6 = 5	10 ÷ 5 = 2	12 ÷ 4 = 3	

Number Correct __/20

166

Test 3—Dividing by 4, 5, and 6

36 ÷ 4 = 9	30 ÷ 5 = 6	60 ÷ 6 = 10	32 ÷ 4 = 8	30 ÷ 5 = 6	54 ÷ 6 = 9	28 ÷ 4 = 7
48 ÷ 6 = 8	40 ÷ 4 = 10	25 ÷ 5 = 5	36 ÷ 6 = 6	12 ÷ 4 = 3	40 ÷ 5 = 8	12 ÷ 6 = 2
15 ÷ 5 = 3	24 ÷ 4 = 6	6 ÷ 6 = 1	45 ÷ 5 = 9	30 ÷ 6 = 5	8 ÷ 4 = 2	

Number Correct __/20

Test 4—Dividing by 4, 5, and 6

4 ÷ 4 = 1	60 ÷ 6 = 10	28 ÷ 4 = 7	30 ÷ 5 = 6	32 ÷ 4 = 8	18 ÷ 6 = 3	45 ÷ 5 = 9
5 ÷ 5 = 1	20 ÷ 4 = 5	42 ÷ 6 = 7	20 ÷ 5 = 4	24 ÷ 4 = 6	12 ÷ 6 = 2	50 ÷ 5 = 10
36 ÷ 4 = 9	25 ÷ 5 = 5	6 ÷ 6 = 1	10 ÷ 5 = 2	48 ÷ 6 = 8	16 ÷ 4 = 4	

Number Correct __/20

167

Test 5—Dividing by 4, 5, and 6

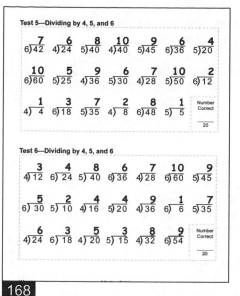

6)42 = 7	4)24 = 6	5)40 = 8	4)40 = 10	5)45 = 9	6)36 = 6	5)20 = 4
6)60 = 10	5)25 = 5	4)36 = 9	5)30 = 6	4)28 = 7	5)50 = 10	6)12 = 2
4)4 = 1	6)18 = 3	5)35 = 7	4)8 = 2	6)48 = 8	5)5 = 1	Number Correct / 20

Test 6—Dividing by 4, 5, and 6

4)12 = 3	6)24 = 4	5)40 = 8	6)36 = 6	4)28 = 7	6)60 = 10	5)45 = 9
6)30 = 5	5)10 = 2	4)16 = 4	5)20 = 4	4)36 = 9	6)6 = 1	5)35 = 7
4)24 = 6	6)18 = 3	4)20 = 5	5)15 = 3	4)32 = 8	6)54 = 9	Number Correct / 20

Test 7—Dividing by 4, 5, and 6

5)40 = 8	4)28 = 7	5)30 = 6	6)60 = 10	4)12 = 3	6)36 = 6	5)45 = 9
5)35 = 7	4)24 = 6	6)48 = 8	5)15 = 3	4)4 = 1	6)54 = 9	5)10 = 2
6)42 = 7	4)36 = 9	6)12 = 2	5)5 = 1	6)30 = 5	4)40 = 10	Number Correct / 20

Test 8—Dividing by 4, 5, and 6

6)36 = 6	4)32 = 8	5)35 = 7	6)60 = 10	4)28 = 7	6)54 = 9	5)30 = 6
4)12 = 3	6)48 = 8	5)50 = 10	6)12 = 2	4)4 = 1	5)25 = 5	4)16 = 4
4)40 = 10	5)40 = 8	6)42 = 7	6)24 = 4	5)15 = 3	4)36 = 9	Number Correct / 20

Test 9—Dividing by 4, 5, and 6

4)40 = 10	6)42 = 7	5)45 = 9	4)32 = 8	5)30 = 6	6)60 = 10	4)8 = 2
5)20 = 4	6)18 = 3	4)24 = 6	6)6 = 1	4)20 = 5	5)10 = 2	4)16 = 4
6)48 = 8	5)15 = 3	4)28 = 7	6)24 = 4	4)4 = 1	5)50 = 10	Number Correct / 20

Test 10—Dividing by 4, 5, and 6

5)5 = 1	4)8 = 2	5)30 = 5	6)54 = 9	4)32 = 8	6)18 = 3	5)45 = 9
4)20 = 5	5)35 = 7	6)12 = 2	5)40 = 8	4)36 = 9	6)60 = 10	4)32 = 8
4)40 = 10	5)10 = 2	6)36 = 6	4)12 = 3	5)50 = 10	6)48 = 8	Number Correct / 20

Test 1—Dividing by 7, 8, and 9

7)70 = 10	8)32 = 4	9)81 = 9	7)35 = 5	8)64 = 8	7)14 = 2	9)63 = 7
8)48 = 6	7)63 = 9	9)72 = 8	7)28 = 4	8)56 = 7	9)90 = 10	8)40 = 5
9)36 = 4	8)8 = 1	7)21 = 3	9)18 = 2	7)49 = 7	8)16 = 2	Number Correct / 20

Test 2—Dividing by 7, 8, and 9

8)80 = 10	7)49 = 7	9)45 = 5	7)21 = 3	8)72 = 9	9)54 = 6	8)64 = 8
8)40 = 5	9)36 = 4	7)63 = 9	8)48 = 6	9)27 = 3	7)56 = 8	8)24 = 3
9)90 = 10	7)42 = 6	8)32 = 4	9)9 = 1	7)14 = 2	8)56 = 7	Number Correct / 20

Test 3—Dividing by 7, 8, and 9

7)63 = 9	8)32 = 4	9)90 = 10	8)40 = 5	7)56 = 8	9)27 = 3	7)42 = 6
8)72 = 9	7)35 = 5	8)48 = 6	9)72 = 8	7)28 = 4	8)80 = 10	7)49 = 7
9)36 = 4	7)70 = 10	8)56 = 7	9)54 = 6	7)7 = 1	8)16 = 2	Number Correct / 20

Test 4—Dividing by 7, 8, and 9

7)63 = 9	8)40 = 5	9)36 = 4	8)48 = 6	7)21 = 3	8)64 = 8	9)63 = 7
8)24 = 3	7)35 = 5	9)72 = 8	7)14 = 2	8)80 = 10	9)81 = 9	8)32 = 4
7)70 = 10	9)18 = 2	8)56 = 7	9)45 = 5	7)42 = 6	8)8 = 1	Number Correct / 20

Test 5—Dividing by 7, 8, and 9

9)90 = 10	7)28 = 4	8)72 = 9	9)63 = 7	7)35 = 5	8)16 = 2	9)72 = 8
8)24 = 3	9)9 = 1	7)56 = 8	8)8 = 1	9)45 = 5	7)7 = 1	8)64 = 8
7)21 = 3	8)80 = 10	9)54 = 6	7)49 = 7	8)32 = 4	9)81 = 9	Number Correct / 20

Test 6—Dividing by 7, 8, and 9

8)16 = 2	9)63 = 7	7)35 = 5	9)72 = 9	7)63 = 7	8)48 = 6	9)27 = 3
7)21 = 3	8)32 = 4	9)81 = 9	7)56 = 8	8)80 = 10	9)45 = 5	7)14 = 2
9)90 = 10	7)7 = 1	8)64 = 8	9)24 = 3	9)18 = 2	7)42 = 6	Number Correct / 20

Test 7—Dividing by 7, 8, and 9

9)63 = 7	8)32 = 4	7)63 = 9	9)45 = 5	7)56 = 8	8)16 = 2	9)54 = 6
8)8 = 1	7)35 = 5	9)18 = 2	8)72 = 9	7)42 = 6	9)90 = 10	8)24 = 3
7)28 = 4	9)9 = 1	8)56 = 7	7)70 = 10	8)40 = 5	7)14 = 2	Number Correct / 20

Test 8—Dividing by 7, 8, and 9

8)72 = 9	7)56 = 8	9)36 = 4	7)35 = 5	8)24 = 3	9)63 = 7	7)42 = 6
9)54 = 6	8)40 = 5	7)49 = 7	9)27 = 3	7)7 = 1	8)16 = 2	8)32 = 4
7)70 = 10	9)18 = 2	8)64 = 8	8)8 = 1	9)81 = 9	7)28 = 4	Number Correct / 20

Test 9—Dividing by 7, 8, and 9

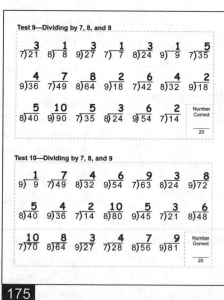

7)21 = 3	8)8 = 1	9)27 = 3	7)7 = 1	8)24 = 3	9)9 = 1	7)35 = 5
9)36 = 4	7)49 = 7	8)64 = 8	9)18 = 2	7)42 = 6	8)32 = 4	9)18 = 2
8)40 = 5	9)90 = 10	7)35 = 5	8)24 = 3	9)54 = 6	7)14 = 2	Number Correct / 20

Test 10—Dividing by 7, 8, and 9

9)9 = 1	7)49 = 7	8)32 = 4	9)54 = 6	7)63 = 9	8)24 = 3	9)72 = 8
8)40 = 5	9)36 = 4	7)14 = 2	8)80 = 10	9)45 = 5	7)21 = 3	8)48 = 6
7)70 = 10	8)64 = 8	9)27 = 3	7)28 = 4	8)56 = 7	9)81 = 9	Number Correct / 20

168   169   170   171   172   173   174   175

Grammar and Reading

Exploring Kinds of Sentences, p. 204
1. a) question mark, b) period, c) exclamation mark, d) question mark, e) period, f) exclamation mark, g) question mark
2. Sample answers:
   a) John is walking his dog.   Amy is reading a book.
   b) Are you ready to go?   Do you like apples?
   c) I like to go bike riding!   I love my teddy bear!
   d) Stop that!   Look at that rainbow!

What Is a Noun? p. 206
1. Nouns that name a person: Tom, girl, man, Maria, grandfather, doctor
2. Nouns that name a place: school, library, backyard, mall, beach, Canada
3. Nouns that name a thing: lamp, pencil, coat, car, tree
4. a) shoe, carrot, basement; b) teacher, bed; c) baby, woman, bedroom
5. a) kitchen, b) Carlos, street; c) truck, house; d) Mom, bathroom

What Are Proper Nouns? p. 207
1. Sample answers: a) Nova Scotia, b) Thanksgiving, c) Toronto, d) Sparky, e) Monday
2. Sample answers: Anna, Tiger, Edmonton, Tuesday, Canada, Fido, Mack, Kelly

What Are Pronouns? p. 208
1. a) She, b) It, c) They, d) We, e) it, f) her, g) them, h) me, i) He

Making It Plural, p. 209
1. a) dishes, b) pennies, c) pushes, d) boxes, e) wishes, f) matches, g) benches, h) buses
2. I got scratches on my arms; b) I saw ladies wearing dresses.

Tricky Plurals, p. 210
1. a) patios, b) zeros, c) tomatoes, d) pianos
2. a) On the radios, they told about heroes. b) Larry sent me photos of potatoes from his garden. c) In the videos, people heard echoes.
3. a) halves, b) thieves, c) wolves, d) shelves
4. The chefs made loaves of bread. b) Leaves blew onto the roofs. c) It is dangerous to play near cliffs. d) Thieves stole my scarves.
5. a) knives, b) fish, c) lives, d) sheep
6. The wives made lots of food for the party. b) Mice ran over my feet! c) Children fed the geese. d) The women saw deer in the woods.

What Is a Verb? p. 213
Students should circle the following verbs:
1. a) jumps, b) flies, c) gives, d) flashes, e) forgets, f) sends, g) see, h) squeaks, i) dance, j) runs
2. a) tells, cleans; b) writes, says; c) builds, explores: d) hears, hides; e) buys, pours; f) remembers, asks, scrubs; g) skips, decides

Spelling Present Tense Verbs, p. 214
1. a) copies, b) cries, c) buys, d) flies, e) tries, f) says, g) hurries, h) stays
2. a) scratches, b) pushes, c) passes, d) mixes, e) catches, f) rushes, g) tosses, h) waxes

Using the Correct Verb Tense, p. 215
1. a) walks, b) barks, c) walk, d) uses, e) decide, f) wants g) flies, h) rushes
2. a) checkmark, b) believe, c) waves, d) checkmark, e) plays, f) checkmark

Past Tense Verbs, p. 216
1 a) invented, b) coughed, c) shared, d) worked, e) borrowed, f) escaped, g) agreed, h) exploded
2. a) chased, b) chewed) c) filled, d) invited, e) played
3. a) past, b) present, c) present, d) past

Spelling Past Tense Verbs, p. 217
1. a) tripped, b) stopped, c) stirred, d) dripped) e) stepped, f) mopped, g) planned, h) wrapped, i) wagged, j) hugged
2. a) cried, b) carried, c) hurried, d) worried, e) scurried

Tricky Tense Verbs, p. 218
1. a) had, b) said, c) ate, d) came, e) gave, f) drove, g) got, h) fell
2. a) We drive to the grocery store. b) The squirrel eats all the nuts. c) I have two pencils in my desk. d) Carly comes to my house every week.
3. a) went, b) drank, c) thought, d) bought, e) took, f) found, g) knew, h) drew
4. We drink juice with our breakfast. b) He buys a new toy for his grandson. c) Anna finds lots of seashells at the beach. d) I think about my best friend.

Future Tense Verbs, p. 220
1. a) will ride, b) will swim, c) will shine, d) will drive, e) will grow
2. a) Timothy will plant a tree in the backyard. b) Carlos and Mary will talk about the movie. c) People will laugh at all my silly jokes. d) Kim will share her raisins with Ken and Beth. e) Josh will wash the car very carefully.

What Is an Adjective? p. 221
1. Students should circle the following adjectives: a) brown, b) large, c) scary, d) playful, e) green, f) slippery, g) loud, h) interesting, i) funny, j) round, k) tall, l) dirty
   Students should underline the following nouns:
   a) mouse, b) book, c) dragon, d) puppy, e) mug, f) ice, g) thunder, h) movie, i) joke, j) table, k) mountain, l) dishes
2. Sample answers: a) striped socks, b) quiet voice, c) fluffy clouds, d) fastest runner, e) pretty flowers, f) sneaky cat

Adjectives After Nouns, p. 222
1. Students should circle the following adjectives: a) funny, b) red, c) angry, d) dry, e) exciting, f) soft, g) cute, h) delicious, i) bright, j) cold, k) tired, l) correct
   Students should underline the following nouns: a) clown, b) light, c) woman, d) towels, e) video, f) pillow, g) baby, h) sandwiches, i) sun, j) water, k) Enzo, l) answer

2. a) *huge* describes *dinosaur*, and *sharp* describes *teeth*;
   b) *happy* describes *children*, and *colourful* describes *rainbow*;
   c) *tall* describes *woman*, and *leaky* describes *roof*

Adjectives Can Describe How Many, p. 223
1. Circled adjectives: a) Three, four, c) two, d) Eight
   Underlined nouns: a) apples, b) pennies, c) squirrels, d) frogs
2. a) several, b) Many, c) Few, d) some, e) many, few; f) several, many

Pronouns for People, p. 224
1. a) He, b) They, c) them
2. a) They played with the puppies. b) She showed the picture to him. c) The doctor and the nurse smiled at us. d) We waved goodbye to our aunt and uncle.

Pronouns for Things, p. 225
1. a) it, b) They, c) them, d) It, e) They, f) them, g) they
2. a) It was too big for him. b) We made them for him. c) They gave them to us. d) They are too big for them to carry. e) We sent it to him. f) Will they sing for them?

Some Adverbs Describe How, p. 226
1. a) slowly, b) quietly, c) loudly, d) carefully, e) correctly, f) gently
2. a) gracefully, b) happily, c) hungrily, d) sweetly, e) boldly, f) silently

Some Adverbs Describe When, p. 227
1. a) during, b) next, c) tomorrow, d) now, e) soon, f) after, g) yesterday, h) next, i) after
2. a) later, sing; b) next, swim; c) tomorrow, visit

Some Adverbs Describe Where, p. 228
1. a) here, hang; b) inside, plays; c) downstairs, ran; d) there, put
2. a) everywhere, b) away, c) nearby, d) anywhere, e) nowhere

Some Adverbs Describe How Often, p. 229
1. a) always, b) twice, c) often, d) never, e) once
2. a) frequently, b) constantly, c) rarely, d) usually, e) seldom, f) occasionally

Using Adjectives to Compare More Than Two Things, p. 230
1. a) fastest, all the runners; b) coldest, all the days of the year; c) warmest, all the coats; d) softest, all the beds
2. a) the cleanest, b) the brightest; c) the thickest, d) the smallest, e) the oldest, f) the shortest

Spelling Adjectives That Compare, p. 231
1. a) better, two things; b) worse, two things; c) the best, more than two things; d) farther, two things; e) the most, more than two things; f) the worst, more than two things

Adjectives That Use *More* and *Most* to Compare, p. 232
1. a) more, b) the most, c) more, d) the most, e) more, f) the most, g) more, h) the most

Joining Sentences with *And* or *But*, p. 233
1. a) but, b) and, c) but, d) and, e) but

2. Ensure that students put a comma before the word *and* or *but*.
   a) and, b) but, c) but, d) and, e) but

Joining Sentences with *Or* or *So*, p. 234
1. a) or, b) or, c) so, d) so, e) or
2. Ensure that students put a comma before the word *or* or *so*.
   a) so, b) or, c) or, d) so, e) so

School Trip, p. 237
1. The girls flipped ac coin to decide who would get the window seat.
2. Sample answers: Other ways to decide who goes first might include picking a number, playing Eenie Meenie Miney Mo, playing Rock, Paper, Scissors.
3. 45 + 20 + 45 = 110 The trip to Niagara Falls took 110 minutes altogether.
4. Sample answer: The fence is probably to keep people from falling into the water and for keeping people a safe distance from the falls.
5. The best part of the day for the writer was taking a boat with lots of other people.

The Magic Wand, p. 239
1. 8 + 3 = 11 Eleven people came to the birthday party.
2. Cousin Leo gave the magic wand.
3. The three magic wand rules were: You cannot hurt anyone with it, you have to use it for something you really want, and you can only use it once, then you have to pass it on to someone else.
4. Answers will vary. You might wish to have students share their wishes with the class.
5. Answers will vary.

Whale Watching, p. 241
1. The family will go to the Pacific Ocean near Vancouver, British Columbia, to go whale watching.
2. The trip takes place in May.
3. It is a good time of year to see whales because they swim around there at that time of year.
4. They saw a humpback whale.
5. It is important to wear raincoats and put on sturdy shoes on a rainy day so they do not slip on the wet deck of the boat.

Sensational Similes, p. 243
1. Sample answers: a) bear, b) cheetah, c) bat, d) fish, e) daisy, f) flower, g) polar bear, h) maniac, i) the Sun, j) kitten, k) truck horn. You might wish to have students share their similes with the class.
2. Answers will vary. You might wish to have students share their similes with the class.

Alliteration, p. 244
1. Answers will vary. You might wish to have students share their alliterations with the class.

Acrostic Poems, p. 245
You might wish to create a bulletin board display of students' acrostic poems.

Cinquain Poems, p. 246
You might wish to create a bulletin board display of students' cinquain poems.

Brilliant Brochure Checklist, p. 247
You might wish to create a bulletin board display of students' brochures.

Social Studies

Trace Your Roots, p. 261
1. The text says that an ancestor is someone who decided to make Canada their home.
2. Answers will vary. **Note:** This could be a sensitive issue for some students. If you wish students to share with the class, ask for volunteers only.
3. Answers will vary. Some students might say that their family members all have the same colour hair and eyes, and similar features.
4. Answers will vary.
5. Answers will vary. You might wish to ask for volunteers to share with the class.

How Pioneers Cleared the Land, p. 263
1. They had to clear the land to grow food.
2. First, the trees were cut down in such a way that they fell into huge piles.
   Next, the men worked to create several large piles and brought in a cart pulled by the oxen.
   Then, the logs were loaded onto the cart and taken away.
   Finally, the long pieces were kept for building barns and houses.
3. A logging bee was when many families helped each other to chop the trees and clear the field.
4. Answers might vary. Sample answer: The work was hard to do and more people working together finished the job more quickly.
5. A farmer used an axe called a mattock to take out the roots.
6. Tree stumps were removed by using oxen to pull them out or by exploding them.
7. The soil was made ready for planting with the help of a plough and a horse or two to pull it. The plough broke up the soil so that seeds could be planted.

Pioneers Needed Water, p. 265
1. Pioneers needed water for many reasons. They needed water to be close by because they had to carry it to their farms.
2. Pioneers needed water for drinking, washing themselves, washing clothes and dishes, watering gardens, and giving to their animals.
3. Water for baths was heated in a large pot over a fire.
4. Rivers made it easy for the pioneers to get to town or move supplies. There were no cars at that time, and the land was covered with trees. So walking or riding a horse was difficult and took a long time. Pioneers found it easy to float down rivers on rafts. They also made canoes out of birchbark and logs.

5. Sample answer: In modern times, people have running water right in their homes. So people just turn on a tap now. They do not need to go get water in a river or lake.
6. Indigenous people showed pioneers how to build birchbark canoes.

Pioneer Life: Building a House, p. 267
1. Sample answer: Pioneers used an axe to cut down trees to make a home, and to cut up wood for the fireplace.
2. Pioneers lived in a tent or a lean-to because they needed a place to live while they were building their log house.
3. Pioneer families worked together to build a log house.
4. Sample answer: If pioneers had no house by winter, they would freeze in the cold weather
5. A fire warmed the house, was used for cooking, and provided light.
6. Pioneer children chopped wood and kept the fire going.

Pioneer Farms: Spring and Summer, p. 269
1. They made maple syrup and maple sugar from the sap.
2. Farmers used horses to pull the heavy plough over the fields. The plough broke up the hard soil. Then, farmers planted seeds.
3. Farmers waited for hot, dry weather to **harvest** the hay. They wanted the hay to dry out in the sun before they stored it away in the barn for winter.
4. Farmers needed a barn to store the hay for winter.
5. To keep fruits and vegetables from spoiling, farmers dried fruits or cooked in water and a little sugar to stew them, then stored them in jars. Vegetables were put in jars that contained salt and vinegar.
6. The root cellar kept the food from freezing in winter, and kept the foods cool during the warmer months.

Pioneer Farms: Fall and Winter, p. 271
1. It was important to harvest the crops before winter came because frost could ruin the crops.
2. Wheat is used to make flour, and flour is used to make bread. Bread was an important food for pioneers.
3. Farmers hit the wheat with a flail to make the seeds come off.
4. On a windy day, farmers put the grain and the chaff on a bed sheet. One person held each end of the sheet, and they tossed the grain and chaff into the air. The chaff is very light, so the wind blew it away. The grain fell back onto the sheet.
5. At the mill, the grain was crushed to make flour.
6. In winter, farmers fixed their tools and repaired buildings and fences.

Comparing Family Chores: Pioneer Days and Modern Days, p. 273
Answers might vary. Sample answers:
Women, Men, Older Girls, and Older Boys: mowing the lawn, watering the garden, shovelling the snow, pulling weeds, mending the fence, fixing the car, painting the house, taking care of the children, mending clothes, preparing meals, planting gardens, helping harvest food from the gardens

Young Girls and Young Boys: helping take care of younger siblings, feeding pets, pulling weeds, picking vegetables, helping clean the house, helping make meals

Pioneer Occupations, p. 274

1. A trade is a job with special skills that is done with special tools.
2. The wainwright and harness maker worked with animals.
3. Answers will vary.
4. Blacksmith: someone who fit oxen and horses with iron shoes
   Wainwright: someone who built the top part of carriages, wagons, sleighs, and coaches
   Wheelwright: someone who crafted many sizes of wheels for carriages, wagons, carts, and wheelbarrows
   Cooper: someone who made wooden barrels, washtubs, buckets, and butter churns
   Harness Maker: someone who crafted leather harnesses and saddles for large animals

Health Care in Pioneer Times, p. 276

1. Sample answer: It surprised me that people got teeth pulled out by the blacksmith.
2. People wash their hands a lot more often to stay healthy, we go to the dentist to get our teeth taken care of, and we go to the doctor's office or to a hospital when we are sick.

Cariboo Gold Rush, p. 277

1. A gold rush was a time when people rushed to a place to mine for gold after they heard rumours that gold had been discovered in the area.
2. British Columbia
3. People dipped a pan into streams and looked for gold in the wet soil they scooped up..
4. People deserted the towns when they did not find gold, and many hotels and stores closed.
5. Sample answer: A ghost town is a place that used to have many people living there, but is now abandoned. Some of the old buildings are still standing.
6. The new settlers began to work in forestry, ranching, or farming.

How Do We Use Land? p. 279

1. Some of the ways we have used land in the past are for farming, forestry, mining, outdoor and indoor recreation, shopping, parks, and living space for people.
2. As cities become bigger, more land is being used to build new houses, apartment buildings, shops, roads, schools, and recreational areas.
3. Many farms have been sold so that new housing and businesses could be built.
4. When we lose forests, animals have more trouble finding homes and food.
5. Forests are cut down because people want more products and more homes.

Urban and Rural Communities, p. 281

Answers will vary.

Urban and Rural Living, p. 282

Sample answers:
Reasons for Living in an Urban Area: people live close to each other so you have close neighbours; there are lots of places to live; there are lots of schools, stores, and recreation areas so there are always things to do
Reasons for Living in a Rural Area: it is quieter in a rural area, people are farther apart from their neighbours, there is a lot of open space

Comparing Features of a Community, p. 283

You might wish to have students share their research with the class.

The Great Lakes, p. 284

1. There are five Great Lakes.
2. Four of the Great Lakes are shared by Canada and the United States.
3. Lake Superior is the largest Great Lake.
4. False. The land around the Great Lakes is good for farming. I know this because the text says that people have lived around the Great Lakes for centuries and the land is good for farming. People still live near the Great Lakes today.
5. Chemicals from farms have run into the water and polluted the Great Lakes.
6. Sea creatures such as zebra mussels, sea lampreys, and a fish called a Eurasian ruffe have invaded the Great Lakes and are making it difficult for ships and people. There are fewer fish in the Great Lakes that people can safely eat.

Fishing Communities, p. 286

1. Students should mention any three of the following: Fishers and their families lived in villages and towns near the sea, rivers, or lakes. Some of these communities were far from big cities and towns, and were hard to get to. People in small fishing communities helped each other through tough times. Today, some fishing communities have large ports with transportation connections, large fish processing plants, shipyards, and fish research facilities.
2. There are not as many fish as there were in the past because of overfishing. When overfishing happens nature cannot replace all the fish that is caught, quickly enough.
3. Fisheries and Oceans Canada decides how many fish can be caught. This is to prevent overfishing.
4. Because there was so much cod fishing over the years, there were fewer cod. In recent years, the government has told fishers they could only catch a certain number of cod.
5. Sample answers:
   Overfishing: reduces the number of fish and nature cannot replace them quickly enough
   Less Cod in Atlantic Canada: the government told fishers they could only catch a certain number of cod; today, more people in Atlantic Canada fish the sea for shellfish such as shrimp, scallops, and lobster, instead of for cod.

Forestry Communities, p. 288

1. Forestry means the cutting down and replanting of trees.

2. Sample answer: Replanting trees is important so people can still have paper and wood for building, and so this resource does not run out.
3. Answers will vary. Students should mention that their chairs and desks are made of wood, their houses and the school are build with wood, and that they use paper and pencils at school.
4. Sample answer: Water is a natural resource because it comes from nature.

Manufacturing Communities, p. 289
1. The word manufacture means to use raw materials to make a completed product.
2. Sample answer: The text says that not all people at the plant work to build something. It says that some people work at a plant or factory to supply services such as medical-, social-, security-, or food-related services, to other workers. Also, people always need products and goods, and manufacturing makes these things.
3. Sample answer: Manufacturing communities make products that people in other communities need.

Science

What Do Plants Need? p. 290
1.

	Plants	People
Water	X	X
Time to sleep		X
Air	X	X
Soil	X	
Warmth	X	X

2. Sunlight coming in the window gives the plant the light and warmth it needs.
3. There is not enough space for the roots to spread out.
4. Answers will vary.

Parts of a Plant, p. 292
1.

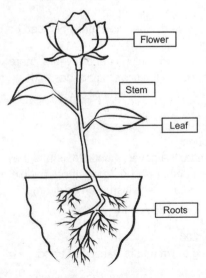

2. stem
3. roots
4. flower
5. roots and leaf
6. flower
7. stem
8. flower

Life Cycle of a Plant, p. 294
1. Labels from top: seed, sprout, seedling, adult plant, plant with fruit

Plant Parts: I Ate That? p. 296
cauliflower: flower; onions: bulb; lettuce: leaf; pear: fruit; melon: fruit; beet: root; peas: seeds; lemon: fruit; zucchini: fruit; corn: seeds; carrot: root; eggplant: fruit; asparagus: stem; apple: fruit

Poison Ivy! Watch Out! p. 297
1. Someone would yell, "Watch out!" because if you touch the poison ivy, you could get a terrible rash.
2. Poison oak and poison sumac can also give you a rash.
3. A poison ivy plant has three leaves.
4. Wearing long-sleeved tops and long pants will protect your body so poison ivy cannot touch you.
5. Take a shower, not a bath, and use soap.

Big Trees in British Columbia, p. 299
1. You can see 800-year-old trees in Cathedral Grove on British Columbia's Vancouver Island.
2. Cathedral Grove is in MacMillan Provincial Park.
3. Many of the oldest trees in Cathedral Grove burned down 350 years ago. Others were cut down.
4. Douglas fir and red cedar
5. A strong wind storm knocked down many of the trees and destroyed some of the trails. Park workers are still trying to fix the trails so they ask visitors to stay on the marked trails.

What Can Forces Do? p. 301
1. pull
2. push
3. push
4. pull
5. Sparky pulled the leash to make Tanya run. Tanya pulled the leash to make Sparky slow down. Sparky pulled Tanya off the sidewalk and through the garden.
6. The change from walking to running (two times) and from running to slowing down.
7. Sparky pulls Tanya off the sidewalk and through Mr. Lee's flower garden.

The Force of Gravity, p. 303
1. Gravity pulls you toward the ground.
2. You move faster near the bottom of the slide. You can feel the change in speed.
3. Without gravity, juice would not fall from the container.
4. Gravity keeps the bicycle w

The Force of Friction, p. 305
1. The towel.
2. A towel has a rougher surface than a glass table. Rough surfaces create more friction than smooth surfaces do.
3. There is more friction when you rub together two pieces of sandpaper. Sandpaper has a rougher surface than regular paper and it is harder to rub them together.
4. A paved road is smooth and creates little friction. Gravel adds a lot of bumps to the surface, giving the road more friction.

How Friction Helps Us, p. 307
1. Sock feet are more dangerous on stairs because they are smooth. The soles of shoes create more friction.
2. Snow tires, because they create more friction on icy roads.
3. The rougher surface on snow tires will slow cars down more. Regular tires slow cars down less. There is no need for snow tires when there is no snow and ice.

Contact and Non-contact Forces, p. 309
1. Contact forces: friction, muscular force; Non-contact forces: magnetic force, gravity
2. No, non-contact forces still work when there is contact between objects. The magnetic force keeps the pin stuck to the magnet even after they are in contact. The rock does not float because the force of gravity is pulling on it, even when the rock is touching Earth.

Experiment: The Force of Static Electricity, p. 311
1. A pulling force, because it pulls the water closer to the comb.
2. A non-contact force, because the static electricity in the comb pulls on the water without touching it.
3. No, a magnet only pulls on iron or nickel only.
   Try It! Students may notice that some pieces of foil shift position, some pieces stand on end and some pieces jump to the comb and stick to it.

Lightning Strikes, p. 313
1. lightning
2. Because lightning is too powerful, happens too quickly, and does not last for long.
3. Lightning is five times hotter than the surface of the Sun. When lightning strikes the ground, fires can start, trees can be destroyed, and people can be seriously hurt.
4. You might wish to display students' posters around the classroom.

What Is a Structure? p. 315
1. All structures hold or support a load.
2. Sample answers:
   An airplane: seats, luggage, people, engine, pilot
   A backpack: books, homework, pens and pencils, snacks, lunch, sneakers
   A shopping cart: canned goods, cereal, produce, ice cream, milk
3. Load: person riding the skateboard
   Purpose: to move a person more quickly than walking
4. Sample answer: Yes, a fence is a structure because the posts support the chain link fencing or wooden planks.

Natural Structures, p. 317
1. Sample answers: birds, eggs, materials used to build the nest
2. circular, shaped like a bowl
3. Sample answers: twigs, grass, moss, string, feathers, mud
4. Sample answers: to catch insects for food, home for the spider
5. Sample answers: the spider, any insects caught on the web, the strands used to build the web
6. No, because it was built by a human.

Structures Word Search, p. 319
anthill, beehive, bike, boat, bridge, cave, chair, coral reef, eggshell, feather, house, hut, iceberg, igloo, nest, snowflake, spider web, tent, tower, tree

E	S	P	I	D	E	R	W	E	B	B
G	T	I	C	E	B	E	R	G	S	E
G	O	N	T	Q	W	B	A	I	N	E
S	W	T	R	E	E	R	N	G	O	H
H	E	G	N	M	G	I	T	L	W	I
E	R	N	E	S	T	D	H	O	F	V
L	C	G	E	R	P	G	I	O	L	E
L	H	H	O	U	S	E	L	T	A	K
W	A	G	E	Z	I	S	L	E	K	B
O	I	Q	C	A	V	E	E	N	E	I
G	R	P	A	B	O	A	T	T	D	K
W	C	O	R	A	L	R	E	E	F	E
F	E	A	T	H	E	R	Q	H	U	T

Structures Collage, p. 320
You might wish to create a bulletin board display of students' collages.

What Is Soil Made Of? p. 321
1. Living Things: ants, roots, bacteria, worms; Non-living Things: water, sand, air, pebbles, rock, salt, sticks, dead leaves
2. Air is found in the tiny spaces in soil.
3. Answers will vary.

Dirt and Soil, p. 323
1. Soil is more useful because it helps plants grow and it important for life on Earth.
2. Soil is a good mixture of minerals, natural material, and the decayed remains of living things.
3. Dirt is dust and grime that is not useful.
4. The best soil for growing plants is soil that has organic material in it.
5. To keep soil from drying out in the summer heat, you can add mulch, which is twigs, leaves, and bark.

Erosion, p. 325
1. Erosion is what happens when parts of the land wear away.
2. Rainfall, rivers, waves, and floods all change the land and wear it away.
3. People made erosion worse by cutting down trees to make room for farming and building.
4. Without trees, the soil blows away in the wind and gets washed away by rain.
5. People can plant new trees to replace the trees that were cut down and help stop some of the erosion.

Air and Water for Plant Roots, p. 327

1. Water pushes air out of the spaces between the particles so the roots do not have access to air.
2. The cup with stones has larger spaces between the particles.
3. Water will flow faster through the cup with stones because there are larger spaces between the particles.
4. The water would flow faster through Abdul's cup. Silt particles are larger than clay particles, so there are larger spaces between the silt particles.

Glaciers, p. 329

1. Glaciers are giant rivers of ice that move very slowly.
2. About 99% of glacier ice is found near the North Pole and South Pole.
3. Alpine glaciers are found near mountains. Ice cap or ice field glaciers sit on top of mountains. Ice sheet glaciers are found at the North Pole and the South Pole.
4. As the planet gets warmer, many glaciers are becoming smaller.
5. Glaciers are very important because they store about 75% of Earth's fresh water.
6. Answers will vary.

Technology Collage, p. 331

You might wish to have students share their collages with the class and ask a few volunteers to read how they use technology in their daily life aloud.